LOOKING
FOR
HARVEY
WEINSTEIN

(WHAT STARTED OUT AS BUSINESS BECAME A CAUSE)

—

SHIRLEY & HOLLY
YANEZ

THE TRUE STORY OF MODERN DAY MICHELANGELO

ACKNOWLEDGMENTS

Our sincere and deepest thanks must go to God who although had to rein The Girls in at times never stopped believing in this project. She is a true inspiration to all women in Hollywood.

Thank you so much to American Express without whom, this journey would not have been possible.

A respectful thank you to Hawthorne Printing for making other people's dreams come true and our friend Robert Evans for his cover photographs.

A deep and heartfelt thank you to all the people mentioned who took the time to read our story before publishing and offered their kind words of encouragement and support. We are eternally grateful to you all.

A great thank you to some essential reading before moving to Los Angeles, 'The How to Penetrate Hollywood Manual.' A book that, although helps navigate you through the corridors of fame and fortune, does not guarantee the door won't be slammed in your face. Some names have been changed at individual request and Tommy Lee's email is excluded to protect his privacy.

For information on the Russian genius Mr Ilia Anossov and his contribution at the 2004 Academy Awards, visit www.truefresco.com and www.academyawards.com

And last but not least, thank you to Steve next door and all the people who gave free pot when a new Chanel handbag was nothing more than a distant memory.

Note for Librarians: a cataloguing record for this book that includes Dewey Classification and US Library of Congress numbers is available from the National Library of Canada. The complete cataloguing record can be obtained from the National Library's online database at: www.nlc-bnc.ca/amicus/index-e.html
ISBN 1-4120-2822-1
Printed in Victoria, BC, Canada

TRAFFORD

This book was published *on-demand* in cooperation with Trafford Publishing. On-demand publishing is a unique process and service of making a book available for retail sale to the public taking advantage of on-demand manufacturing and Internet marketing. **On-demand publishing** includes promotions, retail sales, manufacturing, order fulfilment, accounting and collecting royalties on behalf of the author.
Suite 6E, 2333 Government St.,
Victoria, B.C. V8T 4P4, CANADA
Phone   250-383-6864
Toll-free   1-888-232-4444
Fax   250-383-6804
E-mail   sales@trafford.com
www.trafford.com/robots/04-0650.html

10   9   8   7   6   5   4   3   2   1

LOOKING FOR HARVEY WEINSTEIN

INTRODUCTION

It all began three years ago as two English, life long best friends, married to extremely good looking American brothers, sat in an extraordinarily expensive, pokey beach apartment with a peek a boo view, literally. They were formulating a plan to establish a possible business, the perfect opportunity for two individuals whose resumes read as follows.

Patrons and benefactors to the world of fine wine, no regional prejudices. Open to all grapes regardless of color. Agricultural herbalists promoting ecological remedies for an all round feeling of well being. Tirelessly dedicated to the legalization of marijuana and both smokers of cigarettes, primarily to indicate one's nationality. One and only true vice. Last but not least ideas people, unconventional enough to excite but business savvy enough to keep the bottom line firmly in focus. Harsh but fair, lazy but honest with passionate aspirations to take social climbing to a new level. Too much hard work leaves little time for pleasure.

The Girls came up with an art gallery. The perfect platform to attract the rich and the famous in LA LA Land and give the folks back home something to be jealous of. And so came about Art Interiors, the perfect business to promote creative genius. It had to be private enough for high rollers to frequent, yet fun enough to be stuck in for hours. Hard work was not their highest priority.

These Girls had big ideas, gorgeous husbands but little else. It was always about champagne tastes on a beer budget. Two bright evangelists with absolutely no idea how to run an art gallery. A minor detail at five pm when the rubbish bin is over flowing with empty wine bottles and the ash tray has taken on a life form of its own.

They needed success. Art Interiors was the beginning of an empire. A monumental struggle which started out with such incredible hopes and dreams. Possibly a tad unrealistic, as you get to know The Girls, two peas in a pod, both the wrong side of thirty five and truly absolutely fabulous. Two great minds between two average bodies but both blessed with above average confidence. Definitely all fur coat and no knickers.

This empowering story is about how two English, fish out of water take on Hollywood and its elusive celebrity to elevate the work of a Russian genius painter and help him promote the revival of Fresco. I know what you are thinking. How ridiculous is that. But believe me when I tell you, these women are, without a doubt, from another planet. Follow their dream and be prepared to laugh out loud.

You are about to hear some ridiculous Tawdry Tales from LA LA Land. Please sit back, pour a large glass of wine, smoke a joint and escape into a long crazy journey through Hollywood all in the name of art. Discover secrets about the only place on the planet where no one ever calls you back and if you're lucky enough they do, odds are, it's to say, no thanks. A place where the word yes is a prehistoric concept and if you have any vices, you need to move. This journey is living proof that anything is truly possible. Read it and find yourself in it.

This book is dedicated, to Mr. Harvey Weinstein of Miramax Films for his commitment to independent emerging talent because like Holly and Shirley, he never takes no for an answer and to all the people who have found the courage and belief in themselves to go it alone.

THE ART GALLERY

"What is from the earth is of the greatest worth."
BEN HARPER

MOVING TO LOS ANGELES FROM THE UK, WHERE THE WEATHER WAS ALWAYS BLOODY awful, was considered quite a result for two best friends from Yorkshire. Marrying good looking brothers who lived in the sunshine was the price. Best friends married to American brothers? Odd in itself I can hear you saying. Well it is the God's honest truth. Hollywood was one of those places one would watch on television and dream about visiting. Oh well we all make mistakes in love. Life there always looked so fabulous and exciting from a dull rainy afternoon in The City. Was it really like that?

Their training, their own school of life had been the perfect world for two unique friends to run a muck but the bright lights of London had lost their luster and the ever growing Coutts and Co. bank account for their thriving business provided little else than trinkets and luxury whenever they wanted.

Both Girls came from northern working class families but with a few elocution lessons, reading the paper everyday and choosing Hemingway over Hello they had managed to penetrate the elite of all social strata, The British Aristocracy. Their portfolio of clients read like the Queen's New Year Honor Roll. Honorables, Lords, Sirs and Viscounts were ten a penny and investment banks with a five star credit rating were deemed inferior. With everything, materially one could ever hope for or in fact need, could they find boyfriends? Not Likely. They had lost their direction and purpose and were looking for love. Moving to America and actually becoming dames was not quite what they had in mind.

It didn't take these fifteen year business partners very long to work out, living in LA was horribly expensive and marrying for looks; well really stupid. It all came to pass when one had a holiday romance and in a moment of temporary insanity gave up everything at home to marry the Californian boy in question. The other, in her moment of madness accepted the job of maid of honor at the wedding. The groom's big brother was best man and you know what they say about best man perks? Leaving close to half a million dollars in their business account, they signed over their City Of London based company to their ten percent partner for nothing. With bulging stock portfolios they felt safe and untouchable. How wrong could they have been?

To cut a long story short, they all lived not so happily ever after in jail somewhere in LA LA Land. In truth the writing was on the wall when one looked beyond the movie star faces of the East Los Angeles brothers. One a Harley Davidson riding loner, an outlaw, the other an insular and repressed computer salesman. Both with fucking bad tempers and a propensity to thump the fridge when things didn't go their way.

The Girls do look alike but are completely different, if that makes any sense. One blond forty something going on sixteen and the other brunette, thirty eight going on seventy.

Having experienced the fast lane, embracing the best and dismissing the rest, it had to be Chanel all the way from here on. No going back for either. They were in it for a good time not a long time. To make enough money to escape jail, purchase a house in Italy, and go home.

So they decided to set up a business together selling art. It was all they could do really, flog their personal collections. Their art was all they had left. LA was brutal to anyone over the age of twenty five and those days were well and truly gone. Starting an art business seemed like the perfect plan giving them all the freedom they needed to escape jail, better known as the marital home and of course become filthy rich once again.

After many weeks secretly plotting and planning while The Jailers were at work, The Girls set out to see what space was available to rent locally. Somewhere they could open a small exclusive art gallery and start working again.

"Ad in the Beach reporter. Fabulous space for rent in downtown Manhattan Beach. It's cheap for the location. Call Clive? Sounds cute. What do you think? Shall we call?"

Being monumental snobs, working by the ocean was expensive but worth it. Manhattan Beach, the Cote D'Azur of California. A place where property is astronomical and space limited. It was the closest they would get to the South of France for a long while. It was decided.

"We need to find a fabulous location to open a gallery and this place is in our price range."

"Cheap and cheerful."

The space turned out to be the size of a postage stamp and shared between two other businesses. As for cute Clive. Fuck. You would've had to have been blind to look at that all day, was the immediate reaction, as he eagerly held out his fat sweaty hand of friendship. When the shortest, hairiest, ugliest man alive squeezed from behind his small wooden desk, packed so close to the wall to give the illusion of more space, it was enough to make even the die hard run in the opposite direction. Was he a giant hedgehog?

Clive Dullard was not a looker by any stretch of the imagination. He was the kind of man one wants to punch in the mouth within the first few seconds of his boring sentence. They maybe should have walked away there and then but beggars could not be choosers and it was cheap for a new business with no capital. A mental note was made. Clive, the hedgehog, just had to go.

The room rental agency on the other side was run by Dom, a cute Italian stallion.

"Now he's someone to have a flirt with on a dull Monday morning."

"Where God closes a door, somewhere he opens a window."

"We'll take it. When can we move in?"

At last The Girls had found the perfect space. Being extremely small turned out to be a blessing as they had very little office equipment and just enough art to fill the walls. Although the visual was good, the reality was quite different. They needed to come up with a way to penetrate the androids, promote some passion and sell some art. The local beach residents had more money than sense to buy their fabulous art. Now it was just a case of networking. Simple. Without the possibility of meeting like minded people, life in LA would be grim.

It was not long before the art was displayed on the walls of the new gallery. Clive the loser, should be given some credit here. He did enthuse about the paintings, as long as they remained in The Girls, precisely measured half of the wall, never to over shadow his pride and joy, a tasteless computer poster from back in the eighties. Clive's one and only claim to fame. From the word go they both wanted to humiliate then exterminate. He was everything one hated in another human being and he was pig ugly. Working with Clive would be tricky but not impossible. They had their ways, insult him to death. The Girls, delighted with their achievements, skipped back to their Beach Cottage to formulate a business plan and celebrate the new Art Gallery. Life long best friends, who could discuss the most controversial subjects with incredible ease, especially after a few bottles of red wine, sat down to prepare a set of rules and guidelines for the new business, easy to follow and never to be broken.

1/ Rules are made to be broken. (The thought always there but the reality never failed to rear its ugly head, these two already aware of their weaknesses.)

2/ Never give up a dream because anything is truly possible.

3/ No drinking before 11.30. (Even these champions had to conform sometimes.)

4/ When boarding a flight, always, always turn left.

So that was that. The Art Interiors business plan was scribbled on a piece of paper and tossed in a drawer for future reference. It was eleven thirty. Perfect timing for the first tipple of the day after a busy morning hanging art and softening up Clive.

"Let's celebrate. Do we have any cigarettes?"

"Can you roll a joint"

With so many things to think about, having a glass of red and a hit on some nice weed, really helped get the creative juices flowing. Well that is their side of the story and they're sticking to it. Los Angeles was certainly not London darling so client divining skills needed to be modified. Any place in the universe with a manual giving clear instructions on how to navigate through it, had to be worth looking at. 'The How to Penetrate Hollywood Manuel' was opened at page one.

"Did you know there is a three P system designed to crack LA? A million ways to face rejection, Patience Passion and Persistence."

"Sounds good reading but we have none of those skills."

"We could concoct our own P system, the practical pursuit of pleasure, much more fitting to our life style don't you think?"

It was settled. With two great minds, lashings of red wine, three packets of fags and a well thought out business plan, the English birds were off and running. After one too many drinks, the aspiring art dealers addressed some stark reality about the new business. Money was tight and they needed more inventory.

"We need more art, more choice. How do you find an artist at the beach?"

"Just roll another and relax, something will turn up, it's Hollywood."

This was typical. They were always quick to put the cart before the horse then spend weeks playing catch up. Back in Europe art was an essential ingredient to living. It was just a question of focusing. And that tells you something important about these two unusual bananas. They think big. The Girls, both convinced if they looked hard enough, they would find the genius they needed to get them noticed.

"A genius is out there. I can feel it in my bones."

"We may have to exaggerate but let's get on the net and mirror image the Tate, find someone to represent and start our own museum"

After surfing the net from The Beach Cottage, the final task of the day was to send a fabulous introduction email to Mr. Ilia Anossov, a Russian Fresco mas-

SHIRLEY & HOLLY YANEZ

ter, starving to death somewhere in Inglewood. He was perfect. Even though he sounded like a character from an old black and white horror movie, the bells, the bells, he had what sounded like an incredible studio filled to the brim with a magnificent body of work, too good to be true and too ideal to pass on. For some strange reason contacting Ilia just felt right.

"I have always had a thing about Russian men. If nothing else he could be sexy."

"Unlikely, he's poor." One a passionate dreamer, the other a realist, that's exactly how they operate. A perfect balance between best mates.

It turned out Ilia was desperate for cash and actively seeking the bright lights of art appreciation. He was waiting to be noticed by the world, something very possible if one hangs with The Girls long enough. For most, hanging with The Girls was, an unthinkable task. It required the constitution of an ox and the balls of a gorilla, a combination they had yet to come across in America. The Russian was invited for a meeting of the minds. He accepted and suggested the following day for a spot of lunch. Ilia had hung with the Russian mafia. For him meeting The Girls would be baby food.

Over their first lunch together, Ilia mesmerized them with fabulous, exciting tales about Russian art and his triumphant, victorious escape 10 years earlier, arriving in the US with only four dollars in his pocket. He had left over a quarter of million dollars of art behind, misappropriated by the mob but had escaped with a body of work of genius level. Not that these two had any idea about being a genius back then. For them it was just a question of bluffing, a skill they had honed and played to perfection.

Ilia Anossov was indeed a gift. In reality he was such a rare find, even the administration had given him genius status to live in the USA and paint freely. Something he had been arrested for numerous times in the former USSR. He was the perfect person to build an alliance with. They rejoiced. His appearance needed some work. His horrific yellow teeth were more crooked than the LAPD and in need of some serious drilling but for once the art duo would look beyond the beast and cash in on the beauty. He didn't fit their profile on the boyfriend front, far too scruffy but with a little change here and there, he had something they could package and promote in Los Angeles. His dedication to resurrecting the dying technique of Fresco filled both girls with incredible passion and his art, thrilled and excited them. This was the perfect opportunity to kick things off for Art Interiors and a deal was struck there and then, cementing their alliance.

The Girls quickly established Ilia was blessed with the perfect credentials to be represented by Art Interiors. A drug taking maniac, with a sexy Russian, accent capable of drinking an alcoholic under the table was an explosive combination to offer clients. The story was hot and Ilia was about to come in his pants as the two evangelists promised fame and fortune.

"Your work is magnificent."

"We need four of your best pieces to display in the gallery."

"We will get you recognized for your genius."

"Now let's drink vodka and see what you're made of"

With an opportunity to test his stamina, they set the bar and Ilia cleared it with flying colors. He could drink and The Girls had a new partner. They made their way back to the beach to plan an exhibition. Ilia's work would make a real statement on the walls of the smallest gallery in the world.

When the art arrived several days later it was carefully unpacked and hung in the gallery. Standing back in contemplation with fingers on chins, The Girls regarded the work appearing like real art critics. Clive, the loser, just couldn't help himself.

"Did your two year old paint that trash?" Ilia's work did have a child like quality but some lucky client would be conned into paying over the odds for it. It was phenomenal. It was real art and it was a bargain. Convincing Americans would not be easy but The Girls were committed to keeping art history alive and Ilia had a dream. He was determined to promote the revival of Fresco, as well as teach the world about his passion for painting and creative expression. If anyone could fulfill his vision, it was these two English aliens trapped and dying in a cultural void. Remember they are crazy and anything is possible in their world.

As much as The Girls loved Ilia's work, it did not offer potential clients enough choice. So the hunt for more talent was now a priority. The Girls, trying to stay on the wagon, it did happen occasionally, spent a slow Friday afternoon at the gallery. A young artist with a limp and a smile, struggling to carry an armful of average paintings popped his head around the door. Looking like the Artful Dodger from the movie Oliver Twist, The Girls instantly felt sorry for him. He begged for a chance to show his work, pleaded in fact, then produced a disabled badge.

"Bless him." The Girls sat through his laborious rendition of "life as an artist" and its' monumental difficulties. He had one piece with a little potential if priced right; dirt-cheap. It was added to the wall as a daily reminder, they needed bigger fish to fry with better collections. A plan came to mind.

"Why don't we contact the Pavlovas?" Someone somewhere had given them the name and telephone number of a talented art couple living in Long Beach. According to the art community they had an exceptional collection, an interesting story, were unusual yet well established. The perfect combination for Art

Interiors. Everyone loves a freak. The Girls made a call to the arty farty couple, who suggested lunch at their home come studio. This was more like it. The Girls were delighted to accept.

"What a result, our first invitation to lunch."

"How charming, let's hope they smoke."

It was always a mission to find others who loved to socialize. Living in Stepford, the new nickname for LA, was slowly killing them both. Maybe, at last, this meeting would not only turn out to be fun but the break they needed.

The two English Girls forever hopeful and always positive had no hesitation when informing the artistic hosts of their requirements for lunch. This was a bold yet rather useful skill they had mastered back in Europe. Ask and you shall receive and never leave anything to chance. Sorting things out ahead of time minimized the risk of disappointment later down the road.

"We drink wine. We love any fish dish and we need somewhere to smoke after lunch." The plan dived south like breasts after childbirth. The Pavlova's were non -drinking vegans, with a strange allergy to cigarette smoke, happily raising a family of tropical fish. Not their kind of friend.

"Shall we cancel?"

With little else to do that week, it was decided to take a chance on meeting the strange couple. If nothing else it would be an opportunity to get out and about in the art community and potentially source some new talent.

The Girls arrived promptly at two PM looking 60s fabulous. Lateness, something they didn't tolerate under any circumstances. The house itself wasn't bad if one still lived in the sixties. Tony Pavlova opened the door talking his head off non stop. He loved the sound of his own voice, that was a given. Would they ever get out alive? Kitty, the mysterious wife, presented to The Girls three hours into the meeting, scared them to death. He let them out four hours later bored to death.

Tony's build up of his wife was out of this world. He shared stories of how they had met twenty years earlier, somewhere seedy in New York. How she was so stunning people would stop and stare, taking endless pictures. How he instantly found himself falling head over heels in love. How she was the epitome of femininity and talent. It went on for hours, seven in fact.

"Wow she sounds too good to be true."

"Bo Derek with a paint brush?" As Kitty, the wife, made her grand sweeping entrance it was immediately evident Bo Derek she was not. Her hair did resemble paintbrushes. The character Medusa springs to mind.

Poor Kitty, sixty if she was a day, thinner than a thread of cotton and just as fragile was rather tragic really. Wearing far too small silver hot pants, her long

14

blond Rastafarian weaves almost touching her wrinkly bony knees, she flirted with them. Was she bisexual? The make up, oh the make up. It was caked on like Betty Davis in 'What Ever Happened To Baby Jane?' and made both Girls feel really young again. For them, hiding their complete shock and disbelief while choking down sparkling apple juice in plastic wine glasses, yuk. Suffice to say a struggle.

Well what ever happened to the Pavlovas will always remain a mystery. The Girls, not known for their subtlety, determined this was taking the piss. They would never be able to convincingly promote the work of the truly bizarre and keep a straight face. They bid the freaks a fond farewell and headed for the nearest bar. Tomorrow was another day with a new challenge. They needed a buzz to continue the struggle and set out to have cocktails somewhere nice.

"You have to promise me you will shoot me if I ever look like that. I mean it."

"Pommaine? My God what next?"

"It's a shame. The art was fabulous. Oh well their loss. Red wine?"

After that awful experience, they needed to get high. It was always easy to find an excuse to get drunk in LA. After all what else was there to do? The two happy friends open to meeting new people, forever chasing a good time, got hammered before returning to jail. It had been quite a day. Inane office shopping could be tackled with a headache as punishment. Although The Girls had failed to source new art, The Pavlovas were a real eye opener as to what might lie ahead in the strange world of LA LA Land.

They needed a new phone system and some flashy headed paper for the gallery. Working with a hangover was a skill they had perfected over the years and working with technology bored them to death so combining the two seemed sensible. If their business was to become a raging success, they had to at least appear to be doing some work. In truth that prospect was about as appealing as having sex with one's Jailer, God forbid.

Dom, bless him, had a fax machine, an item relegated to an unnecessary purchase when considered against the new season's Chanel sunglasses, screaming come in and buy me. Clive, the geek, had 3D technology coming out of the wazoo, bringing to the forefront another of The Girls oh so important principles. Why have a dog and bark yourself? With female charm they set out to make Dullard do some work, hooking up their network and connecting their internet access. Finding office furniture was the perfect job for the jailer husbands. Keeping them busy and off the war path was definitely a priority. All in all, things were beginning to take shape at the new gallery. They had some Russian Art, Clive had the technology, Dom had a fax machine and the Chanel sunglasses looked fabulous. The only thing missing was an essential line of credit.

"Gold American Express cards, that's what we need, someone else to pay, temporarily"

Being poor, was not an option. The Girl's had been forced to open the art gallery in the first place after making the fatal mistake of marring for looks not money. Living in LA without cash was brutal. They liked the good things in life far too much. American Express would become their new sleeping partner and finance some essential client entertaining until they managed to sell the art. Yes American Express would do nicely for the time being.

The carefully completed application form winged its way to Credit Card Land and within days their first piece of mail was delivered to the gallery.

"How fantastic, two gold cards with Art Interiors, proudly punched and firmly embedded."

"Let's do lunch at the Peninsula Hotel."

"According to W. Michael Caine often pops in there."

"Good. He might buy some art." Art Interiors, the company was now liquid providing the perfect excuse to have a celebration lunch, just to try out the card of course.

Their first corporate business lunch proved to be tricky. They didn't have a client to invite although no clients had ever stopped them lunching before. Always hopeful, forever positive they felt sure their first art buyer would be sitting at the next table.

The Girls had a global theory. Going out for lunch was about stalking the rich, getting the tab picked up and hopefully having some sport on the side. Their strategy never failed to work wherever they found themselves in the world. It was simple logic and about truth. Go to the best and one will encounter the best and if one is going to drop one's knickers for a boy and we all do at some point, make him pay for the privilege. So the hunt began for a rich, old client with failing eyesight and a bad memory. The Girls could spot them a mile away.

Making a reservation in such a popular eatery needed careful planning to pull off. The request, for a highly sought after table, had to be delivered with style and self importance.

"Good afternoon. We would like a table for lunch in your fabulous restaurant. I wonder, do you think you might squeeze in two ferociously hungry Europeans on a table outside? We smoke more than we eat. We drink as much as we smoke. We hear you have an impressive wine list. What was your name?" The Girls had a reservation and a fabulous adventure out was anticipated. American Express would treat. They hated overt rudeness in any form but being pleasant to people in Los Angeles got one nowhere. Attitude was everything to avoid being trampled on. Unfortunately, if you sound like someone difficult in LA LA Land, people automatically assume you are someone important. That's how it works.

When the day of the lunch arrived coincidentally, both were dressed identically in vintage black and white Chanel. They never planned it that way. It just happened like that. A clip from the twilight zone, two focused women ready to face the world of endless possibilities having lunch in a Beverly Hills hotel. The perfect opportunity to drink wine, smoke, then bag an art buying elephant just like Bud Fox in the classic movie, Wall Street. Take Tinsel town by the balls? How hard would it be make friends with Michael Caine? They did know him from Langans Brasserie, Stratton Street, London, after all.

They had no worries leaving the gallery unmanned while they lunched. Art Interiors had taken over; paintings on every wall, filling every space. Dom loved it and Clive Dullarce, as they had now appropriately nick named him, had no choice. He was under their spell. Flirting with a giant hedgehog sober was not easy but having someone to answer the phone if it rang, crucial. Their feminine charm always worked on the ugly ones. Dullarse, one of those star struck wannabes, always fell for it, making him the perfect stand in receptionist.

"We are off to lunch with Michael Caine, 'Don't shoot those bloody arrows at me.' Remember Zulu? If the phones rings be a love and answer Art Interiors. We are at the Peninsula if it's urgent."

The Peninsula Hotel, Beverly Hills was busy that particular day. Obscenely rich folk mingling around the front entrance all checking each other out. What stupidity. The Girls confidently glided by the busy crowd with one mission in mind, to get to their table, have an aperitif and a much needed fag. It was 11.30am, perfect timing. A large gin and tonic with a huge slice of lemon beckoned.

"Nice place, real linen."

"Looks like we could be in trouble, the water list is more extensive than the wine list. Is that not odd to you?" No matter how much they tried to work out the LA lunch protocol, they didn't get it. They liked to linger, savor the moment and make lunch last for hours. The whole rushed eating out experience in Los Angeles just didn't do it for them. Always looking to be proved wrong they spotted a potential victim, a bald overweight Arab in a pale blue suit, greedily guzzling a nice big bottle of expensive champagne.

"Things are looking up, alone and rich."

"You flirt with him first. Didn't you shag an Arab once?"

"That's why now it's your turn. Smile." With the tilt of a glass and the flash of a thigh, the fat Arab was lulled into a false sense of security. He found himself at their table and at their mercy, principled Slappers' salesmanship at its very best.

Little did he know, at that point, any sexual contact was a no no and just by joining their table, he was in for footing the bill.

He stank to high heaven of rather cheap aftershave. The stench was overpowering as he tried to kiss them both on the lips. Brave. His gold jewelry was abundant, real yet horribly tasteless. Not the most perfect shape to be dressing in pale blue but all things considered, he was quite a pleasant chap for an Arab. He introduced himself as Ali Khan, playboy and gambler, with a passion for curves and cards. Perfect. He liked playing games. The waiter, heading for a hefty tip, swiftly came through with a deck.

"So Mr. Kahn what exactly do you do?"

"Fancy a little flutter? Bridge is our game."

Questions were casually asked as he kicked their butts. Two on one with a blind hand and they still couldn't beat him. It could only happen to these two. It turned out the portly Middle Eastern gentleman, the potential art buying rich client, was nothing more than a slimy arms dealer from Kuwait and certainly not the kind of customer one wants to associate with an up market art business. Good thing really as he didn't buy a painting. He did leave them with the telephone number of his art loving brother Aga however, a collector who lived in the Carlton International Hotel, Cannes. Ali had insisted The Girls call him before he retired. Their cellphone didn't run to international dialing so Plan B went into immediate effect.

"We'll just finish off the champers darling then join you for pudding in your suite. What number did you say?" As soon as Ali Khan was out of sight, The Girls rather large lunch tab was charged to suite four five four. They made a swift getaway but not before penning a thank you note for lunch, citing some major catastrophe at the office and leaving it at reception.

They were covered. Cannes was their favorite place in the entire world and Aga could turn out to be an ace in the hole the next time they found themselves with a free night in paradise. The Girls had spent the last fifteen years building a powerful international Rolodex. Aga Khan was the latest addition.

"This is our ticket to the film festival."

"So much for bumping into Michael Caine."

"Just means we will have to go back."

The drive back to the gallery was filled with chatter about lunch. One of the many downsides of lunching in LA was having to trick someone into paying the bill. It was so frightfully barbarous. In England, boys always paid for girls one way or another. For The Girls it was a much better system.

The Girls faced each day with verve and gusto. Just because one marries an American, it does not mean one has to become one. Getting up in the morning and going into the gallery was actually quite a treat and became the perfect excuse to escape jail. LA had offered them little excitement or opportunity up to now and the gallery instilled some hope they were on their way to becoming rich again. It was all about creating one's own destiny. There had to be someone out there to buy their art.

These girls were English and proud of it. In order to penetrate the rich art buying community, they had to have a solid plan. Of course marrying for money would have been a better plan. Oh well, there was always marijuana.

Was Los Angeles just a cultural void after all? Walking along Manhattan Beach Boulevard to the new gallery was not quite the same buzz as the days on Wall Street. Manhattan Beach was a ghost town at 10.00am and there was certainly no sexy pinstriped bankers anywhere in sight to buy their art. They were lucky if they spotted one other person. They made friends with Mark. He owned a small surfing and skateboarding shop, selling take out coffee as a sideline, to counteract the slow season. He was not a potential client but that was easy to overlook as he was quite definitely a young sexy guy to flirt outrageously with. Having the opportunity to lust after younger, good looking boys was crucial and they searched high and low to find one every day.

Mark wasn't a banker but he fitted the profile perfectly in the looks department and it was not long before The Girls had their very own coffee tab. It was the ideal solution to their cash flow problems. Mark could not take American Express for just one coffee but they could pay their tab with it at the end of the month. Now they just needed to find a way to park the car for free and life could not have been rosier in the fabulous world of Art Interiors. Well that was until they had to face Dullarse with his irritating habit of stating the obvious. The rent was late.

Dullarse had this annoying ability to wind them up with his small minded attitude to any dilemma. His monotone negativity was delivered with slip off your elbow regularity but The Girls never became accustomed to it. He couldn't grasp their solution as opposed to problem concept no matter how hard they tried to ram it home. In reality the poor chap had no idea what he was dealing with. The Girls had still not managed to sell one single piece of art so the rent payments were tough but with a little juggling here and there and lying when absolutely necessary, Dullarse had got his money. Somehow the rent had to be paid.

Ilia was very good for the gallery but far too focused on saving the fragile and ancient tradition of fresco. The Girls spent hours on the net just checking out the who's who in fresco but the reality was few had heard of the likes of Michelangelo in Los Angeles and to most, a fresco was a type of soda. Their research always seemed to lead them back to the religious connection to the art. The Vatican kept popping up like a Jack in the Box. Not the most perfect client for The Girls. Sharing a drink and a fag with the Pope didn't really do it for them so the prospect of selling fresco became an impossible chore. The Girls needed exposure, more exciting prospects. Something a little more stylish and a little less religious. Taking on more artists was the only way to attract new clients.

"How about putting an ad in a glossy?"

"Art in America looks good."

"Art Interiors, gallery of fine art and art agents to the stars, seeks genius to represent. Anyone can call them selves an art agent, right?"

"Where do those types hang?" And that was that. The internship into the world of advertising began. Placing an ad to attract a genius made complete sense. Hanging with the players in cool places was next on the agenda. By chance The Girls spotted an advert in the back of the art magazine. Christies Auctioneers, Beverly Hills were having a sale the following Monday evening, the main attraction going under the hammer, one of Andy Warhol's Poppy Series.

"Warhol's story is not dissimilar to Ilia's."

"Elton John likes his stuff I think."

"Do we need to be a member?"

The Girls never daunted by big ideas, both fearless and desperate for a sale, decided to take the plunge and attend the show. One has to think about the reality of such a bold move. Two English art dealers with not a pot to piss in, prepared to try anything for the sake of the art. Most people would run a mile. For The Girls, having to give lip service to important agents from New York, wealthy buyers from Japan and serious art collectors would not be so bad. There had to be fun somewhere in LA. It was just a case of sniffing it out.

Getting ready for such an event, easy and getting out on a Monday evening, a result. The perfect opportunity to have a few glasses of wine somewhere full of good looking, rich men, and stalk a potential art buying client. They picked out their most impressive attire. Black trouser suits with white crisp linen shirts, high heeled gold Gucci sandals, always a must when trying to impress anyone, and the faithful Louis Vuitton pouchettes. Looking hip and impressive, they were both ready to take on the world of fine art, strategizing at its best. Getting to Beverly Hills was straightforward. The car could get there on its' own yet in an attempt to look flash they hired a nice man to drive them. This gem of an idea created the perfect opportunity to smoke a giant spliff on the way. Just for Dutch courage you understand. As they reached their destination the unobtrusive entrance looked impressive. Welcome to Christies. The driver opened the door and out stepped the nicely buzzed Girls loving the attention of whispering passers by. Everything was perfect as they entered the huge marbled reception area. To be greeted by an over made up stern receptionist was not part of their plan. Was she a transsexual? Christies needed to revamp their H.R. department, she was awful.

"Good evening, we are here to look at some art."

"Perhaps you would be kind enough to point us in the direction of the bar?"

"You are kidding right? This is Christies?"

Always trying to get their priorities right but not tonight. There was no bar at Christies. It was one place where having a stiff drink after spending a wad made absolute sense. Surely they would have one in London? It was another reason to get rich and get out. In the blink of an eye Elvira, the receptionist turned into Inspector Clueso, demanding whether or not The Girls actually had an established account with Christies. Scary questions for a Monday evening. When The Girls gave it one more shot, one would have thought they had asked her for a free painting.

"Fill out forms?'

"What is our agreed credit limit?"

"She needs the details of our private accounts? Who is our private bank manager?"

"Not showing up in the London database?" Inspector Clueso's sympathetic and up until now silent sidekick told The Girls about Prego, a small Italian restaurant next door, the perfect place for a glass of wine and filling out the necessary forms at their leisure. This was music to their ears. Thank God she'd piped up. They had their excuse to leave, collect themselves and engineer an infallible Plan B in private. They spat out a quick thank you and escaped through the revolving door onto the busy street.

This was becoming a nightmare. Their bank balance was well below zero and their account, frozen solid. As you can imagine, this dilemma caused serious concern for the wannabe art dealers. Credit limit? That was tricky. Writing a forty dollar check for a catalog in its self a calculated risk just in case the thing bounced.

The first bottle in Prego disappeared virtually before the poor waiter had a chance to pour it, neither did nerves very well. The restaurant had outside seating. That was a blessing, something positive at least. The second bottle helped with the butterflies and gave The Girls a more confident approach to their dilemma.

"Just out snob. Its not Christies London is it darling?" Before the guard dog on reception had time to blink, The Girls had slipped through the net and seated themselves on the front row of the impressive auction room. Experts. The silence was deafening and the atmosphere electric, as the sexy black auctioneer, stylishly graced the high podium. She began to build a quiet chant. The Girls hearts pounded in their chests and they weren't even bidding. The sharp eager eyes of the room watched and waited, as the thrill of the exciting bidding reached its climax. A twelve inch by twelve inch painting by Andy Warhol sold for four hundred and twenty five thousand dollars to number five five five. Wow that was one hell of an orgasm for someone. This had to be a time to completely break the rules.

Apparently, according to company rules and auctioneer etiquette, one should never turn and gorpe at the buyer of a piece, however The Girls could not resist. They wanted to see who it was. Anyone stupid enough to spend close to half a million dollars on a Monday evening, on a painting the size of a record cover, had to be stark raving bonkers and quite possibly a potential client for them. It transpired the buyer was not even in the room. A broker had bid on his client's behalf, so once again the elusive art buying client was no where in sight. An art sale with no clients? Is that fucked up or what? It was back to the drawing board.

Although the whole evening had been a waste of time and somewhat dull, the same table in Prego was still empty. No one smokes in LA so everyone sits inside, even when it's hot as hell. On this occasion the same table was a blessing as they had stashed the remnants of the second bottle from earlier behind some potted geraniums nearby just in case they returned. They snaffled clean glasses from the next table and prayed they wouldn't get busted. Smoking like traders and people watching the arty crowd as it turned out of the auction they hoped to spot some corruptible passing crumpet to buy them another bottle.

"For God sake where have all the buyers gone?"

"We are in the hub of the art world and not a bite in sight." Things looked up when something sexy and fun glided by their table. Not bad looking and rather debonair. They forced their victim to a halt. Was he another art agent?

"Hello handsome, what's your name?" He joined the table and lit their cigarettes. He introduced himself as Rupert Durrant, art agent to the rich and famous. He was more handsome than George Clooney but bent as a nine bob note, just their luck. Life had to be about veracity and the two women shocked him talking openly about anal sex. They loved it and asked for some tips. He was a light at the end of a dark evening but he had nothing to offer their business. Rupert Durrant had no clients. Art Interiors he had no clients. Was this common in L.A? No matter how much experience one had or how many qualifications one had, it appeared no one had any clients except Christies and they remained anonymous protected by the austerity of the suited staff lined up on telephones relaying current price and bidding when instructed. Personal services redefined for The Girls. In truth, Rupert was no closer to selling a piece of art than they were. The

Girls quickly put his sketchy client list to shame. It was obviously just a question of who could drop the biggest name. Was he independently wealthy and just liked the title art dealer? Was it that impressive? The Girls didn't get it. They extinguished their fags, finished the wine and bid a fond farewell to Rupert Durrant. It was a good job they hadn't ordered another bottle. He didn't offer to pay. It was time to re think the plan and find new ways to source rich clients. They would sleep on it.

After a long day at the gallery following the Christies fiasco, The Girls decided to take a break and delve into a much needed bout of escapism, a hot bath, a little pot and some porno. The perfect plan to make up for the lack of sexual pleasure from The Jailers in the bedroom department. What luxury. The movie, 'Private Parts', jumped off the shelf in Blockbuster Video, ideal viewing for the evening ahead. The Girls headed back to jail, forever hopeful, always positive a miracle would happen and they finally might get to come. As it happened 'Private Parts'" had nothing to do with porno. It was Howard Sterns biography, a hilarious satirical story of the quirky genius journalist's rise to fame. What a fab flick. It was amazing. Would Howard come to the rescue and help them with their art? Packaging two middle aged women, well past their sell by date, for the sexy, controversial Stern would be tricky and a little unrealistic in the cold light of day, but if anyone could do it, they could.

"What could one do to get Howard's attention, when one cannot rely on thirty four, twenty four, thirty six?"

"I am not prepared to be humiliated on national TV, not even for a creative genius. The man is brutal."

"I'll do it. I will show him my body, it's good."

"Not in his world, trust me. He lives at Scores."

The Pussy Galore notebook was dusted off in search the perfect body for Howard. It was the only way they could think of to get on the show. Howard was fussy and they knew what he liked. Based on the movie, the art alone would be useless. The sacrifice chosen, young, tall, thin, blond and completely shaven down below. Howard was wild and things could potentially go a rye so The Girls would assume the position. Brains behind the beauty and the essential damage control for the fabulous free spirit who told the truth better than anyone else in Television Land. He was the perfect person to build an alliance with, especially if they could come up with a sexual pitch to tickle his fancy. The red was open and breathing and a giant spliff was rolled. The Girls took a trip to the Land of Creative Ideas, where anything is truly possible.

"He likes to play games. How about strip poker? "

"Forget it. He'll have us all naked."

"We take the naked blond along for eye candy, get Howard and his gang drawing their interpretation of a clitoris from memory, then plug the art at the end of the show."

"An art come sex game. Draw the perfect shape of a clitoris. Tricky for men. Clitoris Pictionary?"

"You are a genius, Howard will love The Pussy Galore Girls." The pitch for "Clitoris Pictionary" was written and faxed over to the Howard Stern Show in New York, asking him to join them for a bit of fun. The media exposure for Art Interiors would be phenomenal or so they thought. Within a matter of hours Howard replied, via one of his throng of extremely pretty interns. The pitch sounded good, something Howard would enjoy but in the land of television, he needed some visual evidence. He needed to know what The Girls looked like before he would consider their fabulous plan.

"Make a mental note, must get some pictures taken." Not trying to run before one can walk was the lesson. They were art dealers not celebrities. Although Howard was someone they loved to death, getting his attention would take much more research. They would revisit that genius later down the road, armor on and better prepared. Clitoris Pictionary was a brilliant idea. If they couldn't use it with Howard immediately, they would surely find a willing participant/victim soon, to practice on.

The following morning a copy of The Beach Reporter was delivered. It was Thursday. Being focused and not too hung over for once, produced another incredible idea to move forward. Sheer genius. The Girls were ever hopeful and always positive.

"Let's place another ad locally and see what comes from it. You never know, the next Rembrandt could be down on the Strand polishing his surfboard"

"Just waiting for a copy of the Beach Reporter to land on his lap?" Writing ad copy comes quite easily when one has an over inflated opinion of ones self. Something these Girls did bring to the party. The ad was written and set in stone. This plan would produce the big break.

"Art Interiors fine art consultants, offering original works and commissions by an array of talented artists. Murals. Frescos. Sculptures. Call this number blah blah blah."

Getting the name Art Interiors out there was imperative and the ad looked amazing as it hit the stands and was given out in droves the following week. There was the small problem of the six hundred dollars to pay for it. Oh that worry had to be shelved on such a glorious occasion. It was almost eleven thirty. American Express having been allocated the minimum payment was still working. A nice celebration lunch beckoned. The card would do nicely.

It was not long before two perfectly prepared cosmopolitans stared them in the face from the long wooden bar in McCormick and Schmit, Manhattan Beach, a local watering hole where one can puff on a cigarette until the cows come home. It was one of the very few places in Los Angeles where one could combine smoking, drinking and eating all while seated at the same table. The very beautiful poor waitress, come actress was about to encounter the experience of a lifetime, as The Girls turned the whole afternoon into a passage from the Pussy Galore Notebook. More than one drink was always fatal. Mimi, the waitress, rather taken with The Girls would become the next entry.

It worked like this. Whenever they spotted someone young and gorgeous, they would try and recruit them for future business events. A hot young girl always comes in handy with dirty old male clients. Sex sells.

THE PITCH

"Have you ever considered how much money you could earn if you escorted a rich older man to dinner?"

"It has to be better than serving drinks."

"You are so pretty, so young."

"No sex, of course. What do you think?" The Girls had ideas for new businesses coming out of the wazoo and an up market escort service was firmly in place for later down the road. The Pussy Galore Notebook, always poised and ready to be filled at any opportunity they exchanged telephone numbers with Miss Mimi Bellini. After too many cocktails the pitch never failed.

"Did we really down six cosmopolitans and a bottle of white wine?"

"Did we really offer that poor girl a job as a hooker?"

"Did she really accept?" Even though they still didn't have a client, it was crucial to plan ahead. Mimi was sold but the moment was over. As The Girls left the restaurant they were ever hopeful, always positive the phone would be ringing off the hook by the time they returned to work.

Back at the gallery boring old Dullarce had already gone for the day leaving Dom Slong Perigon alone in the hands of two drunken liberated women, desperate for a flirt and some mischief, before returning home to The Jailers. Facing a dead corpse and an over sexed maniac, neither capable of downing a full glass of wine made the thought of playing mind games with Dom much more interesting.

"Fancy a game of Clitoris Pictionary?"

"It's an English dinner party game."

"You just draw your interpretation of a clitoris"

"Do you know how many men get that simple task wrong? One retard drew a square." The sound of Art Interiors' telephone ringing for the first time in ages let Dom off the hook. Mortified, ripped to shreds and humiliated beyond recognition he grabbed his coat and high tailed it out of there bidding good night, to the two tipsy women. The excitement of someone actually calling sobered them up and activated battle mode. The Girls answered with aplomb, fingers crossed they were about to close a deal. It was Ilia ranting on about a meeting with a potential client. Fabulous. At last.

Another day without a deal, but Ilia had come up with a lead that could potentially make them some cash. A lunch to discuss business made complete sense to all in the moment and was something to look forward to. Were they mad? Tomorrow they'd be hung over as hell.

Texas Tech University had an opportunity for everyone concerned. An outside table at the Bottle Inn, Hermosa Beach, a local eatery where the owner is renowned for his liquid lunches and the minestrone soup isn't bad was chosen to discuss the finer details. Ilia arrived promptly at the gallery at noon, a cross between Picasso and a Russian Mafia boss, moody and dangerous. Surprisingly less hung over than anticipated they both found him sexual in a primitive way, making them compete for his attention. Ilia loved the flattery. He was a good manipulator who always had fags. Three people, all smoking needed strategic planning. He impressed his two new evangelists thinking he'd planned ahead. Not. The white serial killer van with a huge sliding door was unacceptable wheels for two gallery owners from Manhattan Beach to been seen in so Ilia was instructed to drive their car, handed some cash and reminded to tip the valet generously.

When they arrived at the restaurant, it was empty. It was always empty come to that. No one ever goes to lunch in Hermosa Beach. A strange concept all three could not get their heads around. Once seated it didn't take long for Ilia to order almost everything edible on the menu. The Girls were satiated by the superb vista from the ocean adjacent patio and their starving artist was in full swing. He downed his second glass of wine while lighting his fourth fag and began delivering his drawn out pitch. Texas Tech University were planning a rare Fresco exhibition, June 2002. Never before seen frescoes from Vatican City, Rome were coming to Lubbock, Texas. Was he sure? One thing was certain, Ilia wanted to be there.

It sounded about as exciting as a glass of mineral water, hardly the most prestigious project on the planet, but there again, optimism. The media attention from such an event would be massive and promotion of their genius, a sinch. Was the Catholic Church ready for The Girls?

As the two worked their ideas into a frenzy, asking the passing waiter if he had heard of a place called Lubbock, Ilia poured more wine and saw his dream beginning to realize. Taking a Russian Fresco master to a huge well publicized art event was turning into a real possibility. After all, Ilia had exhibited his work in the Treticov Museum, Moscow. It was clear Texas Tech needed an expert, a modern day genius and they had one out to lunch.

It was time to pin Ilia down and make him sign a contract. Selling his paintings in the gallery was one thing but managing his genius would take investment, something they did not have much of. It took many packets of fags and too many bottles of red to kill his ego but a deal was eventually struck. They would go back to Texas Tech on Ilia's behalf and pitch the job. The profit to be split three ways. The whole idea of working with a museum on a religious period of Fresco history was not the most realistic symbiosis, especially after such a long lunch but The Girls decided to embrace the opportunity and enjoyed a glimmer of possible success. The next day the reality of the project began to set in.

"The Vatican? Where the fuck does one start when one wants to stalk the Pope?"

With monumental two day hangovers and full of drunken remorse The Girls arrived at the gallery hoping Ilia had got it all wrong and the stupid exhibition, was just a figment of his bizarre imagination. No such luck. There written in bold italic writing, looking very impressive on what normally appeared as a rather dull website, the Texas Tech University proudly announced their up and coming Fresco exhibition. Ten, thirteenth century, never before seen frescoes, were being flown courtesy of Continental Airlines from The Vatican for all to see.

"Look here it says contact Lee Brodie, the curator." Pitching their first project with a high profile art consortium was somewhat daunting for two birds from Yorkshire. Although they both had a fair knowledge of art history, Ilia was the expert on Fresco. Could they pull out enough key lines to convince Lee Brodie Art Interiors was the answer to her prayers? That was the all important question before making the call. It was decided. They would go back to The Beach Cottage, have a pow wow, drink some wine and prepare. It was at that point in their business, the "How Many Bottles Of Wine" canvas call was invented. The rules were pretty straightforward.

THE ONE BOTTLE CANVAS CALL
Enough "Dutch" courage to call those they knew would at least take the call and be somewhat polite in the process.

THE TWO BOTTLE CANVAS CALL
Sufficient joie de vivre for folk they had called in previous drunken sessions. Most of whom now had some inclination, these women from Art Interiors were stark

raving bonkers. They were inclined to hang up immediately and last but not least;

THE THREE BOTTLE CANVAS CALL

Euphoria. The perfect opportunity to stalk the unattainable and make complete fools of themselves. They loved these calls, always working towards perfection every day.

The system worked very well although a damage control policy, "Plan B." was put in place to always ensure things ran smoothly in their everyday business antics. Always one step ahead, Damage Control was designed to swiftly clean up any mess or possible negative come back. An ingenious policy, which turned out to be a complete waste of time, as no one ever calls you back in Hollywood.

Lee Brodie the curator. Her name alone was enough to make a nun turn to drink. The Girls batted the task of calling her back and forth. It was executed after two bottles. The English accent always seemed to make the job of bull shitting a little easier as Lee spilled the beans. She wanted Ilia to attend the exhibition the following summer, June 2002 and present a live demonstration of the Fresco technique to awaiting audiences. The queues predicted sounded horrific. It would give visitors an insight into what to expect from the Vatican exhibition apparently. It sounded too good to be true. Then she dropped the bomb shell. They had no spare cash to pay anyone. Ilia would have to find his own sponsor? The Girls resorted to bull shitting and pulled out some big names. Micro-soft, Mercedes Benz, Miramax Films, all companies recognized for their philanthropic contributions to the arts. Getting sponsorship for such a project would be plant food. Wouldn't it? They had her ear and were ready to close her. Lee was excited by their energy. They left her with something to think about.

"Ilia is currently in the process of setting up the First American Fresco School here in LA. This would be an ideal opportunity to offer his talented students the chance to really paint fresco."

The frescoes created by the students during the live demonstrations would be used as gifts to the corporate sponsors in appreciation. Lee was sold. It was amazing what one could pull out of ones' arse in crisis. She told them to put their proposal in writing. She needed to run it by the museum board of directors and then organize a trip for the art trio to visit Lubbock. This was a major result for Art Interiors. Now it was just a case of raising some funds to set up the school and finance the project. Harvey had to have some loose change to throw at art. He was a collector.

After having the door well and truly slammed by Sherri Lansing's people at

Paramount, rude bastards, phoning Miramax to ask for help seemed like a good plan. They decided to go for a gentler giant or so they hoped. How hard would it be to talk to Harvey Weinstein? He was just a bloke after all. Someone they both admired for his independent approach to the movie industry, the expert bridge builder between creation and execution and someone they would love to meet. Nerves aside, they called Miramax Films, New York. The level of excitement was explosive. They had something fabulous to tell Harvey.

After being transferred from assistant to assistant it was soon clear, getting to the top was not as easy as one would think. Let's not forget, these two are good, experts in fact. The outcome of the call was plain. All requests had to sent by fax to his office and someone would get back to them. They had been shut down. It was decided to call Ilia and get him motivated. They had money to raise. Writing to Harvey and the rest of corporate America was a job to be tackled sober the next day.

The sun shines every day in Manhattan Beach. It made getting out of bed a pleasure for two such lovers of life. Having something creative to focus on, their project with the Vatican, made living in Los Angeles not that bad. Over a cup of coffee and a fag in the gallery, the two bragged about their triumph and new dealings with Miramax. Dullarce had dollar signs in his eyes, the rent needed paying. Dom was impressed. Composing a begging letter was the first task of the day. They needed a sponsor with lots of cash and an interest in art. Writing to Harvey was easy. They had already decided he was their number one choice and honored him by asking him to be the Patron of the First American Fresco School. In return for his support to the Vatican project he would receive the contemporary fresco panels to be created during the exhibition and shown beside the ancient relics from across the sea. The fax was sent to New York with a true belief that Harvey would come to the rescue and save the day. Stalking the rich and famous for money to support art was quite empowering that day and induced an impromptu lunch with Ilia. Celebrating success was an essential ingredient for future success.

Getting to understand the mind of a Russian genius was always fascinating and Ilia moved in dangerous circles. Having lunch on his turf excited them both. Three days hence? How come he was so busy all of a sudden?

That first visit to his small concrete gray apartment was a swift realization of his poverty status. Whatever he was up to was certainly not lucrative. It made the mission to elevate him even more essential as they collected their artist for lunch.

His choice of venue, a small local drinking haunt filled with Eastern Europeans and renowned for its selection of vodkas. The food was simple. Fried whole chickens served by a toothless chef in a dirty apron, singing his head off to Italian Opera. It was pure theater, quite a find in LA.

Ilia introduced the English Girls as his new agents to three men on stools at the bar and enthused about finally being recognized. This lunch was on him. Ideas for the project began to emerge as the three active imaginations merged in art, life and aliens from space. If they could pull this off anything was possible. Lunch turned into cocktails as the sun set and the sky blackened. Telling Ilia about begging Harvey for investment gave The Girls such a high. If anyone deserved fame and fortune it was the starving genius.

After hours drinking vodka shots interspersed with cheap red wine, everyone in the bar looked like a potential client and selling art to anyone who would listen, their top priority. Playing pool with two hard nosed Russian customers to promote art seemed like a good plan and The Girls moved in on their victims. Mixing business with pleasure had always produced results in the past. All was well until Ilia delivered some vital information about the dodgy duo. These guys were not there to buy art. They were on the run from the Moscow police department after actually shooting two gallery owners in 1999. Suffice to say that was enough reality to bring the mayhem to a close.

The following day, hangover alert! A board meeting was held to discuss the state of play with Art Interiors. The ads in various magazines had not worked and finding a client was like finding a needle in a hay stack. Unlikely.

"We have a potential project but no money to pull it off and no way of letting the rest of the world know."

"We have a genius with a rare skill"

"We need a press release."

The day was spent on the computer creating a story that would get the media jumping. Someone out there in LA LA Land had to understand their plight. After all it's not every day an LA artist is asked to work with the Pope. The fax machine almost blew a gasket as the clock struck eleven thirty. Every news channel including Larry King had their story. It was now just a matter of time before someone came to the rescue.

A few days passed and some basic communication took place between Lee Brodie and Art Interiors. Texas Tech had received the proposal and liked what they heard. She just needed the nod from the top. Harvey Weinstein had still not responded to their kind offer of becoming Patron of the school and it seemed that the news media didn't give a toss about art. The phone was not ringing.

"If at first you don't succeed try and try again. Winston Churchill said, never ever give up."

Calling Harvey sober to follow up was essential. They knew from previous calls that getting to him required a sharp mind and honed stalking skills. It was time to build a relationship with someone in Miramax who could get them Harvey's ear, the assistant's assistant. Making friends with someone too busy to even take the call, was the first hurdle. It seemed that even his assistants were impenetrable as The Girls were politely told, yet again, to put it all down in a fax and re submit their request. Back to square one.

Promoting the Vatican exhibition, even though they didn't quite have the go ahead, was the only way to get Ilia noticed. They had already put the details on their redundant yet fabulous website www.artofinteriors.com.

"Appointed art consultants for the Vatican exhibition, June 2002." A slight exaggeration and a little premature but my God it looked impressive, especially to The Jailers who were now convinced the art business was just a cover to get completely smashed now and again. As if? The business had a real art project and The Girls were full of it, telling anyone who would listen. Clive Dullarse suddenly seemed more confident about getting his stupid rent check and as for Ilia, he was blown away with the Girl's dedication to art. At last they had a purpose. It was just a case of waiting for further instructions.

One afternoon completely out of the blue, they got a call from ABC news Lubbock. A rather loud woman, Rebecca Cruse, no relation to Penelope unfortunately or Tom for that matter, called about Ilia's attendance at the exhibition. How did she know? Was it official? She wanted to interview him? Not bad for the only call of the week. Being interviewed by the media was a huge result for The Girls from Yorkshire and capitalizing on every second a must. Once again they had their excuse, a celebration lunch. As The Girls planned for their first taste of fame and fortune it was excitement all the way to the bar.

"Fame at last. We have to be at the CNN building at ten."

"You know we need to loose 10lbs. The camera makes you look fat"

With little time for preparation after an essential early night, they left the gallery the following morning looking amazing in matching black leather pants and black T shirts. Always good to slim one down. The destination, CNN on Sunset Boulevard, home to Mr. Larry King. America's answer to David Frost. They were ready to take on the great and magnificent but first they had to collect the star of the show.

Sometimes nothing works. Being interviewed by the media was the first step to get Ilia his much needed exposure and he looked terrible. His off white shirt had seen better days but sadly, never an iron. It did not match his only pair of heavy gray flannel pants. He was unshaven and his hair was, well, let's just say "unkempt". The yellow nicotine stained teeth posed a potential problem for the camera but hopefully CNN would stretch to a good make up artist. The Girls made a quick plan and gave him some much needed advice.

"Just sit there looking deep and artistic, we'll do all the talking."

"We don't want to give Larry heart failure."

"It's live TV darling, your big break, can we rethink the outfit."

"Have you showered recently?"

"Something a little more updated, Picasso with a twist perhaps."

Ilia had no other wardrobe options so The Girls added a few accessories of their own. An Hermes scarf, a Versace belt. Better. They arrived at the impressive CNN building full of spirit and ready to tell America about fresco. Everything was perfect. After signing the visitor's book, the unlikely trio made their way to the green room. It was not remotely as The Girls had expected. In fact it was nothing more than a small room with cheap furniture and paper cups. The first class lounge at Heathrow airport? Not even close.

"Well it's not London is it darling?"

"A stiff drink and some peanuts would go down a treat now, steady the nerves."

It soon became evident to all concerned being interviewed was not remotely glamorous and certainly not the way it played out in the movies. CNN needed some art on the walls. It was a television studio for Gods sake. Two young girls wearing scruffy jeans and baseball caps, no older than 20, suddenly entered the room. They had come to escort the three guests to the small, poky studio with a blue skyline backdrop. Nothing flash about that either.

"Excuse me but do we get an opportunity to go over our lines before we meet Larry King?"

"Surely he doesn't broadcast from such a small studio?"

"Where is Larry?"

It was clear from the young girl's blank expressions they were just temps hired by the hour. The studio had been booked by local ABC news in Lubbock and satellite video did it all. It had nothing to do with Larry King. In fact it had nothing to do with CNN.

With no time to think they were miked up and raring to go. Ilia, stuck in the middle, was grinning like a Cheshire cat on crack. The invisible reporter on the other end of the phone with his deep Southern drawl, made the whole thing fun. They certainly got their first taste of life in Television Land, even if Larry King was nowhere in sight. They told the world about Fresco, about Lubbock and about Art Interiors. They made Ilia sound like the next Michelangelo. The interview was magnificent, so polished. Poor Ilia, couldn't get a word in. It was perfect. Feeling extremely positive about their gritty exciting performance, they were shown back to the green room to freshen up before heading off for a celebration lunch. The Russian artist was over the moon, his head so big it blocked out the sunlight.

"One interview and he thinks he's famous."

"There is only one famous man here, we need to find Larry."

With a new found taste for fame and fortune, they decided to try the Ivy, on Robertson for a spot of lunch, a rather flash expensive eatery in Beverly Hills. They were on that side of town. It was the kind of place one might catch Tom Cruise having a bite to eat. The paparazzi lining Robertson Boulevard was evidence of that.

Inviting Larry King along was the plan. They could tell him their story over a chilled bottle of Chablis. Picking up the in house phone they dialed every extension until bingo. This, something these two divas had down to a fine art. It turned out Larry's assistant was busy powdering her nose, so they got the temp assistant, who was standing in for the assistants, assistant.

Larry to join The Girls for lunch? She had no idea what to make of the bubbly request but she was helpful within her own limited capacity. Put the request in writing and fax it across to Larry's first assistant, who would deal with it when she returned. But they were in the building. They didn't understand. This was their first taste of life in the land of celebrity. It was enough to confuse Confucius. Oh well one thing was clear. They didn't have their fax machine handy so Larry would not be joining them for lunch.

Valet parking is such a luxury, being made to feel special regardless of status and The Ivy knows just how to get it right. Both being big headed sods, The Girls liked that. Once seated, in a chintz covered corner on the patio The Girls gregariously ordered some oysters to show off, two huge platters of translucent, succulent mollusks on ice with a twist of lemon and a dash of Tabasco. One compared the oyster experience to swallowing precious pearls from the bottom of the ocean, delicious. For the other it was more akin to swallowing a dollop of male sperm, disgusting. And Ilia? Well he would eat anything as long as it was free.

The Girls with their Russian painter, told anyone in The Ivy who would listen about the ABC interview. As the appointed art consultants for the up and coming Vatican exhibition it sounded so fantastic, so impressive. Such a lie but what the hell. This was Hollywood. Didn't everyone lie? It is amazing how the name dropping theory works in LA LA Land. Their small table was heaving with interested bodies from inside tables out to smoke. Those strange American people who say they don't smoke but like the occasional one after food? Everybody's mobile was ringing off the hook. The Look How Important I Am syndrome made The Girls puke. Then out of the blue, their mobile rang. It never rang.

Were they in the twilight zone? They did want to join the Hollywood jet set. This was perfect. The three European drunks interviewed by the media and working with the Pope, suddenly had every ones attention. Looking extremely important and very professional, the call was answered.

"Please do excuse me for a moment it could be the Vatican." Don't hold your breath it wasn't the Pope. Dullarse was chasing the rent. The phone went dead, click. It's amazing how bad the reception can be in LA.

This tale is full of long lunches. In fact it is one big lunch from start to finish. However lunch that day ended at two sharp as the staff hovered over any lingering luncheon patrons. It truly was a one hour power lunch that day. The staff had a private party to prepare for so without further incident another day came to an end with no clients and not a sale in sight.

One would have thought being English in Los Angeles advantageous but seemingly not. They had met several supposed art buyers out socially and had exchanged cards on more than one occasion but no one ever rang back when The Girls called to follow up. Lying was so prevalent in LA LA Land it was a job in itself to separate fact from fiction whenever one met anyone new. It hit them like a club. Making powerful connected contacts, who didn't need to lie was the only way to go. This model had worked like a charm in London and their business had flourished. It was decided. Using the news story over lunch, had made them feel positive and focused. The Girls began the essential celebrity rolodex and Larry King's name was added next to Harvey's. He had to be useful for something in the world of art. It was just a question of finding him the right job.

"Patron for the Fresco School?"

"Harvey isn't biting our hands off for the job."

Ilia had been pestering The Girls for ages to find someone famous for the role. They were committed or needing committing. I'm not quite sure which at that point. Was Harvey just another geezer with short arms and deep pockets? Was Larry a good choice to visit Lubbock and hang with the Pope? So many questions. It was time to find out some answers. A three-bottle day was looming, as they drove away from the Ivy and the sun set over LA LA Land. At nine am sharp a well written begging fax, faxed its way to CNN, as instructed by the temp assistant the day before.

Dear Larry,
We are The Girls. We represent a Russian artist with a rare gift, a Fresco master. One of five in the world. A genius, a modern day Michelangelo and a man you should meet. We are seeking a celebrity Patron for the First American Fresco School, here in L.A. Our mission is to take this Russian genius to Lubbock Texas

and ensure he gets the recognition he deserves. We need your help with some high profile media attention to help promote the revival of Fresco.
Regards.

That letter marked the beginning of the junior stalking phase and The Girls liked it. Sending a fax to a media giant and asking for help with art, seemed the ideal solution. With someone as powerful as Larry King on their side, the task of promoting Ilia's dream would become much easier. Getting to famous people was the only thing to do.

A few months earlier they had met a celebrity chef on a wild night out in Hollywood. Thatcher Pike had bragged all night about his list, a complete spreadsheet of Hollywood celebrities' agents and publicists, all with telephone numbers and addresses. The thing was priceless. His old crumpled business card was retrieved from the bottom of a pouchette and the call was made.

"Did you snog him?"

"For The List, what do you think?"

It turned out the kiss and some random suggestion of dinner at home for twenty worked as The List was immediately faxed over. They could not believe their eyes. The Girls now had personal phone numbers for everyone from Tom Cruise to Elton John, what a stroke of luck. This was just the break they needed.

Making big calls to the Hollywood elite after three bottles of red was easy. They went straight for the ICA agents to the best players in town. The receptionist was good as she swiftly put them onto client information. It was a question of grilling the assistant like a kipper and finding out who worked for whom. How naive they were then. It would take more than three bottles to bag this elephant. Even the assistant had a pit-bull terrier assistant positioned and growling on the other end of the line. She was putting no one through to her boss's, boss's boss. Poised to abort the call she cast them aside like old rotten rags and then had the nerve to slam down the phone. Without even saying goodbye. Whatever happened to manners for God sake.

Getting an agent to promote art to their list of celebrities looked tricky. So much for representation. This was impenetrable shielding with an electromagnetic twist. A new plan was needed and fast. A good observation considering The Girls were thinking about opening a forth bottle of red.

The stakes got higher. One name appeared over and over again. Cece York seemed like the ideal victim to impress. She looked after a whole group of the being they called illusive celebrity including Catherine Zeta Jones. They needed an angle to get by the ever present assistant. Reluctantly, they were forced to lie.

"Rusty Lush, editor of Hello magazine London. I am in LA and would love to gossip with Cece. We have the same hairdresser."

"Rusty Lush?"

"Is she free for a quick word?"

The assistant was not being fooled. She told them to fax over any requests they had in writing. It was another dead end. Although they had failed miserably to get to Cece York, they did get a taste of how the closed shop works.

"If it's that hard to talk to the agent, imagine trying to get to Harvey?"

This California jungle was becoming a surfing safari for The Girls. They wanted to say something important about art but no one would listen. It was maddening. They spent the next hour thinking about who they should contact if Larry King turned them down. They needed a big shot film star, Hollywood clout with a religious twist. Someone the rest of the world would take notice of. Having done some research on Hollywood's art collectors, Charlton Heston's name popped up. Steve Martin, Dennis Hopper, Jack Nicholson and Sylvester Stallone were the other choices but Moses was selected. He was a Hollywood legend, older than God and still working, bless him. No recent mega roles but he still had pull in Hollywood circles. If the truth be known they thought he'd be the easiest to close. The Girls composed a fax begging Charlton Heston for his help with their art projects. Would he consider being Patron of the Fresco school? He had played Michelangelo hadn't he?

They scanned the list for his Hollywood publicist and there it was. Charlton? Would he save the day and become their El Cid? Surely it was better than a B role in True Lies with Arnold Schwarzenegger? Pissed as farts the fax went to Agent Land, hopes were high, fingers and eyes crossed. Things were looking quite rosy in their stewed state. They now had a plan and a potential celebrity. All the ingredients one needs for a whopping big success story, anywhere other than LA LA Land, were in place. They returned to jail happy.

The following day with huge hangovers, the fun was over. It was already October. Time to take the plunge and visit Lubbock and the museum. It was not the most exciting prospect but someone had to do it if a contract was ever to materialize. Lee had still not firmed up a plan and the clock was ticking. It was essential to sign a contract with Texas Tech, in order to hook the necessary sponsor.

Trying to do research on Lubbock led them straight to a dead end. It was impossible to find anyone who had ever heard of the place let alone actually been there. However a contract, was a contract, was a contract, as they say in Jewish circles and so the first Art Interiors business trip was planned for two weeks hence. The good old American Express card was dusted off and taken out for a spin. Three flights were booked. Fourteen day advance fares. They were forced to take

Ilia along for his knowledge of fresco. The Girls rarely intimidated, as their knowledge of European art was pretty good, but the museum mob sounded duller than dish water so Ilia had to pull his weight. The museum loved the spontaneity and embraced the rendezvous. Two weeks notice was obviously spontaneous in Lubbock. That was scary in itself but Lee gave instructions on where to stay and how to get to the University campus. All was well.

The day of the trip started out sunny and optimistic, as the three art experts left home for the airport. Things had been less eventful than usual at the gallery so they were all ready to go gangbusters. They walked through the terminal with a hint of snobbery and a taste of Russia. Everyone was staring. The Girls always put on a good show whenever traveling. It was a showing off kind of thing. A skill one is born with. Always carry posh luggage and wear the right shoes. Unfortunately when traveling with South – West Airlines, turning left put them right slam-dunk on the Captains lap so the first rule of the day when flying was swiftly broken.

It just had to be one of those times, when one grits ones teeth and makes the most of a terrible situation. Shock. Horror. That explained why the tickets were so cheap. What was this nightmare turning into? The Girls flying economy?

"This could be fun boys but you have a plane to fly and we have a drink to order."

The air steward was very nice once he got with the program. A promise of a blow job in mid air was made if he kept the drinks freely flowing. He was very naïve. He never got the blowjob, bless him but they said they would call the next time they were forced to travel cattle class.

As the three fell off the plane in Lubbock pissed as farts, in temperatures below freezing, the shock was enough to sober up a judge. (An English one of course)

"Fuck where the hell are we? Siberia? It's fucking freezing."

"Let's just find the nearest bar and pray to God we are in the right country."

Three drunks in a snow storm with not a cocktail in sight, wearing high heels and little else for a day out in a blizzard, The Girls were about to encounter a situation one would only find in pure hell. A place with no alcohol? What was this? The Middle East? Someone somewhere had to have booze. They just needed to find it.

They arrived at the hotel desperate to clean up and relax before hitting the night life. The hunt for red wine began, praying the hotel had its own rules and could provide a well stocked mini bar. No such luck. The over weight male receptionist, needing a sun tan in the worst possible way, informed the three visitors drinking was not prohibited in public places or sold by stores. Lubbock was indeed dry.

After much complaining, some Russian clout and a twenty dollar bill, the fat receptionist got with the program. The small bar down the road would do under the counter take out. This was typical American behavior, a dry state where everyone drinks? Ilia was sent back out into the fray and instructed to come back with goodies. In the meantime they would check in.

The Girls got more and more distressed as they reached the fifth floor of the hotel. It was awful. Much worse than a motel, gray and dingy, dull and cheap, a tasteless example of bland living.

"The reception wasn't that bad was it?"

"Hardly the South of France is it darling?"

The museum trip was looking grim. Even Los Angeles was not this backward and that was saying something. Ilia, the stud, returned loaded with all kinds of necessary evils, red wine, white wine, Marlboro reds, beer and chips. The much needed supplies were graciously received, all things considered. It was going to be a long night in the hotel room as Lubbock night life looked less and less appealing by the nano second.

"Whatever happened to another fucking sunny day in paradise?"

The evening in that hotel room was a blur for all involved. Suffice to say it came to a crashing end around five am. Shirley was throwing up in the freezing cold bathroom while Holly pumped her huge, overfilled and painful breasts both vowing never again. Ilia chased a chambermaid round the bedroom, claiming she was a virgin but obviously lying. She had no top on. He was soon unconscious. The museum meeting was less than eight hours away.

As the morning sun beamed through a gap in the cheap tasteless curtains, a gust of icy wind blew in through the broken window. It was almost eight o'clock when they awoke to face the damage. The room looked like Hiroshima. Always trying to think ahead the perfectly rolled joint next to a pile of headache pills, left in preparation for immediate relief the night before, was exceedingly welcome. Of course two million bottles of Evian sat patiently waiting to try and arrest the horrible dehydration. Both Girls lifted heavy heads before making any comments about the night before. They had all shared the smallest bed on earth, no bigger than a coffin and really only suitable for a single anorexic midget. Ilia in his drunken madness had fallen asleep, naked, trapping both girls under his heavy carcass. The meeting was doomed before it had even begun.

"Perfect photograph for the Architectural Digest, Art Interiors, fine art consultants meet prestigious museum with monumental hangovers in a dry state"

"Can someone please block out that light and call the paramedics, I can't feel my legs."

The neatly pressed designer suits chosen to impress the museum gang, hung on large hangers, ready to wear. It was questionable which looked more life like, the hangers or The Girls. Fresh make up was applied to tired old skin, covering a multitude of sins. A general disaster area. Their lips, black as the ace of spades from far too much cheap red wine, looked like they had taken a good beating from Mike Tyson. Usually the one and only negative thing they had to say about drinking the stuff.

"Did you remember to bring toothpaste?"

"I feel sick, these stains are terrible."

"What the hell were we thinking of?"

All the medicine in the world, including the pot could not ease the pain. Drunken remorse filled the air and irritatingly lingered. Ilia tried to pull himself together, lighting a fag and downing a half filled glass of red wine from the night before. Getting him ready would be pure hell.

Calling ABC news Lubbock and telling the lovely Rebecca of their visit was the first task of the day. Delighted with the news Ilia was in town, the reporter got her skates on and arrived at their hotel with a camera and crew, shortly after the call. Rebecca wanted to do an interview on local television. Thank God for Chanel make up. The exhibition was a sell out and having a Russian Fresco master in town was big news. They had some time to kill before meeting Lee so indulged Rebecca with her second interview. They had not yet seen the footage of the first one and capitalizing on knowing someone in the media was crucial. She could buy them breakfast.

The lure of bright lights was always appealing to The Girls. Ilia was fabulous, sharing his stories of lime putty and pigments drawn from the earth. He wanted to give the museum and its visitors a true understanding of a dying technique. He plugged Art Interiors and the potential support from Hollywood. The Russian mob were thrown in, here and there, adding a splash of color. The interview was a major success and would be aired every hour on the hour throughout the day to promote the exhibition. The fact they had not closed a deal with Lee yet, didn't cross anyone's mind. Rebecca just assumed contracts were signed and The Girls didn't see any harm in bending the truth a little. Any media was good media.

Feeling somewhat more like human beings, the interview under their belt, they ventured back out into the snow. The conditions were treacherous as the small rental car slid from one side of the highway to the other. Ilia was at the wheel. His stories of life as a bus driver, one of the many jobs he had had to overt the attention of the Moscow Police from his art did not instill confidence in The Girls. They felt sure they were going to crash. A huge sigh of relief was exuded by all when they finally arrived at Texas Tech University.

You know the feeling you get when you first walk into a deathly quiet dentist's waiting room, smelling far too clean for words, with everyone looking shifty and nervous? Welcome to the museum. Then to be greeted by Lee Brodie the curator. Yikes. Lee was not their kind of client. She looked too much like a maths teacher in a bad mood. Chatty she was not as she led them into the huge impressive office of the Museum Director. It was pretty clear from the start this was never going to gel. Lee, sporting half rimmed glasses and no make up, indicated where each of them should sit. It was like being back at school.

The main man was seated at the top end of the large mahogany boardroom table next to David, the PR director, hired liaison for all communication with the press. Whoops. Once seated, The Girls nervously began to sell their vision for the exhibition. It was a bit like the art council meets aliens with hangovers from Mars. They tried, fuck they tried but taking Ilia along for his incredible knowledge of fresco, turned out to be a complete waste of time. No one could understand a bloody word he was saying. Boring the already boring, is just how boring Ilia could be at times and always the wrong times. Of course the museum would be paying for the project so with nothing really to lose, the Girls went into overdrive and gave the performance of a lifetime, desperate to sell their concept.

It soon became evident that unless they could find a huge sponsor, their project was indeed dead in the water. As usual the client wanted something for free and they were not budging. The Girls would have to find the money from the elusive Hollywood celebrity after all. Maybe in the twilight zone, back at the gallery, there would be a message from Harvey. Things really went down hill as the PR guy got a call on his mobile. Someone in his office informed him Ilia was on the local news as the appointed fresco master? Shit. Busted. You could hear a pin drop.

Lee ripped their heads off for talking to the press. Rebecca Cruise at ABC News, had called Art Interiors without the permission of the museum and the art council were extremely pissed off. It was a tricky situation for The Girls and Ilia. They had rather jumped the gun by telling the world they were already the appointed consultants on the project. Normal business antics, coupled with some European arrogance. It was not really a lie, just them predicting the future, or not in this case. The TV woman had called them after all.

They used some charm, flirted a tad and turned the potential disaster into getting out alive. If they could get Charlton Heston to open the exhibition, all eyes would be on Texas Tech, the PR invaluable and Ilia would have his gig. The museum director liked their spirit and a deal was struck. Ilia would go to the ball (attend the exhibition) and Art Interiors would somehow pay for it. A contract would be in the post. The journey back was a celebration. If nothing else leaving the worst place in the entire world called for doubles all round.

"Cheers guys, I think that went quite well considering."

"Considering we've promised them a Hollywood celebrity before Charlton has even replied."

Ilia was over the moon and drank South West airlines out of vodka and gin. How he did it with a hangover will always remain one of life's mysteries. He just wanted a real project for once and finally he was convinced The Girls could pull it off. How wrong could he have been that night as they all flew back to LA LA Land.

*

They never heard another word from Lee Brodie and Texas Tech except for a polite bog standard letter stating the live fresco idea was something the museum wanted to consider. The project that never was. The Girls felt quite happy in a small way. Having to work for a living would always be tricky but for the church? That had never really felt right. Ilia was suicidal and drunk for six days.

So here they were with this art business, one week spent stalking celebrities, the next pitching the Vatican exhibition, neither prospect looking even a tiny bit lucrative. None of the celebrity begging letters had worked and they still had no sponsor. There had to be other projects in more interesting places. It was just a case of sniffing them out. It was decided they would concentrate their time on finding a Hollywood celebrity to be Patron of the Fresco school and help them get some necessary funds raised to promote art. Charlton Heston had not accepted the role of Patron to the school. A good thing on reflection, as it turned out he was the president of the California rifle club, tirelessly lobbing for no gun control. Over eleven thousand gun homicides in America last year alone, obviously, not enough for him. On reflection not the kind of person one wants associated with an up market fine art business. An emergency board meeting beckoned to discuss the future of Art Interiors, fine art dealers with no clients. Lunch, always a good plan, they drank endless glasses of red wine, smoked too many fags and put on their thinking caps. A great new idea sprang to mind.

"Corporate America? Let's approach the big top ten like IBM, Microsoft, Mercedes and ask them to support the arts."

"If we can raise some cash, we can then pay a celebrity to become Patron of the school."

"It's always the money, if you won't help because you're charitable, do it because you're a greedy fucker."

Stalking is not the easiest job in the world. It takes great courage and much red wine. Starting off with corporate America's CEOs, would afford them practice before attempting to break down the doors of the impenetrable world of celebrity. What they needed to find out was who really did support the world of fine art. Larry King had still not replied to their request for help and Harvey was looking suspect at that point. Approaching the big corporations still required the 'How Many Bottles Of Wine' system. After all, how does one go about stalking Bill Gates?

Bill was just a bloke who liked computers and according to Forbes magazine, liked to throw money at art. However he was a big wig so this call definitely scored a three bottle level. As The Girls dialed for dollars the wine kicked in nicely.

"Bill has an automated operator who blocks his call. It's unbelievable."

"All that money and he can't afford a receptionist?"

Dissatisfied with the robot, they got straight back on the phone. After ten re-dials and some ingenious skull-duggery they got through to a human being, not the brightest star in the universe but never the less, a real person.

"Bill Gates please."

It was like asking to speak to God himself. The poor human failed to understand. Then she did something really annoying and very rude, put them back to the beginning of the food chain. The fucking automated operator.

"What is wrong with these people?"

"I don't get this place. It's not like Bill has fabulous English women calling him every day."

"He needs to get his organization in order so he keeps in touch with real life."

That kind of automation was one thing The Girls really hated about corporate America. Talking to machines didn't cut it for them so a fax was composed, as instructed by the robot, asking Bill for some of his spare change to support The Fresco School. The Girls were prepared to find money from anywhere to keep their dream alive.

*

The art side of the business had failed to produce any revenue. Nobody wanted fine art at the beach. It was all about cheap prints in two hundred dollar frames, hardly stylish. Success in Europe had always come so easily to both of them. America was not going to beat them.

After so much practice, the begging letters had improved tremendously and a really jolly request winged its way to Micro-soft. And if you can't beat them, don't join them, bring something new to them. A great philosophy and so simple. The same letter was sent to IBM, Mercedes and half a dozen other large corporations, asking for support. With so much energy out there it was time to re-plan and re focus. Maybe a celebrity Brit to throw in the mixture was the answer.

"Sarah Ferguson has taken America by storm holding out her arms to the fat community. You know she works for weight watchers"

"Mid- America has something in common with a Duchess? Are you sure?"

The Girls didn't quite see it themselves but she would be a perfect person to get on board with The Fresco School. They knew Sarah, like Queen Victoria was an artist and before one had time to curtsy, they found the name of her publicist on the invaluable list, Mr. Jerry Casonove. He was English. What a result and so easy to get through to. Something they loved about England. You can call anyone, even the Queen.

Jerry had a sexy voice and politely listened to their plea for Fergie. He was very pleasant, telling them the Duchess loved to paint herself. They already knew that. She was working with other charitable organizations in America and if they sent him a request in writing he would make sure she got it. Not that old chestnut from an English chap. Another automated operator promoting the ever popular fax machine? What was it with these people? Jerry had obviously lived in the States far too long.

The Girls now hardened to rejection sat down and composed another begging letter asking the Duchess to consider the role of Patron to the Fresco School and sent it off to Celebrity Land. Unfortunately The Girls' timing was terrible. Although Sarah was working with Weight Watchers and other charitable causes, she was too busy to help them. At least she had had the courtesy to reply. She was forgiven. She was English and royal let's not forget. The Girls liked the idea of working with a duchess. Just being loosely associated with the British aristocracy made them cream their pants. They would go back to Sarah later.

Dom had a lot of admiration for The Girls' dedication to selling art. He was young, from a good family, not rich but some money. Running Beach Cities Roommates was not his dream but a necessity to get through life. He could see The Girls were under pressure to sell some art and came up with Bill Farley.

This was a different league. Mr. Farley was right hand man and confidant to sex king, Huge (sorry Hugh) Hefner, the giant publisher of girlie merchandise. According to Dom, Heff liked art and Bill was approachable. Sex and art, a good combination and a great fit for their business. A call of this magnitude would take at least three bottles. They packed up for the day and headed back to the Beach Cottage to drink wine and smoke pot before stalking the Playboy Empire.

"Just imagine this. If we make contact with Heff, we might get an invite to one of those Jacuzzi parties at the Playboy mansion, dirty martinis and more sex than an orgy."

"We could be a little past our sell by date for his taste, I think he prefers his women younger."

The Girls did love Heff's philosophy. Why shag one blond when you can shag ten? Why be a stiff suit, when one can be more comfortable and relaxed in silk PJs. Heff lived outside the box and they respected him for that. He also knew every celebrity in Hollywood. They all wanted invites to his wild parties. He would be a great person to form an alliance with.

After only two-bottles and a call to Dom's friend The Girls had the number. They dialed with excitement. They got blocked at first by Heff's assistant, Mary. Nothing new about that. It took four attempts but she was easy to out snob and finally put them through to Bill himself. After weeks and months of getting knocked back by agents' assistants' assistants, hard work and dedication, finally paid off. Bill was charming of course. He loved women. Well he did work with Heff don't forget. He was direct and told them straight. Heff would not meet them without some important facts being established first. That's how it works at The Playboy Mansion. He wanted bra size, hair color and pictures. If Heff liked the look of you, the prize, an invite from his social secretary to one of his bashes. This was a tricky situation for The Girls. They had no really good photographs to send. Since moving to America there had been so few social occasions where one dressed up and looked sexy enough for a photo opportunity. A barbecue in the back yard hardly qualified. Maybe the time had come to branch out and have some professional publicity pictures taken. Howard Stern wanted photographic evidence too. It seemed in fickle Celebrity Land looks really did matter after all. They enthusiastically thanked Bill for the advice and set out to investigate ways to find a genius photographer to take some sexy shots with a way to get to someone really famous and potentially, if they played their cards right, get laid in the process. They needed pictures but had broken through. One step closer to the elusive celebrity. Heff, like Harvey had started at the bottom with a dream. Surely he would help them with their art.

*

It was strange running an art gallery with no clients in LA LA Land, Life with The Jailers was about as exciting as watching paint dry so having a fraction of a taste of marginal success made them smile. Bill Farley was lovely and with photos, they could find a huge Hollywood celebrity to attach to the school. With every media outlet wanting to cover the story, Ilia would finally get noticed. Being the best, proving impossible. They needed that hit and soon. Thoughts of Playboy caused lingering over the last glass of wine before heading back to jail. Did The Girls have something to celebrate?

*

Everyday brought them a little closer to making that important first sale. Contacting high profile celebs just had to be possible in the middle of Hollywood. How hard could it be to find someone really famous with a conscience to help them? The famous were everywhere it was just the conscience bit that was lacking.

Getting to Bill Farley was the beginning of a long journey. Mr. Hefner was the fourth name added to the celebrity Rolodex under Charlton Heston. They would commence their celebrity stalking internship and beat Hollywood on the head about the art if that was what it would to take. The following morning began with a gem from Architectural Digest.

"Why don't we get hold of Sylvester Stallone. He paints."

"Get him to use some muscle and lift his heavy wallet to buy some of Ilia's art."

"His publicist is a woman according to the list."

So Stallone was the next Hollywood target. If they couldn't get to him they knew his wife, Jennifer Flaven, was on the Home Shopping Network. The necessary Plan B. It was time to head back to The Beach Cottage for some stalking antics and of course the red wine for Dutch courage.

After three-bottles they discovered his publicist didn't have an assistant. That was a first. She answered the phone herself? That was a first too. A real human being actually existed in the cold impenetrable world of Hollywood? This was extremely good fortune and obviously meant to be. Taking the bull by the horns they pitched her their idea.

"Do you think Sylvester, as an artist, will help us get the First American Fresco School off the ground by attaching himself as school patron?"

"We cannot pay him but we can give him some free Russian art in return for his support."

"We understand he is busy but we are desperate. Please just ask him."

She loved the idea but said he would hate it, too busy writing Rocky ten. They were reluctant to let her go but couldn't close her. She dismissed the call without a care, barely saying goodbye. Sly's wife Jennifer was contacted several times but they never heard a peep out of her either. The Hollywood Celebrity

Stalking antics would take more planning. They would have to, work the shaft, jiggle the balls and get to Stallone another way.

The corporate world had still not come to the rescue with offers of sponsorship money. In fact no one had even bothered to reply. Not a soul was interested in becoming Patron of the school and not one single person had purchased a piece of art. It was a sad state of affairs. Finding new artists took their minds off the constant rejection from Hollywood. Maybe with more art would come bigger opportunities. The Girls had a good eye.

Being stuck in the Gallery was boring and Celebrity Land was on hold for the time being. Always open to being surprised they were optimistic when an artist from somewhere in the valley contacted them through their web-site. He seemed dull on the phone but by the look of his emailed work he liked the naked female form and they fancied a day out. They would drive to The Valley, see the artists work, sign him, then find somewhere for a spot of lunch. It seemed like a great plan.

When they arrived three hours later, the place was a dump in the back of beyond with about as much style as a Gucci jacket on a wire hanger. They emerged from the car, hot and agitated regretting the decision. Being trapped in hell, in one hundred degree heat was neither Girl's idea of fun.

"Oh my God was this your stupid idea? Where the fuck are we?"

"Don't shout at me. We need some new talent, so let's just get it over with."

For a moment they considered doing a runner but were stopped in their tracks by Nick Lamonty as he came out to greet them. He stood in all his glory with what turned out to be Rosemary, the wife. She was definitely pushing the "California Girl" look just a little too far, a giant white blob of flesh wearing knee length socks and cheap trainers. Her hair, covered by a baseball cap the wrong way round, needed a new perm in the worst possible way and her big baggy shorts, roomy on an elephant. These two were not looking like the Girl's kind of genius for sure. The Girls were not perfect by any stretch of the imagination but they knew how to make the best of a bad lot. Rosemary and Nicholas, unfortunately, did not.

"Sorry we're a little late. We don't get out of Beverly Hills very often."

"How nice to meet you."

The nice American couple hero worshipped the British royal family. Anything English did it for them. The Girls rolled their eyes. Could this get any worse. There was only one thing for it. Be terribly snobby, very British and then do a runner. It was terrible, Americans trying to be English and failing miserably. Why do Americans always think England is so small everyone knows everyone? Rosemary generously prepared afternoon tea. Hot homemade scones were presented except instead of the traditional strawberry jam and fresh clotted Devonshire cream, they were smothered in peanut butter. When tiny bites of the unappetizing faire were attempted both Girls secretly worried about several loose crowns. Dentistry was extremely expensive and a luxury they couldn't afford. The lead weights were surreptitiously stuffed into napkins when the Lamonty's backs were turned. They couldn't risk their teeth. The tea sounded somewhat better and certainly less dangerous until it was poured. Rosemary had forgotten to use the tea strainer and the dark wet tea leafs floated to the top of the I love England mugs. It was just like being in Yorkshire trying to flog art to coal miners. When Rosemary politely inquired did they know Diana, the meeting needed concluding.

"We didn't know Diana but Sarah is a friend."

"May we please see the art now."

Nick led The Girls out to his shed come home made studio behind what seemed like a breeding compound for pitbull terriers. They had visions of Dr Hannibal Lecter popping in for lunch, English meat. Was Nick Lamonty a serial killer with a paint brush? He looked like one. He opened Pandora's box and the art was surprisingly magnificent. His pitch left a little to be desired, slow as a snail and as interesting as a dead worm but he was someone they could potentially work with if they could shut him up. The nudes would be a perfect gift for Heff in return for his celebrity help.

"If Heff had one of your paintings in the mansion, just imagine how many eyes would see your work."

"We need some of your best pieces for the gallery to show clients and a six-month commitment for exclusivity."

"We take 20% off the top."

As they offered him fame and fortune Nick was sold and signed there and then. It was that simple. With the art neatly packed in the back of the car, The Girls made a quick getaway in search of a restaurant with outside seating for a much needed fag and a chance to recover from meeting the nerds.

It took a while but they eventually found a possible eatery half way back to the beach, a small French type bistro not quite getting the ambiance right. It was owned by a Mexican family? That explained it. The Girls sat down at the plastic table to be greeted by Ernesto their crazy waiter. He was trying far too hard to be a Frenchman and failing miserably. When The Girls threw out a few lines in French he smiled a cheesy silent smile and shrugged. His teeth were enough to make a dentist give up practice, huge stubs of yellow decay with gold accessories. French Kisses? No thanks. He was not French and not pretty but he did have a wine list. The Girls had important stuff to discuss about their art business.

"We would like a bottle of red. A packet of Marlboro Lights and a chicken salad, it's a tight trouser day."

Over a year had passed by with not a single bite. Hollywood didn't seem to give a fuck about them or their art. It was sad. Had they not been made of stone, the rejection level would have been enough to make a drunk give up booze. That prospect was far too scary to even think about. Feeling really depressed about life they guzzled the wine to numb the pain. Drinking today would be about drowning their sorrows. When all hope was seemingly lost Jack the restaurant manager appeared. Was he a real Frenchman?

"There is a God after all."

Finding a sexy Frenchman in the middle of California was quite a result and needed acting upon. They collaboratively lured him in over a glass of red. He seemed to like their casual approach, feet out, jackets off, talking about everything, laughing at nothing and complimented them on their choice of wine. Most Americans preferred to drink water. He wanted to join their table. They were happy about that. Lunch with a sexy Frenchman was a major result after such a relatively dull day. Things were beginning to look up. Their bill would be his and the Lamonty experience would be history.

Unlike Ernesto, Jaques had perfect teeth and loved art. He teased The Girls about life in Hollywood. An out of work actor just waiting for the right movie opportunity, not in a position to buy any art but he made life a little more interesting that afternoon. Finding great looks in a small out of the way place was always a plus and having a flirt with the European man just completed the picture.

For The Girls life was about networking, making the impossible happen and building a powerful Rolodex along the way. Jaques was quite the lad with endless contacts in the business. Maybe he could help them sell their art. Numbers were exchanged and promises made to be in touch. The day ended with farewell kisses on both cheeks and a perfect addition to the Pussy Galore Notebook.

It was another day without a deal in sight and once again, no messages to return. They had nothing concrete to work on. The postman must have been on vacation. They had not seen him for ages. Ilia, still desperate to promote the fresco route, was convinced someone wanted to help. The Girls didn't quite see it that way and began hanging the new art on the walls. They had to come up with something before the next rent payment was due.

"Elton John collects art. He is rich and generous and he's on the list?"

The music legend, the English piano man had a lady called Fran Curtis looking after him, his publicist based in New York. Her telephone number was dialed from the Hollywood list and initial contact was made. Elton came from the North of England just like the two art dealers, or so they thought. His Watford days made him almost like a brother. That made no difference to Fran Curtis. She wanted a written fax detailing what they wanted and why. That old chestnut yet again. It was like climbing a mountain, reaching the top, then some idiot pushing you straight back down to the bottom. Was it that hard to make contact with famous people about art? Fran did throw The Girls one crumb. She told them Elton collected Andy Warhol, the early stuff. At least they were right about that. A mental note was immediately made and another begging fax faxed its way to Celebrity Land, asking Elton to be Patron of the school.

It was almost Christmas and money was getting really tight. The holidays were a time The Girls loved so much. No matter what time is was it was always justifiable to be holding a drink. They normally would push the boat out but financially things were bleak. They needed a get rich quick scam to tied them over and push them into the new year. People always spent money at Christmas. They racked their brains for an idea.

"Why don't we teach Americans how to decorate a traditional English Christmas tree?"

"You are joking of course? What the hell is wrong with you?"

"Busy people pay very well for artistic flair. We can always rope Ilia in to help."

It was settled. They placed an advert in the local Beach Reporter, announcing the new arm to their business, Tree Decorators Extraordinaire. Christmas tree decorating could easily be seen as a fine art. It was all about being able to be multi-task. The most terrible thing happened a week later.

"Shit this crazy woman in Manhattan Beach needs a tree and she wants us to go to the house and meet with her this morning."

As they pulled up outside her house, it looked like the new client might be a hit. The house on the Strand was tasteless but enormous. The walls sadly bare except for a handful of tatty prints in broken frames, cats and other animals, too awful to describe and the interior décor, old family crap cluttered in every possible corner. She was not an art buyer that was for sure and so they were relegated to Tree Decorators. It was enough to make anyone want to get drunk.

"Some people have no taste. Hello there Art Interiors. Where's the tree?"

It didn't take very long to work out this was a woman, under the thumb. She was not the Queen of her castle. She had her own jailer. The husband said little as the excited Girls pitched a thousand dollar fee to decorate a six foot Christmas tree. She was sold. Unfortunately her jailer was not. He told his wife to do the bloody job herself and dismissed The Girls like common street peddlers.

What would it take to make a sale? It was another failure in the crazy world of Art Interiors but as it turned out, quite a blessing. Selling tree decorating services to cheap Americans was never going to cut the cake. The Girls needed so much more.

"Rejection is positive, let's have lunch somewhere nice."

"One might spot Tiger Woods the famous golfer having a bite at The Local Yolk."

"Do they serve alcohol?"

It was back to the celebrity-stalking world once again. This time The Girls had a real incentive, Tiger was cute. A tall slim body, fit and rich with a tight bum, a loose pocket and he lived in Manhattan Beach. They could get over the fact he drove an Oldsmobile or some other gas guzzling monstrosity. He was the perfect celebrity to buy them some lunch. They had no idea if he was an art buyer and had heard rumors of a law suit against a Venice Beach artist for sketching Tiger's image then selling it for food but The Girls couldn't rely on gossip to disqualify him from the running. He would certainly be a high profile Patron for the school, exactly what they needed.

"He will love our energy and want to jump on board. A hole in one."

Of course on that day, Tiger had chosen somewhere else to eat lunch. Probably somewhere that served wine. The Girls were so unlucky. The most was made of their sober, celebrity free lunch back at The Beach Cottage by drinking too much red and ending the day, pissed. The three-bottle calls that day were very productive and The Girls dug the afternoon celebrity stalking much more than just trying to flog art. The following day with marginal hangovers, all things considered, they needed a rest. Being fabulous was not always that glamorous and sometimes just getting stoned helped with the failure. The Girls indulged themselves in a little European flavor and made a trip to Bristol Farms, a rare find sandwiched between Taco Bell and MacDonalds. They had real Belgium chocolate, dark and unmistakable, excellent cheeses and a fine selection of wine. A cross between Selfridges and Harrods Food Hall, absolute paradise. With the shopping cart filled to the brim with goodies, The Girls ventured home to roll a giant spliff, before experiencing the best things to come out of Europe. Waiting for the high to wear off and the munchies to set in paralleled anticipating a third orgasm but those shopping excursions always made life seem perfect in the moment. It was like being home.

Even with good food and wine life at Art Interiors was never perfect for very long. The phone didn't ring, the post never arrived, the clients were invisible and The Girls hated to fail. It seemed almost impossible to make life in America work for them. Even the world of the Hollywood celebrity now appeared shallow and not remotely glamorous. They needed a project and fast.

Like a bat out of hell Ilia came up with another of his ridiculous plans. Some big wig from Inglewood council had a possible city art project. The council was actively searching for a young, local artist to paint the streets with new colorful life. They had big ideas about large fresco murals in dark dingy car parks, visions of lush green trees in places where trees would never grow. Ilia was their man.

The council dream team was led by Mr. Jerry Givens, the appointed art director. A new client who loved art? It was a miracle from heaven. The Girls made a completely sober canvas call and planned to meet with Jerry, himself, the following day. Working for the council was hardly the big time but it would pay some bills and keep Ilia focused for the time being. Ilia was overjoyed. Public art always enthused him far more than any offer of a private commission even if the money was terrible. This project was not prestigious by any stretch of the imagination but cash was tight for every one and The Girls needed something to keep them afloat. Working close to home would be ideal for the Russian.

Dressing for the meeting was simple. The corporate business look out again in force, black suits, white shirts and the ever faithful pouchettes. They arrived in Inglewood before ten, their mood positive. They were early.

Jerry was black with a tooth paste campaign smile, ecstatic to be in the presence of artistic genius despite the depressing interior of his office. Hardly the big time. He stood over six feet tall, though his childish excitement made him non threatening. He insisted the trio take the weight off their feet and partake in some coffee. Oooh la di da. Apparently after many days spent surfing the web for fresco talent Jerry had drawn the conclusion Ilia was quite a find in Inglewood. Halleluiah. Someone got it. Well he was one of only a handful of people in the world with this unbelievable gift. Obviously Jerry loved art having already convinced the mayor, colorful murals would attract new business to the depressed downtown area, concurrently making living in Inglewood a total joy for local residents.

Jerry's plan was simple. Put Inglewood back on the map. Ilia would paint four large murals on the side of some extremely ugly local buildings, giving the illusion of color, space and beauty to the main street. The theme, "ethnic" but to be decided upon with creative input from the artist. It was clear he had ambitious ideas to win the vote.

"So how much money do you have exactly?"

The politician became shifty and changed the subject. The council had some extra money to place art in one local shopping area and a small communal garden but Jerry had a dream to create a peaceful haven for the under privileged families though out the city. For Inglewood council, a much more expensive dream of course. He endeavored to make the job appear more attractive by looking to the future. Filling Inglewood with fabulous art and a Starbuck's coffee shop would put Jerry on the map. He could sell his plan to the local airport, LAX, and raise finance to make the area more attractive to visitors. Then local business would thrive. If The Girls worked on it with him Inglewood Council would pay Art Interiors a reasonable fee. He warned payment would be slow. It was the local council after all.

It was decided. Jerry needed Ilia to help make his dream a reality. Art Interiors needed spondoolies and sharpish so the challenge was accepted and a business proposal including fees, prepared. The work could commence immediately with the assurance of payment in full once finance was raised. Buying materials alone would set them back a few bob. Money they just didn't have. With Jerry's deep love of art, taking him out to lunch would be a pleasure. The Girls somehow needed to squeeze money out of him for expenses. Jerry suggested TGI Fridays, Inglewood owned by basketball legend, Magic Johnson. Things were looking up. It was not their kind of place but Magic was a celebrity and they still needed a patron for the school.

*

On arrival at the restaurant another miracle occurred. Jerry was a drinker and a smoker. It was a first. An educated art loving client with political clout, showing the English art dealers social skills they had not seen in years. The idea of food was soon dismissed as the conversation flowed with the wine. Jerry knew his stuff and spent most of the lunch talking about Italy and France almost coming in his pants when describing seeing "The David" for the first time. The three were attentive with one eye on Jerry, one looking out for Magic. Meeting him would round off the day nicely and make staying on into the evening much more justifiable. Jerry had to return to some pressing business at the council building but thanked the three for lunch. He reminded them of the urgency for their proposal and handed over his card. His home number on the back was a surprise. Was he mad? The Girls were elated. Finally they had a gig for Ilia. Getting the media involved for maximum PR exposure was imperative. When the world saw the genius, the commissions would roll in. All that was left to do, Jerry had to approve payment. Getting the first installment of their invoice would be fish food.

"It's been an absolute pleasure."

"Our proposal will be with by tomorrow afternoon. Once all the pieces are put in place we need payment within seven days."

Kissing both cheeks, a custom rarely used in America, Jerry was smitten. He excitedly informed them the man behind the finances would be calling within days. He bid them a fond farewell. As one giant left another arrived. It was Magic Johnson. Could they really predict the future? Magic, the giant, stopping to say hello? Did they stand out? They were the only white faces in the place.

As they stood to greet him, smiling at his navel wasn't going to work. Craning their necks they peered heavenward. The air had to be thinner up there. Pitching art to a giant in a few seconds is not an easy task but butterflies were overcome. The moment had to be capitalized on. Take the bull by the horns and impress the fuck out of him.

"How lovely to meet you, it's such a shame you just missed councilor Givens. We are going to help him make Inglewood look fabulous, painting the town with modern day fresco. We need a kind celebrity to help us gain exposure for the project and become Patron of Ilia's school."

Magic was impressed and gave The Girls his card. Dropping in the name of a local politician always works, giving them the edge and hopefully making him remember them when they rang. The day ended superbly. Life was good. Ilia had work. They had Magic's number and American Express did nicely. The proposal, created the following day after endless arguing with a greedy Russian, was hand delivered to Jerry's desk promptly, as promised.

*

Days passed with no word and no check from the council. Phoning Jerry was pointless. They had already filled his voice mail with pleas and tears. They needed money to pay the rent and continue the struggle. A minor panic attack later, like a gift from God the phone rang. It was the man with the check book from the council, Mr Mackintosh. Brilliant. Was he Scottish? It was imperative he be treated to a slap up lunch anyway. They would flirt with him and get him to expressly clear their invoice before anyone else was paid a penny. It was simple. They needed him pissed and pinned down by the end of the day, writing them a big fat check. He agreed to meet them in Magic's place. Was he another drinker? Two drunks for clients in one week would be a miracle indeed.

The rest of the day was spent going through the rolodex and calling the likes of Harvey, Larry, Charlton Heston and Elton John. Not one celebrity had even bothered to reply. They couldn't get through to anyone and had to be satisfied with leaving yet more messages. It was such a disappointment, they just got drunk.

Having lunch twice in the same place in a matter of weeks would normally be a no no. In this case, they made an exception. Magic would have received their fax by now. Maybe they could kill two birds with one stone and close him too. Ilia was too busy sketching Inglewood High Street to join them, so it would just be The Girls and checkbook Mack for lunch.

Mr. Mackintosh was fashionably late, completely bald, smoked like a chimney and definitely not Scottish. He did rather aspire to the better things in life and ordered some decent red wine. That was a result. Was he paying? Unlike Jerry his passion for art was lukewarm but the man had hollow legs and it was not long before the wine kicked in. The money man's purse strings loosened as the deal got closer to the close. He wanted The Girls to meet the appointed architects, shit another obstacle however then a check could be drawn for Art Interiors, the first installment.

The deal was looking OK. They negotiated a meeting, as he negotiated himself into a waiting cab, all the while smoking a smelly cigar. Magic was no where in sight but the happy girls didn't care. Being surrounded by sexy black men desperate for white pussy was rather thrilling for middle aged women with Jailers at home.

Within seconds the bubbly waitress, spied earlier as a possible entry into the Pussy Galore Notebook, delivered two glasses of wine. A tilt of her head indicated who they were from. Dressed like an advert for Nike, he looked famous but who was he? They couldn't put their finger on it. He was rather wide, with high cheekbones and twinkling brown eyes. It came as a surprise to him he was at their mercy and not the other way around. As it turned out, he was not famous just very sexy and very friendly. With arms flying every where like a frustrated octopus, he became the entertainment for the rest of the afternoon. Black men certainly got right to the point and The Girls liked that. No beating around the bush so to speak.

The bar now buzzing as the late afternoon cocktail crowd began to arrive. The giant octopus fell by the way side, no staying power bless him, as The Girls now legless and full of life, broke through the pain barrier and ordered another bottle. Two Seal look a likes winking from across the patio were the next victims. The Girls lulled them into a false sense of security and before one could sing 'Waiting For You', they were sitting bang opposite the drunken women. Thornton and Clifford seemed like very nice boys. Both a little on the short side for men but sweet all the same and open to free natural conversation with two complete strangers. Little did they know these women when drunk. The excited, sex starved art dealers could get very demanding, forcing people to order more wine, light cigarettes and play Clitoris Pictionary. Could the black men draw the perfect shape? Both boys were Hollywood musicians out on a bender. Were they famous? The rap scene was not The Girls best trivia category. Still listening to The Sound of Music meant little knowledge of anything else. The conversation steered revealing the underlying universal subject, sex.

"So you two music men, what exciting plans do you have for the next few hours?"

"We assume being in the biz you have some fabulous party to go to?"

No matter how hard one tried, living in L.A. was always about meeting celebrities, networking, flirting ferociously and hanging with the right crowd. The boys plan was a midnight jamming session in the studio of the famed Hollywood record producer, Mr. Bombastic. The Girls secured an invite. Inglewood TGI Fridays was turning into an amazing place, celebrities popping up everywhere. Was it starting to happen? A crack of light? A glimmer of hope? Was the unattainable finally becoming a possibility? The Girls wanted to meet the Hollywood producer so badly. Bombastic could potentially open some giant doors in Celebrity Land. Stumbling around in Gucci strappy sandals, the drunken girls paid the bill. Whoops. Had they been sober they would not have considered in a million years clambering onto the back of two custom Harley Davidson motor bikes. Drunk was a different story all together. It was a high for them both, remembering days gone by in "The Life and Times of Two Best Friends in London." Chauffeurs and Bentleys had been the norm. For now, Inglewood and black bikers would have to do.

*

Disheveled, delirious, dazed and terribly high, The Girls dismounted their shiny metal horses and with John Wayne legs made their way to the entrance of Bombastic's studio, an excuse for a piece of architecture if ever they saw one. The studio was even less impressive from the inside. Dank, dingy and disappointingly small for such a supposed big shot. Hardly Abbey Road. Bombastic was very short for a man. Was he height impaired? It was hard to tell but probably not worth mentioning just in case. He really loved himself as he snorted cocaine and flirted with the playful, clever duo. Unhindered by too much wine The Girls set to work, grilling him like bacon for celebrity information. Admittedly there were contacts but none The Girls had heard of except Rene Russo. Once again they had more names to drop than he'd had hot dinners. Did I mention how it works in LA LA Land.

"We are working with Elton you know. He is considering helping us."

"Maybe we can introduce you sometime"

Bombastic wasn't remotely impressed with their contacts. He wasn't forth coming with Rene Russo's telephone number either. They decided he had obviously put too much coke up his conk and shagging a musician and collecting herpes before passing go, was not an option. They were learning the rules fast. Unless the Hollywood producer had something meaningful to say, hanging with a cocaine sniffing midget was pointless. It was time to bid a fond farewell and head back to jail. Another day was over and they were another step closer to the unthinkable, Check Out Girls at Ralph's grocery counter, the local supermarket. The council deal was good for exposure but it was hardly the big time. Something amazing needed to happen and soon if this art business was ever to survive.

The following morning found both rather perky all things considered. They sent another wonderful fax to Magic Johnson asking for his financial help. Having Magic on the team would tie the whole thing together very nicely. With backing for the council project, they could get paid and Magic would be a marvelous patron for the school. The Girls went over their future. Forever positive, definitely sinking but always hopeful they prayed their knight in shining armor was just around the corner. If Magic decided to help them, all their troubles would be over.

Finding rich clients with celebrity status was the only way to go. It would never be possible to promote fine art to clients until the artist collection was elevated and they had a high profile client at the table spending some money. The more work they did on the celebrity stalking, the less time they spent in the gallery. According to Dorothy Lucy on Fox Eleven morning news (the entertainment segment), Hugh Hefner was planning a seventy fourth birthday bash at the Playboy Mansion. According to Bill Farley, Heff had it all and The Girls wanted some of it. Having failed to find a photographer to take some sexy shots, for free being the stumbling block, slipping into his party by other means was their goal. They must offer an alternative to pictures. Something sexy yet challenging enough to secure an invite.

"He has to be taking Viagra for God sake. Think about it, one man having sex with ten bimbos? All with helium balloons for tits and not a brain cell in sight. And at the ripe old age of seventy four? This guy is something else."

The Girls sent a fax to The Playboy Mansion asking Heff to join them in a private game of poker. He liked cards. They liked to rip people off. To spice things up they promised to dress as naughty school girls bearing champagne and other treats. He was sure to go for it. The reply from Bill was swift. He reiterated Heff still needed visual stimulation before he would consider their proposal.

"Make a mental note, must find a good photographer."

"Who else needs a kick up the arse?"

"Fran Curtis? She's not replied yet."

"Let's send her some flowers for ignoring us."

Elton had turned down the first of a dozen or so different pleas for help so killing Fran Curtis with kindness was the plan. At least they had had one no out of her. It didn't matter how many times the celebrity turned them down, they had no fear in bouncing back with something bigger and better. Elton was a huge celebrity and someone they knew would love them, the minute he set eyes on them. Maggie Smith and Judi Dench (Tea with Mussolini) in spirit. Absolutely Fabulous in person. Yes. They just had to keep trying to get in front of him. He was busy touring, holidaying and having fun and although The Girls were very sad about that they understood. The beautiful expensive flowers were chosen and sent to the 5th Avenue office of Webber Shandwick Public Relations. If nothing else Fran would feel important for a second thanks to American Express.

Ilia was busy running around the council shopping center telling everyone who would listen about fresco. He was painting for the greater good after all. The Girls spent an hour or so working on another boring amendment to their proposal for Jerry Givens. He wanted all red tape cutting before any payment could be made. The Girls had an appointment at three with a new artist, Amanda and needed the Inglewood stuff completed by then. She sounded serene on the phone and wanted someone to represent her talent. Maybe she had the collection for Elton, or perhaps she could help Ilia with the mural commission.

*

Amanda was a younger version of Joni Mitchell, a throw back from the sixties wearing a cheesecloth dress and brown leather Jesus sandals. Not really Elton's type. Oh well. The scent of lavender enhanced her calming, spiritual attitude to life. The Girls both closet yoga queens, loved her whole "Deepak Chopra" world. Amanda was their kind of person.

"Hello. Welcome to Art Interiors. Love the beads. Take a seat."

"My God look at your work. It's fabulous. The dance. Tap. Jazz. Very Fluid. Very good."

Amanda was impressed. She liked them, loved Ilia's work, surprise, surprise and The Girls reaction to her work was encouraging. She signed very quickly making a most welcome suggestion. A glass of wine and a fag somewhere close by? This was another first. She was an American? Once again they were faced with finding somewhere one could not only drink but smoke as well. Amanda, quite the expert knew of several places The Girls had let slip through the net.

*

Lilly's, Venice Beach was the kind of place one might spot the odd street entertainer or magician having a bite. It was cool on the back patio surrounded by trickling fountains and wind chimes. The three new friends ordered a bottle of house plonk and spent time swapping tales about life in Hollywood. Amanda pulled out a pack of Prada tarot cards. Wow, her only designer accessory but it was a good one. The Girls had their own mystic Meg sitting at their table about to predict their future. This was fab.

"Come on Amanda don't keep us in suspense."

"Please, I am going to get laid soon? This is just too much to bear. Poverty, OK. Celibacy, sorry"

She told The Girls to shuffle well and place down seven cards in the shape of the letter H, three cards on each side and one in the center. It would be interesting to see if she hit on their checkered past. The Girls, so excited to have their fortunes told, almost pissed their pants in anticipation. Amanda began to predict their future.

She told of a friendship stronger than the ocean and more solid than a rock, the greatest chaste love affair ever. She was good. Her reading made both girls smile. Pushing her to tell them more, she shared stories, surrounding their business. She could see struggle, rejection, misery and pain.

"So tell us something we don't know."

The final cards held some warning for the future. If they were ever to make anything of their lives in Hollywood, they had to become independently wealthy. They must learn the biggest lesson of all, no one cared about art in Los Angeles and never marry for looks. That only worked in the movies. Amanda saw wealth as the key to their success. Without it, the high life would be a distant memory. Selling art in Surfboard City, was futile. Their dream for the art would be realized in Europe. Italy, maybe France, she wasn't sure but the USA had a long way to go before it embarked upon its own renaissance. The Girls were delighted with the reading. They were going home and on that note ordered more wine.

The next day the Tarot reading induced a new plan of action. It was time to try and put the puzzle together and develop some kind of picture. Everyone needed chasing up. The first call was to the council office. For once it was The Girls demanding payment and not Dullarce. His invoice was mounting by the second, as Ilia shopped for paint like a woman buying shoes in the sale.

Jerry had left for the day and Mackintosh was at the dentist, apparently. The Girls were getting the runaround. There was no money there. Even Magic, the gentle giant who'd insisted they call, was now avoiding them. This was just too much to bear. Not one celebrity had called them back. They needed a new one to stalk, perhaps Tom Cruise would be receptive? Get the list out.

Calling celebrities sober was not an option and only to be attempted, from The Beach Cottage in the afternoon. They couldn't leave the gallery. It was only nine thirty. With no wine readily available less stressful stalking tactics were considered.

Opening up email they prayed for a miracle and low and behold someone was listening. There in black and white, a client inquiry from Don Fury somewhere in Florida. So many questions without any answers but a client was a client was a client and they needed cash pronto. He described a rare and valuable oil on canvas. A painting of the movie icon Steve Reeves as Mr. World in the early 1950s. The artist, a quasi famous gay painter with somewhat of a cult following. Mr. Fury sought a buyer. It sounded quite good and a way to earn a bit of extra cash. It was just a question of finding the right client then doing a quick turn around. A huge celebrity art collector perhaps?

"Arnold Schwarzenegger, action hero. He collects."

"Wasn't he Mr. Universe himself back in the seventies? You're a star.'

The now dog eared celebrity list was dusted off and low and behold Arnold was on it. He had an agent in LA but no publicist. Calling an agent, following the Cece York, Rusty Lush lunacy, was a whole new ball game and made the Girls a little jumpy.

"We don't have to be afraid of the agent. It's exactly what we do. They get a percentage on the deal"

"Fuck what a great job. I could do that. It's just like head hunting."

"We can talk to anyone for God sake. We are English."

The number was dialed, a cigarette lit and for the very first time in almost six months, they got straight through again. It was panic stations. The Girls were about to pitch a gay oil painting to a film star without actually ever seeing it? Tricky, but not impossible. When in doubt just lie and flatter.

"Hello there Sarah. What a lovely name. Art Interiors here, fine art dealers to the stars, clients include Elton John, Harvey Weinstein. We find the right piece of art and match it to the celebrity's life style and taste. We have stumbled across a rare piece for Arnold, MR World 1956."

Sarah was a sweetheart telling them to put a photo of the painting in the post and she would get Arnold's attention. What was happening? A nice agent? This was yet another first. The Girls, thrown for a second, soon realized this sniff needed capitalizing on. What other celebrities could the lovely Sarah offer up as sacrifices for their business?

"While I have you on the telephone, perhaps I may pick your brain for a moment. We are looking for a high profile celebrity to consider the role of Patron for The First American Fresco School. Do you have anyone you represent who springs to mind?"

No was her immediate retort. Sarah was an art lover but her clients unfortunately were not. Far too busy to chit chat she hung up. Oh well worth a try. Sarah, seeing Arnold that afternoon promised to pass on the information. At least things were looking up on that front.

The Girls telephoned Don Fury telling him to email a color photograph of the painting as soon as possible. They potentially had a huge celebrity client interested, someone nearly as famous as Tom Cruise and time was of the essence. As they waited for the image of the painting to arrive, they researched some other works by the same artist from around the same period. They were shocked.

"Fifty grand for that. It's a misprint"

Twenty percent of the sale price was the agent's fee. Things were really looking up. It was almost enough to make one run out and spend the money. The Girls were sure this was it, the deal that had eluded them up to now. That was until Don, the big fat liar's fax arrived. It was a painting of Mr. World for sure but what was he wearing? The painting was so ridiculous for Arnold. It made having cocktails with alien visitors seem a real possibility.

"Tight nude silk shorts? Even Kate Moss has a waist bigger than his."

"What is that on his head? A blond wig?"

It was not the kind of thing one would send to The Terminator. Far too puffy and far too glossy for the aspiring conservative Californian governor. A more favorable result would be achieved pitching this visual to someone like Liberace. Yes. Unless they could find another flamboyant celebrity, who was still alive and not in politics, they were toast.

"It must be half eleven by now. I need a drink before I kill myself."

"What is it with this business? Every project we touch turns to shit. Are we ever going to get a break?"

"Arnold running for governor? Anything is truly possible"

Sometimes it was just so obvious why these poor girls had to drink. Even the first second of each working day started with a harsh reality, The Jailers complaining over breakfast about The Girls lack of success. There was nothing they hated more than failing over Raisin Bran. If this life in America for two English fine art dealers married to yanks, representing a Russian genius was ever going to take off, The Girls definitely needed bigger fish to fry.

*

The small gallery never resembled a Hollywood Agents office. The only calls ever made were outbound. It had been months without any success. The American Express card was not doing that nicely, as the stakes got higher and the bank balance, lower. Day after day Clive and Dom watched the confident, vivacious Girls in action, making calls to huge unattainable celebrities asking for help with art. In the beginning they would show off. Their energy, unbelievable but the day to day reality was brutal. The phone never rang, the invisible postman, late again and nobody gave a fuck about them or their art. Clive Dullard really put life into perceptive for The Girls as he sat in the small shared bathroom off the main office. Good god. Dullarse, about as subtle as an orange ball gown on a fat Nigerian opera singer was taking a dump. Was this their real life? The life they wanted?

"We need to upgrade this gallery situation if this whole business is to ever take off."

Although the door was closed there was no soundproofing. Dom's headphones protected him the onslaught of disgusting noises that ensued but when Dullarse proudly emerged leaving the bathroom door wide open, The Girls pent up frustration reached boiling point. The stench was overpowering, just like pig shit. They wanted to kill him. He escaped for lunch, in the nick of time, leaving everyone, gagging and holding their breath. It had been coming for weeks. The Girls wanted out.

They had not been to lunch alone for ages. They needed the chance to sit and chat somewhere quiet, blow out the cobwebs and do some brain storming before they killed Dullarse. It was time to put the thinking caps back on and come up with a gem of an idea to keep the business afloat. The place they chose was quite a find, music pounding and sexy cute waiters in tight black pants with Rock Hudson smiles. Were they out of work porn stars? Delicious food smells permeated the air heightening The Girls senses. Their mouths watered, involuntarily. They were starving thus an embarrassing combination could be forgiven.

"Two Chocolate Martinis and we'll share the fish and chips."

"I hope no one English heard that."

After two bottles of very nice chilled white wine and uncovering the out of work porn stars were actually gay and not interested in flirting with over made up middle aged women, they entertained each other by inventing strange possible situations. You know the kind of shit one talks about when one is too pissed to make sense.

"Who would you like to find yourself stranded on a desert island with and why? He has to be famous."

"Harvey of course because he's strong and independent, rich and powerful, successful but still down to earth. A player, a cad and a gent."

"You know a lot about him considering you've never even met."

"He looks like he'd shag like a rabbit and on a desert island, what else is there to do?"

"You know he's Jewish. You'd never survive without bacon sandwiches, never in a million years."

"Good point but when did you last see a pig and a frying pan on a desert island?"

That was the first time his name was really mentioned properly, well socially. Harvey was sure to help once he realized their dream to save the art and corrupt him in the process. Lunch ended late but no one cared. The rent was due yet again and with no hope of paying it, having to face Dullarse after his performance in the bathroom, sucked. Deep down they had to go back to the Beach Cottage to drink wine and ease the pain. As the fourth bottle was added to the tab tomorrow would be tricky.

*

Code Red. Hangover Alert! Facing Dullarse without the rent was unthinkable. They declared the day National Hangover Day and worked from The Beach Cottage. Sprawled across the sofa with warm coffee and pot, chatting about life seemed like a much less painful plan. It was on this day, sober might I add, The Girls decided to give up the gallery and work from The Beach Cottage. It made sense really. Unless they had clients, a space was pointless and an unnecessary outgoing. Now it was about prioritizing. The money would be better spent getting ones hair cut somewhere fancy. The Girls made a pact.

"Let's just trim down, one phone line, one fax line and if we ever do find a client, we say we work from home."

It was settled and quite a relief. Dullarse, happy to see the back of the crazy English "Witches Of Eastcheap", used their deposit to pay the final months rent. Dom was sad and told them to keep in touch. Mark presented the coffee tab, two hundred and fifty dollars, oops and the art was moved to The Beach Cottage. After several calls to the nice but slow men at the council office, The Girls smelled a dead rat. Jerry kept rambling on about the fabulous art and how they needed to have faith. Yeah right. Were they con men? Mackintosh didn't have the cash to pay for anything, it was always in the system being processed. The Girls considered drastic legal action, just to be paid back the money already invested in the deal but they didn't have the energy to fight anymore for another invisible project. The Girls pulled Ilia off the job.

The time had come to take Art Interiors to new heights. A place where anything was truly possible and clients had more money than sense. The Land of the Rich and Famous. They must confront the beast head on and enter the world of the Hollywood elite full time. This bold move produced a new concept in their lives, the five-bottle canvas call. Making friends with people like Harvey Weinstein was not easy. Unless they could find a sponsor like him, Ralph's checkout counter was all they had to look forward to. Harvey really was the crème de la crème of Hollywood Society but the right man for the job, they were sure of it. It was time to stop being art consultants. Their stalking internship was complete and becoming professional, celebrity stalkers, their only option.

CELEBRITY STALKING

"A road with no access leads to a place of wisdom."
JIM MORRISON THE DOORS

IF CHRISTOPHER COLUMBUS COULD SELL HIS DEATH VOYAGE IN 1492 SURELY THE Girls could sell art to Harvey five hundred years later. Little did they know then, it may take five hundred years.

It was a new year and a new start. Christmas had been quiet and uneventful, a couple of token gifts and a glass of Harvey's Bristol Cream. That is what happens when one is poor and married to a jailer. Getting back to the Beach Cottage at least furnished some hope of escape and over a large café latte, The Girls went through the post and checked the voicemail. There was one melancholy message from Ilia wishing them a Merry Christmas. Both Girls eyes prickled as they swallowed throat lumps and struggled to clear blocked noses. Oh how things had changed. The memory of another life was still vivid and real, attending gallery openings and private showings. When they were art buyers everyone and their mother was one too. Evenings were spent with collectors and celebrities alike vying for a moment with the illusive artist. A hop, skip and a jump across an ocean and art was not revered and admired, it didn't even figure in the minds of most people including the powerful and seemingly creative names in Los Angeles. The dream of moving to America and it all working out was beginning to look doubtful. All they wanted to do was help a struggling genius get the recognition he deserved. Life at Art Interiors would be incredibly dull for two birds from Yorkshire, unless they had unlimited cash and more success.

It was clear after months pounding the streets of Celebrity Land, cracking this safe would take more than opening an art gallery. Concentrating on landing a big fish to help them break down the indestructible walls of Hollywood was imperative. If you can't beat them join them. Their main priority was to penetrate the impenetrable and get the full attention of Harvey Weinstein.

Despite how grim the future looked The Girls were delighted to be back at work. Seven days spent watching 'The Three Stooges', 'Charlie Brown's Christmas' and 'It's A Wonderful Life' was enough to finish anyone off. The Beach Cottage now the full time gallery with a view of the ocean not worth dying for. The 9-foot leopard-print sofa flown all the way from London, when cash was more plentiful, filled almost half the room. The polished wooden floors gave one a feeling of space, as the ever present rays of the January Californian sun beamed through white chiffon drapes. This was more like it. The Girls immediately felt at home as they placed their struggling artists work on the bare white walls.

"Leaving that loser Dullarse behind was the best thing we could do. If one surrounds ones self with "Belows", one becomes one."

"We can hang the art, make some calls and then introduce ourselves to Ashley."

Ashley's Deli was the new liquor store just around the corner. The Girls quickly found out the owners name was Steve not Ashley, as getting a tab was essential. The American Express card was not always doing so nicely, these days. The bill needed paying.

The first morning passed by with a flurry of activity at the new location. They called Ilia, thanked him for his sweet message and suggested he pop round. He wanted to make sure his work looked good on the new walls. He stayed for a glass of wine before rushing off to promote Fresco. Amanda was delighted with her art. The warm sunlight, reflected off the ocean, giving the abstract work a strange sense of reality. She had to dash but hugged them without reserve and promised another reading soon. Even the strange Lamontys dropped by to wish them luck. It was rather embarrassing as they ushered the artist around the two tiny rooms. They had still not sold a single painting to anyone. Heff needed to view their vital statistics before Lamonty would benefit from his genius. One day they would show the world their passion.

It was soon clear the move was a good one. The Beach Cottage was much less expensive than the commercial gallery space and they could focus on getting their art business into a profitable place without the constant nagging of Dullarse in the background. It was time for the battle to commence. They needed a new calling.

"Getting to the Hollywood elite is impossible. That we know from experience. Asking celebrities for help for free is like getting The Jailers to shop at Chanel, impossible. Somehow we have to become famous ourselves."

"Are you suggesting what I think you're suggesting? We could be a little ripe for Hollywood."

"Speak for yourself honey. Look at Liz Taylor. We need someone who knows the business to help us. According to the 'How To Penetrate Hollywood Manual' we need a Red Light executive."

"I think you mean Green light darling."

"Green light, Red light, Bud light. Who gives a damn, as long as he works in the business and recognizes genius."

And that was it really. The Girls had to find a green light executive. Con him into going to lunch. Then pick his brain like a carcass. Remember anything is possible with these two maniacs. Unless they could reach a broader audience for the genius they were going nowhere. Taking someone from the world of television out to lunch would be a first and could be fun. Most channels were full of rubbish anyway. How hard could it be?

"Let's open some wine, smoke some pot, then make some calls."

"Just like any other sales call. Fearless."

After a three-bottle call, far too much high and butterflies in tummies, The Girls had a powerful name. Jeff Shore at E! Television. He was a green light executive with a friendly assistant named Donna. She could feel their energy over the phone and their ridiculous call made her laugh out loud. The Girls had her ear. She soon warmed up and listened with interest to what they had to say. It turned out Donna adored life in London. She'd been there before with her Mum and her Mum's best friend. They tantalized her offering free hospitality in London in return for putting their call through. Always kill them with kindness and get them on your side was strategic planning at its very best. Holly, fully loaded, went in for the kill.

"You don't know much about us yet but you will. We want to talk to sexy Jeff your boss. Is he free?"

Style Entertainment television had it going on and they wanted to make friends with a big wig. Jeff Shore was the chosen someone to get them noticed and help promote their art. Donna let down her armor for one split second and The Girls were through. It was great. They were pitching a television executive all in one afternoon. Maybe becoming famous was not that out of reach after all. Sadly The Girls were still as green as a fresh bag of chronic when it came to the world of television.

"Jeff, how are you darling? We love your assistant. She is coming with us to London. You should think about coming too."

"We would love to take you for lunch to pick your brains and pitch our idea. You have such a sexy voice. Are you married?"

Always flatter. It never fails. The poor green light executive from E! had no idea what to make of these women or what they were rambling on about for that matter. Not surprising really as it was a three bottle call let's not forget. In this case however, flattery was the key. The easily bought green light man was coming to lunch. He mentioned his favorite eatery, Orso, on 3rd St, a place to spot Hollywood heavy hitters engaging in the one hour power lunch, apparently. The Girls loved it already. They had stalked the impossible and bagged an elephant, all in about two seconds. The Beach Cottage Gallery come office was working out nicely.

They called the restaurant and flattered the poor Maitre D' to death. They needed the VIP service. Getting creative, when one was as high as a kite never failed. These two were experts.

"Hello there. We need your best table for an important green light man next Tuesday. Mr. Jeff Shore from E! Television, do you know him? If you are looking for work as an actor, maybe we could introduce you."

Their first shot at Hollywood was now firmly in place. The waiter, waiting to be an actor, was over the moon. He gave them his undivided attention and assured them of the very best table in the house. It was booked for half past twelve. For The Girls having lunch with E! Television was a rare opportunity and something they had to capitalize on.

"We are celebrity stalkers trying far too hard to sell art to Hollywood. Hugh Hefner hit the nail on the head. Photographic evidence. We need to make a film for Jeff. He needs to see the power of the art."

"Have you really lost your mind? You're hardly Woody Allen darling"

"Check the making a film section in 'The How to Penetrate Hollywood Manual.'"

The book was turning out to be quite handy for two strangers in a strange place. Clearly written in black and white were more valuable instructions to move forward. Step two meant coming up with a pitch.

"A pitch is a short synopsis of what the show is about. It's what sells the concept."

"OK we have art. We have potential ways of getting to celebrities and we are crazy. How about The Girls on E! A show about celebrity stalkers trying to flog art to famous people. That's hilarious in itself"

"It says here once the pitch is accepted, one then needs a pilot. Not the flying kind, the film kind. We need to film ourselves with some celebrities talking about art."

"Why is everything we tackle always so bloody unrealistic. How the hell do we find a celebrity and make a film by next Tuesday, Sherlock?"

And that was it really. The pitch was born and typed on headed paper. It looked impressive. Achieving the impossible for them was like taking a red rag to a bull. They could do it. They just needed to focus and come up with a solid plan to find a celebrity, make a film and move to the next step.

"Remember the volatile painter Grimaldi. A celebrity photographer lived next door, Challenge Roddy. Maybe we should contact him."

And this is where the worst film makers in the entire universe come into the story, Challenge and Polly from M 2 M Studio, Venice Beach. The Girls got the number and made the call. Challenge was delighted they had remembered him and listened with great interest to what they had to say.

"We are looking to hire a genius. You came highly recommended. We have no money to pay for your time but if you do a good job, your film will be before the eyes of E! Television by next Tuesday. You'll never look back."

Challenge was hired. They had a filmmaker. Well technically a celebrity photographer but he did have real creative talent and more importantly aspirations to take on Steven Spielberg in a head to head. Challenge wanted the chance to make a film and with zero budget he was all they could afford. It was settled. He would follow them around with his digital flair and make them look fabulous. Turn the footage into an Oscar winning pilot and Jeff would be sold. Finally, The Girls would have money to elevate Ilia. Someone had to save Fresco for God sake.

The day came to an end with a feeling of achievement, a great start to a new phase and a new year at The Beach Cottage. It was strange for The Girls. For once they didn't feel remotely pissed. Having something new to think about was fun. This must be what people called working.

As luck would have it, the following day brought forth fruits at breakfast from one of The Jailers. He mentioned some guy from his basketball crowd had junior celebrity status, often seen hanging around the beach with soap stars and offered up his card up like the sacrificial lamb. By ten thirty am The Girls were secure in the confines of The Beach Cottage and dialing his number. Childishly flirting with his LA ego Lee Raymon had met his worst nightmare.

"Hi there. We are The Girls on E! We got your number from a friend who tells us you're a celebrity and rather a good looking one at that."

"We would love to meet you. We need your help to make our new pilot."

"E! Television are coming to lunch and we want to tie in a celebrity with art. We need to come to your house and film you."

The Girls, experts at selling ideas, had his full attention. Like a greedy dog with a bone he invited the bubbly women to a celebrity party at his home on the Strand that Saturday, the perfect setting for Challenge to film the pilot and take some pictures for Heff. Challenge could not believe his luck. The Girls had delivered a celebrity venue and a great opportunity for him to shine. Now his dream was about to come true. Lee was smitten, silly man.

"I wish I'd known years ago how easy the television business is. Looks like we're all about to become famous."

For the rest of the day they plotted and planned the content of their film. It would be natural showing English art dealers, drinking, smoking and talking to celebrities about art. In short, the perfect film to impress Jeff. If Rachel Ashwell and Shabby Chic could do it then so could Art Interiors. When aspiring to success model on success. Famous last words.

It was Saturday lunchtime on a beautiful clear day. The sky was the brightest of blues and the air was crisp for Southern California. The Girls kicked things off with a strong Bloody Mary and a hit on the joint. Performing in front of celebrities would take much Dutch courage. They were out of practice but working at the weekend was a bonus. The Jailers could not get their heads around art suddenly becoming movie making. The Girls gave vague answers to their probing questions desperately trying to discourage them from further quizzing then snuck off to the Beach Cottage leaving the Jailers to the TV, the remote and the sports page. To The Girls life had to be simple but they did want to participate.

"Jailer one thinks we are stark raving bonkers."

"Just remember they're the crazy ones."

"You need more foundation. Show some breast."

"I said young, not tarty. I want people to take me seriously. I sell art remember."

The Beach Cottage was alive like an aging film stars dressing room. Endless rows of filled joints, fags and red wine adorned the dressing table. The much needed fuel to take on such a massive adventure. Getting ready for fame and fortune sent them both into a panic. Hollywood stars? Were they mad? They both needed major restoration, just like Ilia's Frescoes.

Waiting for Challenge to arrive seemed like a lifetime. He was horribly late which made them nervous. When he finally showed up he looked just the ticket dressed from head to foot in black leather and silver studded accessories. Challenge had a way about him. He was always relaxed and sported his wide dimpled smile. Always positive forever hopeful, hanging out with their genius photographer would make them look young. Life was perfect as they set out to make their pilot for E!

Property on the Strand sold for millions. Lee owned one. They could not wait to meet him. He had to be somewhat stylish and liquid, surely. Challenge would capture the whole afternoon on film and for the first time in ages, they would have a chance to show their art to the world. As the tall, over suntanned gonk lurched in the doorway, it was soon clear things needed to improve, if this pilot was to fly. His plastic smile and his limp hand shake, made The Girls grimace as he invited them in. Lee was revolting. Oh well, it was too late to start worrying now. The nicely high girls burst into his kitchen. Like bulls in a china shop, they pushed his large uncoordinated frame, to one side in search of the bar. Was he a Munster? The small exclusive crowd watched in amazement as The Girls demanded attention and Challenge filmed like a demon.

"Hi. Beer only?"

"How terrible."

"Can we smoke?"

"On the balcony? Why?"

This was not looking much like a celebrity bash. The Girls had heard rumors David Kelley and Michelle Pieffer lived on the Strand but there was no sign of them. A man with binoculars spotted a pod of dolphin way out to sea. They had hoped for Jack Nicholson and got Flipper. Getting drunk was quickly becoming their only option. Then The Girls could rip the place to shreds and at least capture some exciting banter on film. After too much beer and some nice strong weed, the essence of the party was captured by Challenge. The celebrity content was weak at best however what people would do for their own fifteen minutes was mind blowing.

The Girls made the party happen, chatting about art, laughing about American boys and sticking up for smoking and drinking. Lee, an out of work talk show host and sports commentator, was desperate to drop his pants. That was on film. The young beautiful soap star from 'Days Of Our Lives' (the hottest daytime soap on NBC, a major network) was kissing someone she should not have been kissing. That was on film. Her gay publicist, who insisted he was straight but just had the misfortune to have a high pitched voice, was also on film. These people were barmy.

The stiff American crowd cracked and by the end of the night, the Miss Daytime Emmy was drunk and very flirty. Bet Lynch always pulled viewers so the daytime starlet had to be a winner for Jeff. They had all the film footage they needed for a fabulous pilot. Mission accomplished. The unlikely trio said their goodbyes and headed back to The Beach Cottage to introduce Challenge to their world. If he was to make a film about them, he had to get to know them a little better.

"This is where we work, our gallery by the sea. We sell the work of struggling genius and promote their art to celebrity clients."

"Challenge put the camera down and have some wine."

Who was this chap who had come to their rescue and offered to help them make a film about art? Challenge, nervous to begin with but after a few trips to the bathroom, opened up like a book. At the time The Girls had no idea what to attribute his confidence boast to but that day they embraced it openly. He invited The Girls to visit his studio the next day. He wanted them to meet Polly, work out a timeline for the film and help him edit the footage. It sounded great. The perfect excuse to escape jail.

Getting out of church was cause for an enormous celebration joint on the drive to Venice. With Drops of Jupiter blaring from the sound system in the truck they stopped off to buy beers on the way. Challenge greeted them enthusiastically when he finally opened the door. Had he just got out of bed? It was eleven am. The studio was a fabulous airy space with rusty red brick walls covered with abstract paintings, some by Grimaldi, the volatile Italian living next door. It was the perfect trendy place to interview celebrities about art. The mood was sultry, under the dim red lights, like a booth in the Moulin Rouge, even though it was the middle of the day. The Girls soon felt the energy of the candle filled room. The unmade free standing bed, covered with white linen was draped in old velvet throws, ready for sex. It was like being on a film set for a porn movie. Working from here could be fun. Challenge rubbed his eyes and suggested they open some beers.

"Darling, not paper cups."

"When was the last time some one did the washing up?"

The Girls sipped the beer from the bottle. Challenge cleared places for them to sit, that large open space a swap meet fanatics' paradise, crap everywhere. Rumblings behind them startled the Girls. They heard a grunt then a cat's meow and as they turned around to investigate a partially clad skinny girl emerged from under a blanket and skulked into the bathroom.

Challenge had an interesting entourage of hangers on, including Polly, loosely described as his girlfriend. She was model thin with straggly blond hair. He called her his angel. On reflection the only thing angelic about her was she looked good in white. When suicide John, bless him, a throw back from the sixties arrived, things started to get more interesting. Within minutes his autistic reclusive patterns were evident. Opening a beer and picking up a guitar, attempting his own rendition of the Bob Dylan classic, 'Like a Rolling Stone' was obviously more comforting than and preferable to making conversation for him. He wasn't bad for a drunk to be avoided at all costs according to Challenge. Manic depressive tendencies when confronted about his life caused him all kinds of problems and yet his James Taylor esque lilting melodies serenaded The Girls. He seemed normal enough. He was in. The Girls topped him up and looked for the positive. So he liked to drink and sing. Perfectly normal, so did they. Based on Challenge's prognosis two entire nations, The Irish and The Scots needed prompt internment at Betty Ford.

A rock guitarist from Idaho lurking in the corner with hair longer than Jane Seymour in desperate need of a good wash was the next person to awaken. What was this? The YMCA? Rory seemed very nice, once he got with the program and realized where he was. He too was quick to pick up a guitar and before The Girls could say Jack Robinson, John and Rory were performing Jimmy Hendrix', 'Purple Haze'. The harmony wasn't bad for a drunk and a heroin addict. The studio, indeed a place for rock and roll, proved hanging guitars and hanging with Challenge could bring The Girls much pleasure.

Challenge shackled to the computer, looked like he knew what he was doing. Polly, now showered, dressed and beautifully made up understood the film making side of things. She even had a few credits along the way. Leaving the pair to edit the film, while The Girls changed the world, seemed like the perfect plan.

After two much beer and far too many verses of a 'New York State of Mind' the film was still not ready and The Girls were drunk. Challenge made some ridiculous excuse about it being new age and far too good to rush. He vowed to stay up all night and complete the masterpiece promising them faithfully they would have a pilot by the following morning, at the latest. E! would be signing The Girls, there and then at lunch. It was that simple. The Studio entourage, now all over the shop, backed him up as they packed The Girls off high and convinced. Returning to jail pissed was brutal but worth every second. They had a new genius on board.

It was Monday morning and with marginal hangovers they set out to go for broke. Having lunch with a television green light executive to pitch a potential show idea would need strategic planning and lots of wine. With no idea where to start they just focused on why they needed Jeff in the first place, to help elevate Ilia and sell his art of course.

"We need to sit down with Jeff and get him excited about the art and Ilia's story. It is explosive. We need to show him how dedicated we are. Getting Ilia's work on television with celebrity collectors is good content for E! and perfect P.R. for us."

For them it was always so simple. You scratch my back and I will scratch yours. By eleven thirty the hangover had faded thanks to the chronic. They would eat a bite of lunch and make a plan. E! wanted celebrity faces. Challenge needed to focus.

"We need some fabulous pictures for Hugh Hefner. Without showing some cleavage he is not calling back."

"He would be the ideal celebrity for our show and now we have a photographer."

"Call Pink Dot and get them to deliver some wine."

Asking Heff to be Patron of the Fresco school was possibly not that appealing but appearing in an art show with sexy older women? That should tickle his fancy. Calling Challenge to thank him for the wild night was the ideal time to talk about the pictures for Heff. Challenge was always flattering. He said the pictures from Saturday looked cosmic.

He promised them faithfully, he would have them printed with the finished film by end of play that day. So much for Monday morning but for once he sounded sincere.

Entering into a new arena with little experience didn't phase either of The Girls. If they wanted to get people like Harvey Weinstein to the table, they needed to understand the business. Making a celebrity art show was going to be their first internship in Television Land and some much needed training. It was important to keep the pilot short and punchy so as not to bore the viewer to death. Challenge was to provide them with a masterpiece to take to Jeff. The plan looked possible. That was until they called him at five o'clock and he had absolutely no idea how to get the film off his computer onto a VHS tape. Their important pitch meeting was less than twenty four hours away. Thank God Jailer One, the computer geek, came to the rescue with invaluable information.

"You need to go to Frys and get a converter. They'll know what you need. It has to be simple if we understand it."

The moment of panic created much doubt for The Girls but they had to believe in Challenge. He wanted the big break just as much as they did. He was all they had. This was the most important lunch since starting their business over a year ago so the next morning having a bloody Mary before half eleven seemed justifiable.

"Well it is a pitch meeting for Gods sake and at this point we have no film."

"Oh yes, getting drunk is our best option."

Challenge had not called so the plan remained the same. They would swing by the studio on the way to lunch and pick up the pilot. Dressing to impress was simple after the Bloody Mary, the staple black trouser suits, white Chanel T shirts, gold Gucci sandals and the ever present pouchettes. Both Girls looked more fabulous than fabulous. Not too young to look past it. Just hip enough to be LA.

Always positive and forever hopeful the drive to the studio was filled with talk of all kinds of possible scenarios. Having somewhere fabulous to go always made work more fun. They now had a real business with a real plan and a way to break into Hollywood. Would the film be good enough? Would Jeff see potential? Were they kidding themselves? As they pulled up outside the Venice Beach studio anything was truly possible. It took twenty minutes and four calls from the cell phone before anyone opened the door. Challenge looked like Desperate Dan on a bad acid tab, the bags under his eyes the size of the new Gucci tote. The film did play well on his computer screen but that was it. You guessed it. The expensive converter software was still in the box and the film was not ready.

"You are joking right. I will kill you."

"Hold me back."

Polly made a quick exit to avoid the onslaught of verbal abuse, as The Girls gave Challenge a mouthful from Yorkshire. His sheepish weakness made him rather unattractive but they did like him and in truth felt a little sorry for him. They gave him another chance. He was to work on the film and have it ready by the end of the day. They would somehow charm Jeff over lunch, pitch him the idea, then Fedex the pilot to E! later that evening. It was a set back but The Girls had no fear. They could sell vibrators to nuns. Experts. Conning the green light man would be a piece of piss.

Arriving at the posh nosh place in Hollywood created a much needed breather. The morning had been seriously stressful thus far. The Girls reveled in being looked after by nice young valet boys. This was more like it. The place had class and The Girls were ready for a stiff one to steady the nerves. Their conversation was always made up of observations then demands. Most people could not understand a word they said but to them it all made sense.

The restaurant theme was white and clinical, rather chic. It was filled with out of work actors, waiting to wait on industry moguls, waiting for their big break. The Girls got their big break when the place had an outside patio, somewhere to drink a large G and T, smoke a fag and discuss the pending meeting. It was their lucky day. The restaurant itself was empty. What a surprise. It was Los Angeles, don't forget, the land of the one hour power lunch. Yet by half past twelve the place would be packed.

Fighting the busy traffic on the way had made both girls think about Barbados for a moment. Oh how things had changed. A gin and tonic always tasted better on the beach in St James but that pleasure was soon reduced to nothing more than a wonderful memory. Today they had to focus and execute their plan.

"What do you think Jeff will look like? "

"Short fat and Jewish. Everyone who is anyone in Hollywood is short, fat and Jewish. Shall we have one more?"

Ordering a second G and T had to be swiftly aborted. The green light man and his exotic assistant Donna had arrived. As The Girls re entered the restaurant, it was amazing. Within the time it took to smoke one fag and guzzle a G and T the restaurant, as predicted, was now completely full.

Jeff was not short, fat and Jewish, quite the contrary. He was tall, dark and handsome wearing Gucci glasses and a soft, pig skin jacket. A major result. Donna had it going on in a big way too. She was just their type, funky and urban, wearing hipster jeans and a great T. Her thick black hair was twisted and hidden under a purple and gold bandanna. She was young and hip and The Girls could see nothing but success ahead. The art of doing good business was always about chemistry. It could not have worked out better if they had planned it. That's right they did.

"You look far too young to be head of E! Television. It makes a change to work with someone so hip."

Jeff loved them right from the gekko, already convinced they had television backgrounds. Why spoil a good thing? Donna opened up by the second, as the four new mates decided to order lunch. Putting them straight seemed unimportant and unnecessary.

"One red, one white? Is that cool with everyone?"

What a surprise, the visitors both opted for water. Jeff said something about not being able to work in the afternoon and Donna was fasting for something. Typical American behavior, always in "Denial" and that is not a river in Egypt. Oh well, more wine for The Girls as they stuck up for the European norm.

"Where we come from everyone drinks at lunch. One won't hurt"

The Girls spent their whole lives encouraging American people to let their hair down a little. It was a well rehearsed speech, said with fun but the green light duo stuck to their guns, sipped their water and proceeded to order their food. Donna turned out to be rather adventurous ordering snail pizza. Was this a first? An American who enjoyed the French delicacy? The Girls were impressed. Jeff went for the chicken salad. Water and lettuce leaves, how sad. Although starving, The Girls stuck to drinking the wine. Doing a pitch with a mouthful of snails could prove rather tricky to say the least.

"In Europe, the food and wine experience tends to be savored over long leisurely periods. We can never understand why Americans opt for in out burgers."

Jeff soon made his argument for fast food loud and clear. Socializing at this point was pointless. He was a busy busy man with a television network to run. He wanted to know what exactly they had to offer him and why he was sitting there. Looking around the room it was very clear the place was filled with people drinking water, eating lettuce leaves and doing a pitch. They needed to wet his appetite. The Girls seized the moment.

"We set out to sell art but no one would buy it. We began to look at Hollywood to find art buying clients."

"We have made a pilot, "Girls on E!". It will be ready this afternoon. Culture, sex and celebrities."

Both girls had their fingers crossed under the table. When in doubt, always, always bullshit. Their energy tickled Jeff. That was evident by the smile on his face. E! Television was on the look out for new celebrity programming. Donna wanted names. Jeff casually mentioned a couple of celebrities he was interested in, Tommy Lee and Jason Alexander, perhaps a late night chat show with a twist? The set, a sultry bed chamber with The Girls as hosts posing the intimate suggestion, Come in and look at our etchings. According to Jeff, famous faces always pulled good ratings. If The Girls could get celebrities like Tommy and Jason in an art show, E! would be extremely interested in their idea. It was amazing for two drunks from Yorkshire. Here they were having a one hour power lunch with a Hollywood green light executive and people said they would end up working in a Troll factory? Maybe now the cold world of Hollywood would open its' doors.

Was this a green light? You bet it was. Stalking celebrities was their profession so finding Tommy Lee the rock star and Jason Alexander the bald sit-com actor couldn't be that difficult. Jeff had given them a challenge and The Girls had The List. This was something they could work with.

As if by magic Donna turned back into the perfect assistant and instructed her boss he had to be in Santa Monica by two. The lunch was over. After a kiss kiss on both cheeks, they said their good byes. Their hourglass had expired but The Girls had a job to do for the head of E! Television. The lunch had been a raging success, expensive but worth every penny.

"These power lunches can really take it out of you. No wonder no one drinks or smokes, there simple isn't enough time, particularly if you have accepted the fact you will never be a size two and would like to eat something for a change."

"How hard could it be to get hold of this bloke Tommy Lee?"

The Girls itching to return to the studio left Orso, just as they had found it, empty. They were eager to impart their good news to Challenge and chatted all the way back to Venice. Challenge would now be filming the great Tommy Lee in a pilot for E! Now that was something to celebrate. When they arrived Challenge was still in the same spot, tied to his computer. Polly his angel was high in the corner still filming the psychotic Siamese cat, Smirnoff. The film was not ready. It was maddening.

"Challenge what exactly is the problem here? You must not over promise then under deliver."

"We had to bull shit our way through lunch without a film. We have promised Jeff a pilot by this evening."

"What do you need?"

He had too much pride, a heavily disguised ego and hated confrontation but the bottom line was he had a screw loose. Something was definitely missing up top but his latent desire to win was packaged in lovable talent. They melted.

"Look Challenge you have to help us here. If we can impress Jeff with a film, you get a job. See how it works."

"The guy told us over lunch we need stars like Tommy Lee. Have you heard of him? Surely with all your contacts someone must have access to his telephone number? Think."

Challenge bless him did have a brain and mentioned three Mexican rappers from the hood, The Filthy Immigrants. They had been the back up band on Tommy's last world tour and Challenge was pretty sure, the rappers still had personal contact with the man himself. This was more like it.

"Set up a meeting and let's get Filthy on tape talking about Tommy. It'll be explosive TV for E! and massive exposure for them."

Challenge agreed to broke the deal and get the rappers into the studio for a power pow wow. The Girls would get to Tommy Lee. Not a bad day's work for two middle aged Hollywood housewives. Although the years had matured the face, the spirit was still very much alive and they wanted success for Ilia more than anything. The studio atmosphere that night paralleled 'Studio 54' in the seventies as The Girls performed like theatrical veterans. Getting ready to come face to face with street gangsters would take some preparation. Challenge knowingly watched from the swivel chair egging them on, secretly hoping they would forget about the film. Challenge's prayer was answered as the high pair piled into the back of a taxi and headed home to jail. He had the nine lives of Smirnoff. Challenge had bought himself more time as he waved farewell to The Girls, his Girls. They would collect the car in the morning.

The following morning was hangover alert but for once they didn't care. They had a plan, a real plan, in fact such a good plan it induced a celebration joint and by eleven thirty, it was time for a cold beer. They could get the car tomorrow.

"I have an idea. Ilia still needs a celebrity patron for the school. We could ask Jason Alexander. He loves art and his career is not exactly booming. We get him to agree to the pilot and then introduce him to fresco. He's educated, trust me, Ilia will blow his head off"

Getting to Tommy Lee would take time. They had to rely on Challenge to set up a meeting with Filthy and that could take forever considering the turn around time thus far on the film. They would concentrate on stalking the big television comedy actor with not much hair and a short body. As luck would have it, the actor had another string to his bow, live theater and was performing in a one man show at the Pasadena Playhouse that week.

"What a stroke of luck. Thank you God."

"Pour some wine, my hangover is dying."

Stalking is not a straightforward profession, but from their days pounding the boards with the local amateur dramatic society, they knew getting through the stage door would be no problem.

STEP ONE

Make friends with the receptionist at the Pasadena playhouse. They would have to get by her first. Her name was Vera. Their accent worked a treat yet again as they made her feel like the Queen of England.

"Oh you would love London. We could show you the most amazing time. By the way, what time does Jason arrive for rehearsal?"

STEP TWO

Con Vera and get into Jason's dressing room for a chat about their proposition. She soon opened up like a mussel, oozing juicy information. Now they knew what time they could catch him.

"Pour some more wine. This will take balls. Tomorrow's the show so we dress up as Beverly Hills florists and deliver flowers for good luck. We insist Jason sign for them himself at the powerful client's request. Vera will be a pushover, just keep her confused."

"You my friend are a genius."

STEP THREE

The note with the flowers had to be kind but informative, just in case they didn't manage to make contact. It's always about covering every possibility.

Dear Jason,

We are The Girls on E! We have an art project to boost your career. It's potentially working with E! Television and a modern day Michelangelo, a little higher profile than Kentucky Fried Chicken. Break a leg.

Art Interiors.

Jason Alexander was now in play. And that was that.

After a celebration joint they called Challenge. He still insisted his film was cosmic and the next revolution. He was stark raving bonkers, don't forget. They told him to forget the old film and prepare for a new voyage of discovery. They had to meet his rapper, Filthy, in order to bag the next elephant, Tommy Lee. Challenge was instructed to get his finger out and do some dialing for dollars.

Time was of the essence.

Two days drinking on the trot took its toll, they were not twenty anymore, so the following morning with giant hangovers, they were relieved to pick up the car from the studio and enjoy an Evian filled day. They picked up the flowers, ordered the day before white and extremely stylish, very European and set off for Pasadena. The American Express card did nicely thank the Lord and the stage was set.

They arrived at the theater and not a Vera in sight? She had taken the day off stupid cow and had been replaced by, what one could only describe as, a smiley King Kong wearing a security mans uniform. This was a disaster for two fake florists from Beverly Hills. Banking on Vera was a key part of the plan. Undaunted, they confidently made their way to the reception desk at the stage door and confronted the Beast. This was a fuck up once again as they smiled for England.

"You do the talking."

"I'm far too spaced to make chit chat with a Gorilla, especially stone cold sober."

"Hello there, Fleurs Des Anglaise. I'm Poppy and she's Rose. We are here to deliver some flowers for Jason Alexander. It was prearranged with Vera."

King Kong was not remotely interested and informed them to leave the flowers with him. He would sign on the star's behalf. They tried to woo him. Make him blush. Do black people blush? He didn't and kicked them out. Oh well, if at first you don't succeed, try and try again. Poppy and Rose had to make contact with Jason. They had invested too much energy to fail. With time running out Plan B was executed.

"Let s check out the building round the back. Maybe we can break into his dressing room and surprise him."

Having good James Bond skills always comes in handy when stalking celebrities. They both watched his films religiously. A smooth crook with style, there was nothing more appealing in a man. At the back of the theater The Girls spotted a tiny window into what looked like the gentleman's toilet. Breaking and entering? It was a possible way in to get closer to the star. Now they were cat burglars?

"I have heard about fitting a square peg in a round hole but a fat arse through that window?"

"I've lost weight. Give me a lift up."

Things were beginning to look up until King Kong came bounding round the corner and caught Fleur Des Anglaise in their act. Both battling huge egos since childbirth being humiliated was probably their worst pet hate. The bloody celebrity was not even that big, hardly Mick Jagger for Gods sake and they were sober.

"OK don't lose your mind. We get the message. You want us to bugger off. Just make sure that Jason gets the flowers. Having to go through this again is unthinkable."

"Well that was a fuck up."

"At least we followed the back up plan and wrote him the message."

"You're right. He won't be able to resist being in our pilot. We're in good shape." King Kong escorted the defeated champions off the pitch and watched their car until it was out of sight. He was glad to see the back of them.

Days passed by with no call and no thank you card from Jason. What was it with celebrities? Forget about ego. Saying thank you was just good manners, something Hollywood sadly lacked. The direct approach had not worked so all their agent stalking skills must be put to the test. They had to get on the phone, make some noise in Celebrity Land and try to make contact with Jason's people. Of course you know by now what that meant, the three bottle canvas call and Thatcher Pikes' invaluable list. Jason's agent was about to get a roasting.

What a surprise, his agent was guarded by the ever present assistant. She had no clue what to do about thank you cards for flowers and put them onto his publicist. The poor publicist assistant was not the sharpest knife in the drawer and put them straight back to the agent's assistant, who was now somewhat pissed off. Was this happening? All that effort just to get a thank you card? It was like banging ones head against the wall until it bleeds. No wonder these girls had to drink.

Persistence paid off when The Girls were fobbed off with Mr. Alexander's home telephone number and the name of his housekeeper, Pip. She was nice and looked through his mail. She came across their card and relayed they were in a pile of things to be dealt with. They would hear back soon. At last they had a result in the crazy world of celebrity stalking. It was just about being patient, persistent and passionate, just like The How To Penetrate Hollywood Manual predicted months earlier. It had been another long day but they were a little closer to homing in on a hit. Maybe tomorrow would bring bigger fish to fry now Jason would be calling them back.

Every day at The Beach Cottage started off pretty much the same. Three cups of coffee and a pick me up joint, followed by horror stories about life with The Jailers. Being married to brothers with an allergic reaction to fun was not a good thing but at least they could sound off each other and continue their fight to escape.

"Today we need to concentrate on getting to Tommy Lee."

"We need to set up a meeting with Filthy."

Had it not been for the lunch with Jeff Shore from E! they would never have thought to contact Tommy Lee and his band, Methods of Mayhem, primarily because they had never heard of him. According to Jeff, if they could get celebrities like Tommy to the table, they could get the deal they so badly needed. Money was tight and they needed a plan, fast. It was time to bug Challenge yet again.

No matter what time they called Challenge, day or night, his disposition was always pleasant. He talked a great story. It was not until much later they discovered his amenable nature was attributed to the pharmaceutical dispensary occurring from his studio bathroom and very little rarely got done. Although Challenge had not finished their film, he had promised to bring bad boys of Rap, The Filthy Immigrants to the table. It was just a matter of time, time they didn't have. The Girls knew from experience pleading with Challenge was pointless. After a few harsh words and a couple of random threats, Filthy was showing up sometime around ten the following evening. Success. The rest of that day was spent preparing outfits for the pending assignment. They had to come up with some sexy but tasteful ideas. If they arrived early, Challenge could take some shots for Heff and The Girls could kill two birds with one stone. This was more like it. Heff was a fussy old bugger and had an eye for the ladies so they arranged to meet at the Venice Studio after lunch giving Challenge plenty of time to snap the perfect pictures before Filthy arrived.

"They have to see us as a power house not to be messed with."

"For Heff we take short skirts and high heels, some cleavage but more mystery. For Filthy we wear Gucci, perfect. English art dealers meet bad boys of rap."

Doing a photo shoot and a film interview with a cutting edge Mexican rap band was quite exciting for two old cronies from Yorkshire. By the time this footage was cut everyone in Television Land would be knocking on their door. After a quick bite and a nice joint, they made their way to Venice for their photo shoot, a mixture of location and studio shots. When they arrived the studio idea was shelved, and the trio headed out and about in Venice Beach. They could get those shots inside later according to Challenge. Over the hours that ensued they hung out in various bars and hot spots. Challenge trailed The Girls around with multiple cameras hanging off his arm, clicking, clicking, clicking. In public Challenge always made them look interesting. Passers by stopped and stared, silently questioning, who were these strange women?

He was funky, the ever present chains hanging from his khaki combat pants and his shaved head permanently covered by a "boys from the hood" black beanie. Fortunately he did take the hat off at The Girl's request, whenever they went anywhere really smart. He always listened and took their advice. Challenge insisted he had captured the ultimate photographs for Heff and the shoot was declared a raging success. It was time for a joint, a fresh coat of lipstick and on to the Filthy Immigrants. Now this was business.

Back at the studio it was almost ten. The Girls changed into power suits and waited for the rappers to arrive. They had no idea what to expect. At ten minutes past ten the door to the studio burst open and in walked the three identically clad Mexican hip-hop gangsters, the Filthy Immigrants. Were they midgets? The long baggy pants showing too much underwear were a fashion disaster. White Nike socks and top of the range trainers just didn't look stylish and the most ridiculous observation of all was their peculiar headdresses.

"Why on earth are you wearing women's tights on your heads? Are they hair nets?"

The ice was broken as Filthy produced a miracle from heaven. The perfect gift to fuse their union, a Dutch. What bliss. Luckily, for The Girls, these guys had a sense of humor. The Girls indulged in the fabulous weed showing the boys they were fly. The high kicked in and before one could say Busta Rhymes, The Girls were doing their own rendition of 'Pass the Courvoisier' and loving every second of it. Hanging with young street people created incredible dialog. Although these chaps came from the same poor background as The Girls, just a different country, they were very bright. Their songs were raw and filled with truth. '911 and the cops don't come.' was about their life growing up in the Bronx. It was magical. Challenge and Polly covered The Filthy Immigrant's action with digital flair. Give them all enough rope and they will hang themselves. In no time at all, Filthy, their leader was happily boasting about touring with Tommy Lee. Things had certainly improved somewhat since the days in the poor suburbs of New York. That was it. Their in. The Girls went for the jugular.

"So how well do you know this dude Tommy Lee?"

"We need a favor. In return for Tommy Lee's phone number, what if we manage your band and get you a gig at the House of Blues."

The English birds had set the bar. How hard would it be to promote Rap? The Girls knew the House of Blues was the place for show casing new talent. It seemed a fair exchange. After another celebration Dutch, the deal was done with nothing more than a handshake. Filthy was euphoric about performing at the famed House of Blues on Sunset. Tommy's number was dialed and a giddy message left by Filthy. Tommy was to expect a call from the two English girls. Like psychotic groupies inside a rock stars penis pouch, The Girls drank wine and reflected. Getting the gig was ambitious but not impossible. They had their ways. With the whole thing captured on film Challenge said the footage would change E! Television forever. They said 'pigs might fly' but one thing was sure. The footage would show networks like MTV that not all 40 year-olds have hearing aids and listen to Perry Como. Life for The Girls had no age barriers. It was all about people finding their purpose then living life to the full. The night ended a raging success. The Girls had photos for Heff, or so they thought, a way to get to Tommy Lee and the rappers had something to look forward to. As for Challenge, he had a film to make as The Girls gave him a reality check before heading back to jail.

"We have to send it to Jeff to keep him hot until we can film Tommy and Jason."

"This is your ninth life in the balance here mate. What ever it takes the new film needs to be ready by Monday morning."

It was clear. Challenge had the weekend to produce a pilot showing The Girls in action and print off some sexy stills. They just needed to rest. The business of selling Michelangelo to Hollywood was becoming very tiring and very hectic for two old timers. Sometimes being locked in jail to detox, was just the ticket.

Monday morning at The Beach Cottage was always great. A whole weekend in jail was about as much as anyone could stand. Thank God it was 11.30. They had things to do.

"Time to make some calls."

"We have Tommy's number now. What should we do?"

"Leave a suggestive message. We can drink some wine, get fucked up and be ready to chat with him later when he rings back."

Jason Alexander had still not responded. They would chase his housekeeper later. After a couple of glasses and a hit on the joint, they dialed Tommy Lee's number and waited like nervous schoolgirls. At first they encountered a recorded message service but eventually got through to his personal voicemail. The man's voice on the other end sounded hoarse and throaty. Steady. This was exciting.

"Hi there Tommy, Filthy Immigrants gave us your number. We are making a pilot for E! Television to expose the work of a Russian genius. We need celebrity collectors who love combining sex with culture. Let's meet and discuss. Do give us a shout back. Peace."

The reality set in. Tommy Lee, rock star would be calling them back? Wow. After another bottle or so they tracked down Pip, housekeeper to the very rude and very elusive Mr. Alexander. They wanted answers, even if they did come from his skivvy. She had no idea who they were already having forgotten she had spoken to them only days earlier. What was wrong with people in this place? Eager to put the phone down and get rid of them Pip said she would pass on their complaint to her busy, busy boss.

"Tell Jason we have a job for him. It's a celebrity art show. We are trying to make contact with him about a modern day Michelangelo and oh yes, tell him it's rude not to say thank you to ladies who send flowers."

The Girls drank more red and slide down the slippery slope into fighting mode. Their interest in the largest name in the independent movie arena began months early. Remember one of them wanted to be stuck on a desert island with him. In the beginning they had used humorous letters about art to tantalize him. Then they tried to sell him on becoming Patron to the Fresco school. They even tried to attach him to the Vatican project, until someone at a dinner party had mentioned they thought he might be Jewish. He must have thought these women from Art Interiors were stark raving bonkers. He was probably right. To try the impossible once again needed nerves of steel. Perhaps Harvey Weinstein, head of Miramax Films would consider filling in for Jason Alexander. They were sure Jeff wouldn't mind they had failed to cast Jason if they could get Harvey as the understudy.

Making calls to Harvey needed so much Dutch courage and three bottles at least. They had already established from previous calls to Miramax he had too many male assistants in his camp and dulcet tones didn't figure. Was he gay? May be girls just weren't tough enough to shield the main man from Hollywood's circling vultures.

It was most strange. Every time The Girls tried to flirt, to get closer to their mentor, it had resulted in the phone being slammed down.

A mad phoning frenzy ensued that day to compile a dossier on the 'who's who' in Harvey's organization. Was Charles more senior than Alex? They needed to understand the Miramax hierarchy if they were ever to land this big fish and make their Hollywood nightmare just a little less difficult. The more real names one had, the more seriously the assistant would take the call.

The information gleaned that day was like gold dust and would definitely help with the name dropping technique when encountering someone new in Harvey's office the next time they called. During their early research of Harvey, they had heard a rumor he collected the work of English rock star painter, Ron Wood. How hard could it be to track down Ronnie Wood's agent? Stalking the best was always easier with a solid plan. If they had him on board, they could go back to Harvey with a painting. Being Harvey's art agent was a good idea if they were representing what he liked.

"You have reached the office of Ron Wood art and music please leave a message."

Without something fabulous to offer Harvey, they knew they would fail. Nobody ever answered the phone and The Girls left another plea for help. They had clients for God sake, who would buy Ronnie's work. It had to be legitimate right? One can't say one's someone's agent if one's not, right? Were they learning at last? Out of the blue and into the twilight zone the telephone rang. Panic set in as The Girls fought about answering the call. Was it Tommy Lee calling back? Talking to Tommy drunk was not such a good idea after all. Neither wanted the job.

After the forth ring one executed. Panic over, it was Ron Wood's elusive and extremely arrogant New York agent, Mark Pines, returning their call. They pitched him on selling a Ron Wood to one of their celebrity clients. They did potentially have Harvey Weinstein as a client, remember. He seemed very interested in building an alliance with these crazy English maniacs and a deal was struck. The new art dealers would be sole representatives of Ron Wood's work on the west coast. It was fantastic, a title and a major result for two birds from Yorkshire. Harvey had expensive taste and a commission would be paid to The Girls for each piece sold. The art was not cheap and they could charge over the odds for it. They now had the solid plan they so desperately needed and a press release was sent over to Harvey in New York. Everything was perfect.

"Art Interiors to showcase Ron Wood, celebrity painter and genius."

It was about the millionth fax sent that month. Surely now Harvey would ring them and order some art for his own collection. He had to use someone. Why not them? As the fourth bottle was opened they couldn't help themselves. Harvey was attainable.

"You know what, he's pissing me off now. What more do we have to do? Fuck it let's just call him."

"Hello there. Please may I have a word with Harvey?"

Their inability to execute him irked them. The annoying frustration, not dissimilar to being two squares off the Rubik's cube. They had to get him on the phone and have a chat. The unfamiliar male assistant was new. He was busy, under pressure and easy to manipulate. They had him by the balls. By sheer good luck and a bit of clever skull- duggery, the assistant, completely confused put their call through to Harvey's personal voice mail. This was the chance of a life-time. Now they really did believe in miracles.

Whatever was said into that machine that afternoon is still a blur however something triggered with Harvey and they were through the door. It had only taken months of blood sweat and half a liver but they had finally made contact with their mentor. He could now connect a voice to the barrage of faxes and requests for help he had received over the last year. The day ended on such a high note, masturbation was in order. Their business was looking good for the first time in months. Tommy would call back, they would have a hit celebrity art show and Ilia could paint fresco until the cows came home.

The next day, hung-over as hell, it never rains in California turned out to be another oxymoron. It was pissing it down and The Girls were trapped in The Beach Cottage for another long day. Calling Tommy again was the first order of the day. Today would be about putting some pieces together and firming up some plans.

"Tommy darling it's the English girls. We don't like talking to your voice mail. Remember you're the boy here. We are not boring middle aged women just after sex. We have business to discuss. In order to move forward with our pilot we have to have a celebrity and we want you. Do give us a shout back. You will love us."

"That was a good call. How famous is he?"

The Girls had a copy of Maxim magazine with Tommy splattered all over the front cover. According to the writer Tommy loved sex. And he was hung like a donkey apparently, a good reason to make contact, maybe. Tommy was extremely good looking in the photos, very sexy. Dressed like a punk and totally covered in tattoos, his soulful eyes and rather gentle coyness were an obvious contradiction. The silver bolt through his lip posed a problem for The Girls but they could soon change that. They loved giving style advice to badly presented Americans. As they read more into the article it became clear Tommy was hot. A major American rocker and much more famous than The Girls had first thought. They were really stalking in the crème de la crème of Hollywood's elite without even trying. It was fabulous. Nothing was out of reach for these two, even getting a sexy super star into bed. It was so unrealistic it was probably possible. The pages of the magazine were earmarked and put away for later stimulation. Back in the twilight zone the telephone was ringing. Maybe Harvey was finally calling.

"If he calls us back you deal with this. I fancy him too much to do business talk. I already want to have sex with him."

"I think he prefers big breasted blondes. He was married to Pam Anderson, quite a hard act to follow. I think you are shopping out of your price range."

"I was talking about Harvey. Oh no please not Tommy sober. You pick it up. I am not doing this."

"Good afternoon Art Interiors, how may I direct your call?"

As one flaked the other always stepped up to the plate. Thank God they worked as a team. It wasn't Tommy and it wasn't Harvey but it was someone really important. Barbara Schneeweiss, Head of Miramax Television, Los Angeles was on the phone. What did she want? Was she about to make their dream come true? How did she get their number? All questions were impossible to answer at this stage in the game.

The rules are simple when caught off guard and out of one's depth. Act like you are in control, then name drop for England. They had already bagged one green light executive. They were on a role. Their effervescent blathering did not detract from the fact Barbara was calling to tell them off. Oops. It seemed Harvey was fed up with their barrage of requests. She made it clear Harvey was not available but inquired as to what it was exactly it was they wanted from Miramax. It was a once in a life time opportunity to jam their foot into the barely ajar door. Like veterans they went into battle.

"We have an idea for a celebrity art show with E! Television. We have been trying to contact Harvey to tell him about art and our modern day Michelangelo. We have Tommy Lee already attached. We now need a heavy hitter like Miramax to produce the show."

Barbara surprisingly loved the idea pulled from nowhere to connect Miramax to their project. She asked them to come in to pitch the pilot on the condition The Girls refrain from bugging Harvey. This was more like it. They could leave Harvey be for a little while at least. Something to really upset the apple chart had to happen. Things never went this smoothly at Art Interiors. She would only accept their pitch via their agent?

This was a travesty and about to open a whole new can of worms. They already knew it was impossible to even talk to an agent, let alone get one out to lunch. They had to think. Having Miramax behind them would really impress Jeff and with Tommy Lee in the pilot, the plan was coming together. Getting an agent had to be possible somehow. Who did they know? Brains were racked, a joint was rolled and they were off yet again on a magic carpet to the Land of Creative Ideas where anything is truly possible.

"Remember that chick, the actress friend of my Jailer? She had to start her own agency because she couldn't find one to represent her."

"Good idea. She only has to lick a stamp. Our pitch gets to Barbara and we get to Harvey. Well done now roll another joint."

The Girls opened some wine to celebrate and made the call to Westside Talent agency. Before one could say William Morris, they had an agent. The friend of the jailer was delighted to help and generously offered them some of her headed stationary for their pitch. She knew how hard it was to get anywhere in Hollywood without the help of an agent. The "Girls on E!" disaster was still stuck on Challenge's computer and not remotely anything they could present with pride to Miramax. Challenge was useless. They needed something much more stylish and more new age. If they wanted to impress Barbara, they had to come up with a new pitch for a real show.

"How about this? 'Celebrity Art Interiors.' A show featuring the artistic side of the famous celebrity. We give Tommy one of Ilia's paintings for free. He hangs it in his house. We do a short interview with champagne and nibbly things. Ilia gets exposure and Tommy becomes a collector, edgy, sexy and cultural. The show will be aired by E! and produced by Miramax. Win win all round"

Always positive, forever hopeful, the pitch 'Celebrity Art Interiors' was typed on the Westside Talent Agency paper and dropped in the post box, first class, to Barbara as requested. All they needed now was Tommy to call back and set up a time to meet. Everything seemed to be falling into place but both girls had to face reality. Life in Hollywood was not that simple.

"What if Tommy says no. Then what?"

"You give him a blow job, whatever it takes. The art is at stake here."

"We need to find six huge celebrities to appear in the show. Just in case."

"We can ask Heff once we get photographs. Tom Cruise might go for it."

"Now we have something to offer, everyone will want to appear in our show, you watch."

Famous last words yet again, would they ever learn? With Tommy and Barbara in play they could relax a little and began compiling some new stalking contacts for the ever present Plan B. It was always a great feeling as they filled their Rolodex with new celebrity prospects. Kevin Morrow, Head of Live Entertainment at the House of Blues was the next name. Even though he was not strictly a celebrity, he did have a powerful job and was in contact with the best in the music business. He also had the clout to get them into the VIP Foundation Room without paying for a membership. Something they would walk on hot coals for. Getting to Kevin would be tricky but they had promised Filthy a gig in return for Tommy's number. Calling Nigel was the answer. If anyone knows, Nigel Knows. www.nigel_knows.com.

How they knew Nigel is still a mystery but his phone number always came in handy whenever they needed anything to do with the impossible. He was a bit like Aladdin's genie except he lived in Las Vegas not the lamp; at the Mandalay Bay Hotel to be precise. He had a Rolodex to die for and Steven Tyler was rumored to be his best mate. He was so connected anything was possible. Putting two and two together, there was a glimmer of hope Nigel could get them to Kevin and dialed his mobile. They had also heard on the grapevine, Nigel had connections at the famed Palms Hotel and House of Blues, Las Vegas. They got it right. They were off and running. Nigel did know and freely gave them the information they needed to get to Kevin and his assistant Walter. Getting a meeting was crucial to keep the deal alive. Calling Walter and dropping Nigel's name would open Kevin's door.

Walter turned out to be the assistant of all assistants and The Girls had their meeting with Kevin, bagels at ten the following morning, their treat. The foundation (room) was in place. Concentrating on the goal for Filthy proved productive. Regarding their own endeavours it was time to get pushy.

"Where is that bastard Tommy Lee? How many fucking messages do we have to leave him?"

Tommy had still not returned their call. It was so frustrating. They called again and again and begged him to call them back. It was getting dull having to chase a bloke so hard. In their world boys did the chasing. Tommy Lee was a tough nut to crack.

The quest to track down Jason Alexander had long since been aborted. Being rude was just not acceptable, especially after the humiliation of being thrown out of The Pasadena Playhouse by a security guard. He had fallen by the way side and it would take more than these good Samaritans to pick him up and dust him off. They wouldn't help him now if he they saw him drowning.

"He might be famous but he is not a gentleman. That is the last time I support his art."

"The Pasadena Playhouse? It's not Covent Garden is it Darling?"

They talked for the rest of the day about Tommy calling back but he didn't and the day ended, finally. They just needed Tommy to say yes to their show and all would be fabulous in the world of Art Interiors. The filming would be tricky even though Challenge wanted the job. The Girls foolishly gave him the benefit of the doubt, both suckers for a good time and prayed for all they were worth Tommy would make a date with them.

Taking coffee and bagels to Kevin Morrow the next day at the famed House of Blues, was something to get up early for. The time had come to get clever and convince Kevin to showcase Filthy. Walter was delighted with his breakfast. The Girls were delighted with him, very cute and very sexy. Was he Bob Marley? The English girls played him like an old Stradivarius, fiddling, plucking, bowing, stroking and always, always flattering.

"Walter you are so much more handsome than we ever imagined."

"Love the jacket."

"The art in this place is fabulous. Who does the buying?"

Walter coyly embraced the energy and told them to take a seat. Kevin was on a long distance call but knew they were waiting. They made themselves at home. Meeting with Kevin served two purposes, a gig for Filthy and a way into the exclusive Foundation Room to stalk celebrities. Maybe they would even get the man out to lunch. An opportunity to ply him with red wine and he would be toast. After a private pow wow with Kevin, Walter popped his head round the door and ushered them into the huge office of his busy boss. They had five minutes. Wall to wall windows provided a spectacular vista of the city and immediately unsettled The Girls. They were not at their best at altitude. The office, overlooking Sunset Strip was stuffed to bursting with autographed memorabilia from signed guitars to Platinum discs. Virtually every well known rock musician on the planet including Eric Clapton, BB King, Jimmy Hendrix and Led Zepplin, were all present and correct in some form or another. The collection alone was worth a fortune. It was evident Kevin had powerful mates and it looked like Tommy Lee might be one of them. There in a photo frame, in the middle of his over filled desk was a picture of him and Tommy golfing. This was manna from heaven to open their meeting.

"Oh my God you know Tommy Lee too? We have just asked him to appear in our new pilot Celebrity Art Interiors. What a coincidence."

"Nigel said you were important but this is fabulous. We should have you appear on the show as well."

The Girls threw out enough information to substantiate the fact they belonged in his office. The name dropping routine worked again and they had Kevin's full attention. It was seemingly uncanny how such outrageous exaggerations gave one immediate credibility in LA LA Land. Kevin had no idea why he liked them but he did. Well as much as they imagined he liked anyone. Kevin was not a looker by any stretch of the imagination bless him. His ginger blond hair, invisible eyebrows and boyish face filled with freckles did little to disguise a bad temper, bubbling and spitting like a latent volcano about to erupt at any second. He was pretty fierce all things considered. He humored their request for the Filthy Immigrants but booking the talent was a job for Walter. Controlling the business and smooching the celebrities was written in bold on his job description. It was clear he needed lunching.

"We have so many ideas to run by you. Let's make this meeting more comfortable, where do you fancy, the Ivy?"

He hated the Ivy but instead chose a small, authentic Italian eatery across the road from The House Of Blues corporate offices on Sunset Boulevard. According to Kevin the place was always packed with famous faces. That was good news for celebrity stalkers. The Girls had a little time to kill but they didn't mind. They would see him in a couple of hours.

The restaurant was heaving with warm bodies, sadly nobody The Girls recognized, as they secured a table and waited for their guest to arrive. They munched on warm bread and fragrant infused olive oil delighted, people on that side of town were lunching for a change. Kevin was fashionably late, like all the other so called cogs in the wheel of Celebrity Land. Sitting down next to one and opposite the other he was simultaneously surrounded and entertained. Most would be terrified but he wasn't afraid. After years of practice The Girls worked men like Mrs. Robinson but even they had to put in some overtime to marginally crack his gruff exterior.

"Red or White darling."

"Let's push the boat out and order two bottles. If you hang out with rock stars you must be a drinker."

Shock! Horror! Poor old Kevin was a recovering drunk, eight years clean and hating every fucking second of it. Shit they weren't expecting that. They were caught off guard without an essential Plan B. in place. The Girls felt an instant empathy for their sober friend. This was something really worth toasting.

Over the years The Girls had given up drinking for Lent a couple of times and thus decided anyone able to go for eight years without a drink deserved a medal. Kevin was amused by their zest for life and appeared to really enjoy their company even though he was sober. As they impressed the shit out of him with their stories about ABC News, the Vatican and "Girls on E!" disaster it didn't matter he was drinking sweet tea. Yuk. Their celebrity show sounded extremely interesting and Kevin wanted to be kept in the loop. Maybe he could help them. It was perfect.

Having lunch with a recovering alcoholic was a new concept for The Girls however things got messy when a suggestion was made to adjourn outside for a nicotine fix. The cigarette smoke pushed Kevin over the edge.

"Why don't you have just one glass? It tastes so good and it lowers your cholesterol. You can do it."

"We promise we won't tell anyone."

Kevin didn't crack. He told The Girls he would think about their idea and get back to them. If they wanted VIP passes for The Foundation Room Walter was their man. The lunch was a raging success and once again they had managed to sell a concept before it was even hatched. Salesmanship at its finest. Having already downed the best part of two bottles, carrying on boozing was the only option. Kevin was dismissed with European flamboyance and the Maitre D' ordered a cab for the Girls. If Tommy didn't call soon, they would need a back up pilot to take to Barbara and Challenge had loads of footage to work with.

It was decided they would drop by the studio and get their filmmaker motivated.

Hanging-out with Challenge and his crazy mates required copious amounts of wine and an endless supply of pot. A heady state would prevent a potential shouting match about the film that never was. They piled into a cab picking up supplies on the way and it was off to the Venice Beach studio. As they pulled up Challenge had good news. The film was still on his computer but it was now the cosmic of all cosmic explosions. He insisted The Girls watch and wait. He could hardly wait to premier it.

If Challenge had been born a cockroach, life as he knew it was over. Dead. Spiked by the heel of a Gucci sandal, crunch, as flat as a pancake. The film was ridiculous and nothing made any sense. The unsteady camera captured endless footage of Smirnoff, the toothless psychotic Siamese cat, older than God. The interview with Filthy had no sound although The Girls' feet did look good thanks to Tom Ford. In short the cosmic explosion was a complete fuck up.

"What happened to the celebrity party on the Strand?

"I had no idea your cat was so talented."

"The starlet from Days of our Lives? The gay publicist?"

"Let's watch the real pilot shall we?"

Sadly, what they had just experienced was indeed his excuse for a film. Polly sat in the corner with her headphones turned up. In reality she was the filmmaker but she didn't believe in The Girls. It was Challenge's esoteric faith that maintained the status quo yet he could not understand why The Girls were so upset. He truly believed his film was new age. Challenge looked sheepish and bowed his head still insisting it was brilliant television. He had no answers to their questions. It was time to get tough and get things back on track. They had to give him a reality check before one of them knocked his lights out. They needed a film and pronto.

"This is not working Challenge. When Tommy Lee calls back and we believe he will, we will have one shot at making this pilot. We have to get it right. Go back to the drawing board and start again."

"Less of your cat and more of us."

"Our faces will be more effective than our feet."

Once again he had over promised and under delivered but it was too late in the day to start worrying about that. All the erratic behavior had to stop. The Girls bit their tongues, choked back their "Don't reward bad behavior" mantra and coaxed Polly into helping. Only she could truly get Challenge focused and working. All they could assume was she must be tremendous in bed. With no more than a half hearted, two second shoulder massage and a few sultry sweet nothings Challenge was momentarily fired up and focused. It was electric and their only hope. Sadly the work was interrupted by a visitor, a good friend of Challenge's from down the street, Mike. Not the best looking vegetable on the plate but Challenge was eager to change the serious dynamic and invited him to stay and hang.

The Girls, queens of procrastination themselves could do nothing except close their eyes and abdicate, voicing an opinion was pointless. Challenge was without a doubt the reigning king of Procrastination Land.

Mike loved the next revolution duo and began to show off. His wide slippery mouth resembled a wet, complicated vagina and his bulging eyes surveyed the scene like a crazy goldfish. He was ugly but there was something about him. Maybe it was the big silver bolt through his long juicy tongue. The Girls instantly found that rather appealing. They were desperate let's not forget. If one closed one's eyes it was easy to imagine one was sitting right next to Billy Joel when he sang. The powerful voice, accompanied by an acoustic guitar resonated off the studio walls. He was excellent. Was he famous? Almost. Mike was a base player and session musician for many famous faces and was currently working with Tommy Lee. Was he for real? Their boat had finally come in? Challenge was off the hook yet again, his nine lives well and truly used up. He always managed to spin any situation in his favor. It was the fundamental element to his charm. The fact Challenge had not put two and two together was typical but forgivable. Maybe Mike could call Tommy from his mobile and introduce The Girls. Of course being a man, Mike wanted something in return for the favor, asking both women "What was it worth?" They had no money to offer but one thing had never failed in the past.

"That silver thing in your mouth looks rather sexy."

Mike was in heaven as he passionately snogged the girl who lost the toss. She was old enough to be his mother but the kiss was essential and the privacy a bonus. The fewer witnesses the better as far as she was concerned. The others were sick, with laughter. Challenge filmed the whole thing then gave his audience a replay. This was hot footage and perfect for the Howard Stern show. Make a mental note, embarrassing footage must be destroyed. According to Mike, Tommy was on the hunt for a new base player. He was picking up "UB40", some bloke, not the band, from the airport and taking him to Tommy's studio the next day. Mike said he would chat to Vignola, Tommy's right hand thug and get a message to the man himself. Kissing an ugly bloke for a rock star's telephone number made going back to jail seem tolerable as the two girls fell out of the studio into a passing cab, another oxymoron in LA LA Land.

The following day was a massive hangover alert! The Girls, as always one step ahead, were determined to start attacking some new stalking possibilities just in case Tommy let them down. They still needed a celebrity Patron for the school and Ilia was desperate for someone somewhere to give him a boost. Challenge had rather taken their time away from him and he did have a tendency to be moody and depressive. They certainly didn't want him going any further down hill.

"Why don't we contact Jack Nicholson about Ilia? He collects art."

"Good idea. He's very sexy. Someone I often masturbate over."

Calling such huge film stars sober didn't seem that impossible. What did they have to lose? They had got to Harvey. Surely they could get to Jack too. Maybe they were mates. They looked down the list and found his publicist, Sandy Bressler.

Experience had taught them they could easily make this call sober. Sandy would have an assistant insisting they pop it all down in a fax blar blar blar so the first brutally hungover canvas call in the history of Art Interiors was made. They got Sandy in person. Shit, that wasn't supposed to happen. He wasn't very friendly, surprise surprise and uncontrollable nerves meant the call was rushed. The panache of absolute calm, usually achieved from a massive bong hit whenever major stars were attacked was severely lacking.

"We would like Jack to consider being Patron to our Fresco school. He loves art and we need a heavy hitter. We also have an art show idea to put to him. He gets a free painting and our artist gets the kudos."

It seemed so strange to both. Here was Jack, a rich Hollywood bastard and here they were poor as church mice offering to give him something for free? With that level of inequity in life it is not really surprising nothing ever got done. Sandy relayed it was a personal thing with Jack and yes, you guessed it they should indeed write it all down in a fax. If Jack had any interest he would contact them directly? Sandy was stern but this response was more exciting than finding a roach when you're desperate. And they hadn't touched a drop.

It was only ten past ten and The Girls had the possibility of three major calls that day, Tommy Lee, Harvey Weinstein and now Jack Nicholson. Was this the big time? Back in the twilight zone the telephone was ringing, now they really did need a drink. Who would it be?

It wasn't a Hollywood celebrity but their Hollywood green light executive, Barbara. She had received the pitch for 'Celebrity Art Interiors' and wanted a meeting with them. Wow. She said the idea looked promising and a meeting was planned at her office, again on Sunset, to pitch their show. Working as Hollywood producers suddenly seemed rather appealing. It was obviously just a case of having the balls to make things happen.

"We have three weeks to make a pilot with Tommy Lee, plus attach five other celebrities to appear later down the road. We need to get stalking."

"Let's bug the shit out of Hollywood and make someone say yes."

Finding celebrities to help with their art had already proved to be impossible. With the Miramax meeting penned in their empty calendar being positive was critical. They had already over promised and under delivered for Tommy's telephone number and he wasn't even calling them back. Their plan was straightforward and simple to them, so why was it so bloody difficult for everyone else to grasp? They drank wine, smoked pot and prayed for new inspiration. Miramax was in the bag but all they had to offer was an unfinished pilot and no celebrity. It was clear they needed more footage and fast. They needed to find more willing celebrities prepared to support the art, and aid The Girls ascension up the social ladder.

In Hollywood, according to 'The How To Penetrate Hollywood Manual', the television industry was all about networking and name dropping. As alien as that was for The Girls they followed the instructions to the letter on a daily basis. They could not fathom where they were going wrong and called Challenge with their news of the Miramax meeting. He was over the moon. His euphoria instantly obliterated as their reality check was delivered with zero compassion. Sparing an ego was a luxury they could not afford.

"To date you're the worst filmmaker in the entire universe."

"We don't know if you're always too high or just fucking useless."

"You must have some other contacts somewhere, you've photographed Gorbachov."

Challenged was challenged but came up with a plan. He had met some woman months earlier who, like Mikhail Gorbachov, had hired him to do a photo shoot. According to Challenge "The Russian Madonna" was a huge star in Europe, had a hit single in the Russian charts and was trying to break into Hollywood. According to her press clippings, she had appeared in one or two movies and had some powerful connections in high places. Maybe she could help. Challenge seriously suggested they take the time to meet her. The Russian bombshell had a television chat show on PBS and was always on the look out for interesting people with fabulous ideas. It was perfect. They finally had a celebrity at their disposal. Challenge would tell the Russian Madonna The Girls had a potential show coming up on E! Television and she could be their first guest. Although it was a little white lie and probably cruel on reflection, they were desperate and she sounded unique enough for Jeff Shore. Did she have big tits? Surely he liked big tits.

"She sounds perfect for our show. We just need to convince America she is huge in Europe."

"Blonde, big tits, singing happy birthday Mr. President with a Russian accent. Was that the road we were going down?"

"We're desperate"

The future always looked brighter after marijuana and today was no exception.

It was the end of another day. Tomorrow would be spent filming a new pilot with Challenge and his Russian pop star and they would finally have a cosmic explosion for Jeff and Barbara.

Going to the studio was always fun and interviewing a celebrity to promote art was exactly what Doctor Jeff had ordered. Challenge needed to focus, film and make sense of the interview. Producing a magnificent pilot from the footage to take to market was the hurdle. Where was Alan Pascoe when you needed him? Hosting Celebrity Art Interiors was the perfect job for two birds from Yorkshire trapped in jail. At last they would save the art, become famous and escape back to Europe with the dignity they now so sadly lacked.

Dressing correctly for television was crucial, the right amount of style with a rock star twist. In truth when they emerged from their walk in closet, the converted Beach Cottage bedroom, they looked like the Banger Sisters, way passed their sell by date. Oh what the hell, they still looked young enough to be fabulous and that was all that mattered.

When the Russian Madonna arrived The Girls stood in total disbelief. Was she a transsexual? Challenge was dead. The Playboy esque pictures did not remotely resemble what was standing in front of them. Was she wearing a wig? Had she been under the knife? She made even The Girls look more fabulous than usual. This was the biggest joke yet. They pulled Challenge aside.

"Where the hell did you find such a creature?"

Ruled by the ridiculous and bordering on insane The Girls knew Americans loved something different and decided to proceed with the pilot anyway. The Russian Madonna? Could they promote her as Euro Trash? Maybe if they kept it dark in the studio. She was probably pushing fifty but thought she looked twenty. Her red military jacket sadly missing a button revealed a tragic tale to the visually astute and her short black hot pants, better placed on a camel, rode up her arse. Her long jet black hair, fake or real? still a mystery, was scooped in a bun and hidden under a black beret. She did have big tits, what a surprise. At least that was a positive in LA LA Land.

Ilia had shared stories about the women in Russia many times but this chick would have sent even him running for the nearest salt mine. Her make up was more plentiful than the contents of a Max Factor warehouse. Not a pretty sight. The deep Russian accent lent itself to what could be described as a very sexy telephone voice but that was about as far as one could stretch the word sexy. Did Challenge have a plan? Obviously so. Challenge shouldered the job of director while Polly created a fabulous set with copious candles and canvases perched on easels from the studio walls. The room was transformed into a bohemian den of inequity, dark and sultry. The quintessential lighting making The Girls look ten years younger. It was perfect. They were sympathetic to their guest. No amount of theatrical engineering could help her.

It was getting late as the stars of the show took their places on the worn orange sofa, directly facing the hot studio lights. The Russian Madonna sat adjacent in an antique armchair by a huge statue of a stone penis. In the relaxed comfortable setting interviewing a Russian was easy. The strange trio talked about vodka and escaping from behind The Iron Curtain, old ground for The Girls. It was just like talking to Ilia and made her feel at home. When all three women had a full goblet of red wine The Russian Madonna insisted Challenge begin shooting the film. Cigarettes burned in the ashtray as the crew obliged capturing the energy. Lights. Camera. Action. This was cutting edge television and Tommy would love it. The Girls had been trained by the best.

As the shenanigans steered an uncharted course The Russian Madonna burst into what some might kindly describe as a song. It was accompanied by the systematic removal of her bright red bodice in what she obviously thought was a seductive fashion. Oh my Lord, what was she doing? Unhindered and unperturbed she performed the pseudo burlesque come opera number with gusto. The Girls just couldn't help themselves. She was terrible.

"Why don't you sing like a virgin?"

"It's a little more current"

Challenge had to stop himself wetting his pants as the Russian Madonna crawled across the floor, warbling something in Russian from the pit of her gut. She sounded like a cross between Pavorotti and a cat being skinned. The two girls sat in amazement. It was not "Like a Virgin" in fact she was nothing like a virgin. The Russian Madonna obviously liked taking her top off exposing her breasts. It had to be said they weren't bad for a woman of her age. She did have some porn star qualities but they were not suitable for a celebrity art show. They wouldn't be able to sell her to Jeff or anyone else for that matter with a straight face. Make a mental note. The only thing that footage could be used for was a freak show later down the road. And so the show was complete. The reality, when the footage was played back was quite different. The show was complete rubbish.

Although meeting the Russian 'celebrity' was a fantastic experience and exceedingly funny, she just wasn't famous enough. Her desperation to get naked was a testament to that. Appearing on real television was her ultimate dream and she insisted on repaying the favor by inviting The Girls to appear on her chat show later that week. She was also making a pilot. What happened to PBS? It was a controversial chat show she was pitching to the networks. Maybe they could nick her film crew and sack Challenge. That would be a result. Any exposure was usually good exposure and they did need more practice in front of the camera. With exposure in mind The Girls agreed to appear clarifying no nudity was required. Before leaving Madonna repeatedly asked what date The Girls show was airing on E! She had a fan club to inform. They didn't see it some how and put her off exchanging telephone numbers before she disappeared into the night.

The footage was hilarious but not suitable for Barbara. A half naked, aging Russian pop star in pigtails? She was a vertical market in her own right. There was nothing for it. They had to pin down Tommy Lee and get him on camera before meeting Miramax.

It was already almost Easter and the next day with horrible hangovers once again they set out to get to Tommy before the holiday. They dialed his phone service and gave it their best shot. Without him, the pilot was dead in the water and all their effort would be wasted.

"Tommy darling where are you? We have everything in place for an amazing pilot about art and celebrity. E! Television love you and so do we. Please, please call us back."

Tommy needed some solid P.R. like an infant needs a nurse and being associated with two middle aged art dealers, representing and saving a starving Russian genius, would give him all the kudos his heart desired, or so The Girls thought. However they still needed more celebrities to appear in their show. They had failed horribly with Jason Alexander and it was looking like Jack Nicholson didn't love art as much as he made out on the telly. A new plan of action was necessary.

"We hit everyone on the list and tell them about Celebrity Art Interiors. It will take a while to get all the names into a database but it'll give all those publicists something to do."

Sometimes having office projects was their saving grace. It kept them busy. Concentrating on a mass mailing made drinking too much red wine and smoking pot less essential. Being forty and fabulous was tricky at the best and worst of times.

Typing all the names and addresses into the computer then figuring out the whole mail merge function of Microsoft Word was a task neither relished but it was accomplished with surprisingly few complaints. As the printer stuttered and spewed The Girls busily began folding the begging letters asking for support and stuffed them into piles and piles of labeled envelopes to every celebrity in Tinsel Town on The List. Suddenly the industrial monotony was disturbed. In a flash from nowhere the phone was ringing. Once again they found them selves back in the twilight zone.

"Don't panic. It will be Ilia wanting a fucking celebrity Patron for his school. Just answer it"

"Tommy? Tommy who? Tommy Lee, Oh my God it's really you."

Tommy Lee had finally returned their 22nd call. This was the call they had waited weeks for. They were floored. Tommy was in a limo on his way to the Staples Center, home to the Los Angeles Lakers, for rehearsals of the MTV awards. They pitched their artist with a passion only cultivated from having manually just produced a 500 piece mail shot. The conversation was beyond fantastic the dialogue gushed like a crack in the Hoover Dam. He loved their idea and was happy to share he collected erotic art. There was silence, then panic, then absolute euphoria.

"The show will be a riot."

"Ilia paints the best nudes in town."

At last they had a rock star mate. Tommy giggled like a giddy school girl telling them to contact his manager, Carl Stubner at Deluxe Management, to firm up a plan. He was up for appearing in the show and promptly blurted out his personal email address, foolish man. kinky@rockstar.com. He did not have the slightest inclination he was dealing with professional celebrity stalkers. Being given a private email address in the world of celebrity stalking was like winning the Oscar. With all their hard work beginning to pay off they had free access to a huge rock star. Tommy had agreed to be in their pilot. Wow. What a triumph. Someone from Rich and Famous Land had come to the rescue.

A fabulous cocky letter faxed its way to Carl in music management world. This was a whole new ball game.

Dear Carl,

Tommy Lee has kindly agreed to appear in our show "Celebrity Art Interiors". We plan to place a free piece of erotic art in his home have a short interview with him and film our pilot for E! Television. We can work around Tommy but it needs to be within the next week. We have a meeting with Miramax scheduled to pitch the pilot.

Regards,

Art Interiors

Challenge was blown to bits by their fabulous news and insisted his film would win awards. They said "pigs might fly" yet again but told him to prepare for the big event anyway. He was all they had. Ilia was confused. He had no idea who this chap Tommy Lee was but said he would sort out a valuable earlier piece to present to the rock star. He truly believed in his girls. The Jailers even had a moment of madness. They loved Tommy and his band and The Girls actually got something usually unheard of in jail, a pat on the back. Wow. This was too much excitement for one day. Dealing with huge celebrities sober was a pattern they needed to break so what better reason to get drunk and celebrate. They called Steve at Ashley's Deli, blurted out their news and within fifteen minutes he was at their door with lunch, a couple of bottle of Chardonnay and the treat of all treats for dessert, two Caburys Cream Eggs. Where he found them The Girls had no idea but they accepted his gift, dazed and adoringly mistaking the six foot grocer for their teenage heart throb.

All the celebration aside, the man who really needed to hear the news was Mr. Jeff Shore. The Girls had managed to bag one of his two elephants, as well as con Miramax into potentially producing the show. Was this now a real deal? Not bad for two fish out of water from Yorkshire, trapped in Hollywood, trying to flog art. They dialed E! Television with a plan to meet up with Jeff again and give him the inside scoop.

"We now have a real celebrity project with Tommy Lee and others attached. Is Jeff free for a quick word?"

Initially Donna was delighted to hear from the bubbly girls. Then something terrible and horribly unexpected happened. Their friend turned into an android assistant promoting the ever-popular fax machine. Fax over their idea? What had happened? They thought she was in Flynn. It was unbelievable and most disappointing. After all, both girls had made a concerted effort to be lovely over lunch. Donna was getting too big for her boots and needed slapping down. Taking the bastards to lunch was supposed to prevent this kind of shit happening.

"Do we need to take Jeff out for lunch again, alone?"

She protected him like the crown jewels. Jeff was not available for calls and Donna wasn't budging. Still on the first bottle they were too sober to tackle the problem. Content Donna would soon realize how they worked, it was left they would send over the fax as instructed. A mental note was made. Donna needed pushing off her perch.

"It says here in the 'How To Penetrate Hollywood Manual', always make friends with the assistant. One day she could be the boss. If we make friends with her she will help us, then we have full access to Jeff whenever we want."

"Isn't that what we've been trying to do?"

Over their two hundred and fifty dollar lunch in Orso that day Donna had let slip her life long ambition to DJ in the underground clubs of New York and Philadelphia. She wanted to learn to scratch. In a world where anything is truly possible, Jailer two had some Mexican buddies at the Budda Company, a team of young scratch talent running an urban underground business. It was perfect. They would invite Donna to lunch at The Beach Cottage and set up a session for her to have complimentary lessons from the best.

"Entertaining is always the key. It happens in every business. It's called bottom licking"

After polishing off the wine they called Donna back and extended the invitation. She accepted the offer like Fagin faced with a pocket handkerchief and insisted bringing her best friend Andrea along. Her partner? Were they lesbians? That would be a bonus. Two black lesbians would be a triumph for the Pussy Galore Notebook and a great gift to offer their new rock star mate, Tommy Lee. The Budda Company got an offer they could not refuse from the tipsy girls. This was E! Television remember and now the scratchers had an audition for a new reality show. A slight lie but Donna did work for Jeff Shore and they were trying to sell their show. As the afternoon progressed the wine continued to silently take its toll. They wanted to talk to Deluxe Management and get Carl Stubner by the balls. What was the hold up with Tommy? The fax had been sent hours earlier and they didn't have the luxury of time any more.

"Call him and pin him down to a plan. Tommy has already said yes for Gods Sake. What is this? Kindergarten"

Calling Carl Stubner to follow up about Tommy was essential. Under the circumstances, dealing with Deluxe Management should have been standard or so one would think, anywhere other than LA LA Land. After being blocked by the ever present assistant Blaine they immediately found out telling the management the celebrities' plans was a no no. It certainly wasn't deluxe. Blaine confirmed The Girls' fax had been received however Carl had a rock star to look after. His boss was a busy man. He did say their request looked do able and interesting. Do able and interesting? The chief, Tommy had said yes. If Tommy had said yes, there would be no problem, was the retort. He told them to chill. This news was just not good enough. The Girls wanted action and sensed they were being put off. They had to talk to Tommy directly and make friends with him. And so they sent their new rock star mate a love letter.

Dear kinky@rockstar.com, We have made contact with Carl and Blaine at Deluxe who seem very nice but a little slow. They are getting back to us. We are going to give you the most amazing painting. We can't wait to meet you. We already love you for helping us. Peace, The English Girls XXX Send.

With their first private communication on its way it was just a question of pulling all the pieces together and making them fit. Was this finally a real business? The Girls found themselves back in the twilight zone once again, the phone was ringing. An agent calling them? It was better than finding a tampon when cramming toilet paper down ones knickers is one's only option. Yes we have all done it.

Finally they had a response to one of the begging letters from the mass mailing. The nice man on the other end, Alan Nerob, was calling on behalf of his actor client, Robert Downey Junior. A Hollywood hell raiser with a bad reputation and a wicked cocaine habit, he was someone who needed good P.R. like a plant needs water and the perfect celebrity for The Girls art show. According to Alan, Robert was unavailable for three months but perhaps would consider appearing in their show later down the road. After going in and out of nick more times than Rodney King, he had been forced back into rehab by the establishment for what seemed to The Girls as nothing more than a personal choice. 'So this is Freedom, you must be joking.' The poor bastard was in jail too. Oh well at least he had a release date to look forward to.

"Can you believe that. The only reply we get back comes from a drug taking out of work actor, who might help us if he can stay out of nick long enough."

It was enough to make a nun loose her virginity. After a big hit on the joint they decided to call Walter. Kevin had not got back to them with a date for Filthy and The Girls fancied a night out. Of course, as always, Kevin was far too busy to chit chat but Walter confirmed he was checking things out and any time they needed VIP passes, no problem. Another day came to an end in LA LA Land, as The Girls headed back to their own cells. Working so hard for no money was beginning to make them sick.

"We could take the American Express out for a spin and just pray it works."

"If this is the last blow out, we need to wait until the right opportunity arises."

It was another fucking sunny day in paradise. Sending the emotional plea to their new rock star mate, the day before paid off. As they opened up hot mail, they had a reply from Tommy. AWESOME!!!!!!!! One world. T xxxx . After two minutes of silence The Girls just didn't get it. Although The Girls liked the whole celebrity thing, they wanted results. Telling off a rock star first thing induced rolling a joint.

"Is that it? Is he thick or what? We tell him we need his help and that's his response."

"Maybe he was busy this morning. He is famous for Gods sake."

"Hit him back. This is for fucking charity."

Dear kinky@rockstar.com, Good morning. How are you? We are so glad you think we are awesome but can you tell Carl to call us? Time is running out. Love The Girls XX. Send.

"Send another fax to Jack Nicholson telling him Tommy is in our show, two bad boys together? Maybe being Patron of the school was not wild enough for him but hanging with a rock star is a whole new ball game"

It was decided and another begging fax faxed its way to Sandy, this time asking Jack to appear in their celebrity art show.

"I was thinking last night, we didn't say thank you to Harvey for sending Barbara our way. We should send him something wonderful. Something just from us."

"For the man who has everything? Something rare and precious, sweet smelling and horribly expensive."

"I know you fancy him but we can't send him a bag of chronic."

Although they had got Harvey's attention for a moment, Barbara had made her point sharply not to bother him. They still wanted to get him to the table though. He was their mentor not the assistant. Researching Harvey's movements would take much wine and many joints. Getting to him would be like getting laid by a jailer, a miracle.

They decided to have a beer then make some calls. They dialed the number and encountered Ben a new recruit. It was their lucky day. He was an "Art Interiors Virgin" someone fresh in Harvey's camp they could manipulate and confuse into giving them vital information. Ben insisted Harvey Weinstein was out of town contradicting The Girls protestation to the contrary. They were wary of being fobbed off. Acting quickly they confused poor Ben to death and delved deeper.

"Of course he is. I completely forgot. Silly me. Los Angeles, this week?"

A good guess and it paid off. They had info on Harvey's whereabouts. It was like winning the lottery. Their man was in town. They would deliver a rare and spectacular gift and make him feel fabulous. He of course would be flattered calling them back immediately and suggesting lunch somewhere nice. The giant Orchid was ordered from their Beverly Hills florist. The card read as follows.

Dear Harvey,
Thank you for Barbara. Great things happen when one connects with style.
Love,
Art Interiors

After calling Miramax L.A. it was established Harvey would be arriving at two pm for an in house lunch, the perfect time to have the perfect gift for their movie giant, delivered. The well rehearsed Texan drawl did the trick with an assistant's assistant in the Los Angeles office. It was always about making a huge impression on Harvey, marketing genius at its best. If nothing else, every single senior person in the room would ask "Who are these women?" The Orchid of all Orchids was orchestrated and now it was just a case of waiting. Surely he would at least call and say hello. It was the only excuse they needed to open some red wine. Speaking to Harvey sober was just not an option. What exactly would they say? Checking hot mail regularly was a new thing but there in black and white they had a reply from Tommy. SORRY!!!!!!! One world T XXXX

"Does this guy only communicate with one word dialog? He must be as thick as pig shit."

"Hit him back."

Dear kinky@rockstar.com Please can you call us. We need a date from you to film the pilot. Talk to us dude. Love The English Girls. XXX Send.

The overall situation was rather grim to say the least. They had one week left before the meeting with Barbara and they needed a miracle. Challenge's pilot was a cross between a cat with a foot fetish and a cosmic fuck up. Tommy Lee was really thick with management resembling the dead. A potential young Hollywood hell raiser was available, if he could resist putting cocaine up his conk and the weekend was fucked because Donna was coming for scratching lessons. It was a mess as usual.

At 4pm they called Miramax to determine if Harvey had received the Orchid. He had, it was confirmed however the top dog had already left for New York. It was a treacherous blow when the receptionist relayed he had casually left their gift behind. Two hundred dollars they didn't have, wasted? Harvey was a miserable git after all. They would make him pay for that later down the road.

The last call of the day was to Deluxe Management. They needed Blaine to connect them with Carl. The clock was ticking and a time bomb was about to blow up in their faces. Blaine turned out to be the assistant of all assistants beating out Walter. He made excuses for Carl but being the nice boy he was he did give them the inside scoop. Tommy was about to release a new album, the first in two years. Carl had a tour to plan and record companies to smooch. The Girls begged and pleaded sharing with Blaine about emailing Tommy directly. It was just a quick shoot. It could all be done in one afternoon. He promised them faithfully, he would put them to the top of his list and get them some action.

It had to be an early night for the frustrated stalkers. They had the Russian Madonna T.V. show the following morning. All the Chanel foundation in the entire world would not help at this stage without a solid eight hours kip. Dressing for television is an art in itself when one is the wrong side of a size ten. Thank God they were experts at covering a multitude of disaster areas. Black, black and more black, extra make up to cover the cracks and a nice joint on the way. They were fine. Remember what she looks like.

Arriving at the television studio as high as kites was a good move. The place looked terrible. Public television obviously didn't spend a penny on their image.

This was the junior league and The Girls were fired up for fun. The perfect situation to practice their talk show skills. The Russian Madonna once again looked more ridiculous than ridiculous, if you can get your head around that. Her half rimmed glasses failed to make her look serious. She looked more like a French street walker than Tina Brown. Her blue and white stripped T-shirt was far too tight and her short skirt had a split longer than the Nile. She was cheap and tasteless but really funny. Wearing the ever present beret and black fish net tights, was she a French Porn star?

She showed The Girls into the brightly lit studio and introduced them to her other guests. Olig, a Russian, film director with a cheeky grin, a good shirt and a terrible accent, was there to promote his new movie, Women in Love or something like that. He was flying to some remote poverty stricken location in South America to make a romantic documentary with a new twist on the mail order bride business. Was he kidding himself? Those folks were starving. They'd say anything for a free ticket out of hell.

Then they met Dr. King, another crazy foreigner. This was the doctor of love not medicine and tirelessly dedicated to helping poor children in war torn countries through hypnosis. He was there to raise money for Afghanistan. Was this for real? It made The Girls story look less and less far fetched by the nano second.

The stage was set, the bright lights dimmed as the four guests seated on two comfy sofas silently awaited "The Overture". The Russian Madonna sat poised, holding court over her happy guests just anxiously waiting to come out of the gate. Her show was all about promoting independent talent and she introduced them all as bright stars of the future. She opened her intro bragging about The Girls up and coming imaginary show on E! Television. It was a slight exaggeration but not that far from the truth. The Girls played along giving themselves a plug before diving into controversial chat with the panel.

"So Olig what is it like to watch complete strangers having oral sex?"

"Do you ever get a hard on?"

The poor guy was trapped on camera and totally floored by the frank honesty of The Girls. Although they had got, completely the wrong end of the stick as to what his film was actually about he had no choice but to answer their questions. He somehow managed to come back. They liked that, a fighter. Madonna was desperate to change the dialog and introduced Doctor King, a very strange Austrian but someone who loved art. His story actually worked quite well for The Girls. Doctor King needed to raise five million dollars for his charity to build a hospital in Afghanistan. He wanted to auction the art of another genius to Hollywood celebrities. It would help raise the cash he so desperately needed. Was he trying to out do The Girls and steal their plan? That was their business. Their egos took over and they had him by the throat. Foolishly they reacted instead of responding. A mistake one should never make on television.

"Five million, who shall we ask?"

"Arnold Schwartenegger? Isn't he Austrian too? We take the challenge."

"It's all about the art and exactly what we do everyday."

He was delighted someone else now had the stress. The Russian Madonna could not believe her luck. She had been trying for months to help Dr. King raise awareness, for her this was great news. For The Girls it was another example of a "Can someone please take my foot out of my mouth" situation. Damage Control. Raising five million dollars for poor kids in Afghanistan, to help elevate art, was not such a bad idea but of course they didn't know anyone with that kind of money except Harvey and Tommy Lee. Always hopeful forever positive Tom Cruise could drop that kind of cash in one afternoon. They were pretty convinced he did not watch public television and being an avid fan of The Russian Madonna was unlikely so stalking his entourage and getting his ear was essential. They needed to make contact with him somehow.

"Fuck another fine mess you've got me into Stanley."

The show finally closed, to dire reviews and a blushing Olig offered The Girls his card. Did he want them to appear in his next movie? What was it with the Russians. The Girls just couldn't get away from them. They thanked everyone and kissed goodbye. Flirting with her film crew produced instant gratification in the form of a VHS tape and a phone number. Visual evidence and a new filmmaker, that was reward enough. The director was insistent they call him. Was he blind? The Girls were flattered but come on.

Dr. King was hanging onto their car door, as they tried to escape his clutches. He could not thank them enough. Having a televised interview had been a fantastic experience and conformation they could pull off their show now without a hitch.

"We'll be in touch, must dash, we have celebrities to pester."

The Patron of the school position had not pulled any interest. Maybe a children's charity, the U.W.I.C.R, (United World for International Children Rights) was the way to go. Surely Hollywood cared about kids. Perhaps this would catalyze Deluxe Management into action.

Back at The Beach Cottage it was time for some wine. It was Friday afternoon and they had Donna coming at noon the next day. They checked the machine to find an amazing message from Filthy. They needed to rest but lady luck was not on their side. Walter had called Filthy directly and offered the promised gig at the House of Blues. They were on stage at 8.00pm that night, supporting legendary Rap artist Busta Rhymes. It was like a miracle from heaven for Filthy and he insisted The Girls dress up and hit the town. The band needed their management by their side and The Girls fancied a night out. Escaping jail on a Friday night was a gift and a chance certainly not to be missed.

"How the hell did that happen? What is going on here?"

"Did we really get those guys a gig?"

The Girls had questions flying out of the wazoo but today nothing could take away the joy of success. They needed VIP passes by 6pm. Calling Walter was the plan. They would get him to leave their names on the list and VIP passes with security. It was simple.

Dressing for the part of rap management was a little tricky. It was a first but they rose to the challenge, appearing from a closet like ringers for Patsy and Edina, the Absolutely Fabulous duo, one wearing black leather pants and a see through top, the other in faded jeans and a funky bandanna. They looked absolutely fabulous. Long black coats complimented by tasteful expensive accessories matched perfectly and the ever present pouchettes completed the picture. A large joint, stuffed with deliciously fresh green weed, and a chilled bottle of French champagne, made the perfect traveling companions. They would certainly help set the evening off with a bang. If they were out mixing with celebrities, Challenge needed to be there with his digital camera. More explosive footage for their pilot was imperative. They called him from the mobile. He jumped at the request to tag along and said he would meet them there. It was cosmic man.

Getting into the VIP Foundation Room at the House of Blues, Hollywood was like getting into Brad Pitt's pants, impossible. So pulling up in a limo and acting famous was the right thing to do. The Girls loved to travel in style. What was the point of being in the music business, if they didn't have a limo? Remember they were with the band after all. There was always a hungry crowd of star spotters to show off to lined up outside. Showing off was all part of the job and well worth paying two hundred dollars for the experience. They had spent that on Harvey's orchid and that had got them absolutely nowhere.

The Girls had massive egos and liked to feel important, sharing stories of their important work. Their driver was cool and let them smoke pot on the way convinced they were Tommy Lee's management. It was never really about lying just sometimes they got their wires a little crossed. The truth was always packaged in there somewhere.

By the time they reached the House of Blues their world was rocking. Too many glasses of champagne on top of red wine, was not a nice feeling. They were tipsy but focused as they pushed their way through the poor bastards, with no hope of getting in. Busta was sold out. The Girls loved the feeling of self importance as they made their names known to the skinny bird guarding the door. She looked far too young to be in charge. What did she know about life? The Girls would eat her alive.

"Good evening we are The Girls, friends of Kevin's. Is Walter around? We should be on the top of your list and make it snappy, queuing for anything makes us crazy."

The stick insect was a fashion disaster if ever there was one with no record of The Girls on her list. Shit. She wore a base ball cap the wrong way round and overtly chewed bubbly gum. This was worse than being turned down by a cute boy. The humiliation was unbearable for two such major snobs. The name dropping technique came out for a spin once again. Good God this was getting dull, somehow they had too exterminate the stick insect.

"Do we look like gatecrashers to you?"

"Call Walter on your radio. We spoke to him two hours ago. We should not have to put up with this."

"Kevin will sack you when he finds out. You know what he's like."

"Under normal circumstances we would not be seen dead in a dump like this. Now, are we on your list?"

She was petrified and out snobbed by the powerful duo. With no choice but to let them through to level one, drinks in a wooden floored shack, she told them to find Kevin or Walter inside and collect passes to get to level two, the gig. The Foundation room was level five. Going for a night in the House of Blues was not their cup of tea unless they could have a table in the VIP room. Downstairs was about queuing for drinks, God forbid and worse that that, no smoking? It was like playing bloody monopoly, pass go and collect a stamp on the way but at least The Girls were in.

They wandered around looking for Walter. They needed passes to the private elevators and quickly. Under different circumstances he would have been easy to spot but every black guy in Hollywood was at The House of Blues that night. It was hard to pick the babe out of the crowd. It took their hatred for failure and razor sharp antennas to spy him alone at the bar.

"Walter darling what the hell happened? We were not on the list and this queuing business really stinks."

Walter apologized like a silly boy explaining The Girls should have got Filthy to put them on his list. Kevin's was already over booked. Busta was a big star and everyone wanted passes that night. The show was a sell out. Walter diffused The Girls arguments to the contrary pointing them in the direction of his boss. There was only one man with the power to greenlight them that night. They were forced to face the enemy. Only Kevin could help them.

"Hello there, sorry to intrude how lovely to see you"

"Walter said you had our passes to the Foundation Room."

Kevin was having a bite to eat with a pretty young thing and nearly jumped out of his skin, as The Girls pounced. In a moment of panic he told them to have a drink and he would see what strings he could pull. The element of surprise had been critical to their plan of attack. It worked. He seemed shocked The Girls had even made it thus far.

They unnerved him, poor guy and he was tough to unnerve. It was always about who you know, not what you know and he didn't quite know if he knew The Girls or not. They were experts at confusing a situation, clouding the issue then winning the war.

It was time to have some wine and relax. Kevin would soon be over to save the day. They were sure he liked them too much and wouldn't be able to help himself. As his intrigue level was reaching a climax, they ordered a good red and some chicken wings. It was going to be a long night and they had been at it since 11.30. Their waiter informed them the wine was on the house? What was this? Kevin a gent after all? Someone buying them a drink because they wanted to and not because they had been coerced into it was a first. The Girls were delighted and up graded the vintage to an expensive sixty nine red, the best in the house, delicious. It was not long before Kevin joined their table. He was curious about these women and their strange associations with celebrities. He had good sense and wanted to make friends with them. They began by charming the pants off him.

"Thank you so much for the wine. Sorry you can't indulge. We have managed to get Tommy on board thanks to Filthy and he said he might pop along tonight, we did invite him. Hope that's O.K."

"It would be a shame if we couldn't join him in the VIP room."

Once again the name dropping worked. Kevin couldn't help himself. Like a fireman to the rescue, he proffered his hose in a grand sweeping gesture, the crème de la crème of all passes. The Girls sheer delight amused him and fuelled his ego. They didn't care. They had access everywhere topped off by an invitation to the top table, his table no less. Wow it was like Christmas all over again. Now they had free range to explore the whole place including the VIP room. This magical pass even got one into the star's dressing room. Perhaps they could sell Busta a painting? He was rumored to like Cristal and shopping in Tiffany. Art was a possibility. Watching three Mexican midgets with big baggy pants and women's tights on their heads, singing in Rap tongue was not really The Girls idea of a great concert. They liked Rod Stewart better although tonight they had to go with the flow and be seen to be enjoying themselves. They were the management after all. Filthy performed five songs before falling off the stage over excited and full of the moment, having just experienced his fifteen minutes. It was quite sweet to watch and The Girls felt maternal for a moment, not. They gushed with pride and praise while insisting on going somewhere more appealing and less noisy to reflect on the performance.

"Where's your dressing room? Let's roll a Dutch."

It turned out the House of Blues did not run to dressing rooms for support bands. The boys were relegated to the tour bus outside. Was this the Rugby Sevens all over again? The bus was packed with cold beers and filled with young groupies. It sounded terrific to Mexican rappers from the hood. A few beers, a few puffs, some footage then back inside to stalk the VIP room before finishing off the night on the top table was the plan brewing for The Girls. It was looking like a good evening lay ahead.

Challenge was late as usual but had found the bus, what a surprise. He was drinking his forth beer and filming the groupies kissing when The Girls arrived. Having missed the gig he wanted a diversion. It was typical of him. He always missed the crucial shot. The Girls hung out with the band and made them feel good with news about Tommy and the show. It had been a mutual trade off and now everyone was square. Challenge was reluctant to leave but he had work to do. They were about to stalk Busta Rhymes. This was one celebrity they wanted on tape for the pilot and The Girls insisted Challenge be ready with digital flair. How famous was he anyway? They had not really heard of him. Stalking the Rap God would be cake with the magical passes. They were Rap managers let's not forget and smoking pot had to be seen as a plus.

Back inside the place was heaving as Challenge followed closely behind the Girls with his camera. They soon found their way down a long hallway, flanked by security and then into a private elevator going up to the Land of Celebrity, the VIP room. This was more like it. The Maitre D' stood like a statue at the entrance to the dimly lit room. It was pretty swanky. Securing the one and only smoking table in the VIP room required balls of steel having to gate crash the party seated and then prey on whomever had the reservation. By chance they were in luck. A group of young trendy hair stylists from Fred Segal, hairdressers to the stars, had the table booked for a surprise birthday bash. They embraced the English girls and insisted they join their party. That was the first problem solved, a seat and a base where one could smoke. The Girls usually found the host didn't object to being sociable. Now all they needed was to get inside Busta Rhymes' dressing room. Maybe one of the hairdressers cut his hair?

"Does anyone mind if we continue filming?"

"We are waiting to interview Busta."

"We are making a pilot for E!"

It was a miracle from heaven for professional celebrity stalkers in LA LA

Land. Eli, the thin blonde birthday boy, did cut celebrities hair. Sadly not Busta Rhymes but planning ahead, they stashed his card. The Girls instantly loved him as Challenge filmed the energy. He definitely had a place in their impending success. Eli accepted the offer of work revealing he really wanted to cut Tommy Lee's hair. No problem, he would be hired as their personal stylist on Celebrity Art Interiors. It was a tall order but how hard could it be? Someone had to cut Tommy's hair. They were confident they could pull it off for Eli. After a couple of fags it was time to venture back inside, stalk out Busta Rhymes and get into his dressing room.

Their first impression of him was excellent. He drank Cristal, always a plus. Then they noticed something rather depressing. His tiffany diamonds out shone theirs by miles. Busta seemed flustered as Challenge was pushed outside by the heavy gorillas screaming no filming allowed. It was clear money could not by style. Trying to talk to this celebrity was impossible and The Girls headed back to the outside table. It was a shame but oh well. They didn't really need anymore rap mates.

At the outside table the hairdressers had been replaced by a bunch of girls from the playboy mansion, or so they said. Challenge could not believe his good fortune. He took endless pictures of boobs that night while The Girls got busy. They needed inside information on how to get past Bill Farley so they set to work, delivering naïve curiosity in abundance. They couldn't rely on Challenge to produce hard photographic evidence so finding Heff's weakness was crucial to their plan.

"Have any of you been to bed with Heff?"

"You all have. Um."

"How does it work with him? Are you rotated?"

Apparently it works like this. To the A girl, a salary is paid and the title of girlfriend bestowed upon the chosen blond. According to these playmates, Heff was fair and a very loving friend but he liked what he liked and they were happy to please him.

It sounded like The Girls kind of job so they kept delving. Apparently the A girl can choose a B girl to join in but that was rare and usually required a bottle of Viagara.

"So does he like to have two of you at the same time?"

"He is bloody 74 for Gods sake."

The evening was turning out to be more fabulous than fabulous. The House of Blues may have been a dump but it was a great place to network and meet people. You scratch my back and I scratch yours. Taking five blonde babes to

Kevin's top table, would give them major kudos but the playmates sadly declined the offer. They couldn't keep Hugh waiting.

The night ended perfectly with Kevin, surprisingly, giving The Girls their first taste of Hollywood VIP. When the show was over he left them holding court on his table with his guests. It was brave but unavoidable. Like the Girls, he was still working and had to go check on Busta and finish up the night.

Trying to create something monumental was about having the confidence to make something so simple become something so magnificent. It was all people wanted to believe in. A big joint was rolled in the limo for the ride home. It had been quite a night for two women with an art dream. They should have both worked for the secret service.

The next day they had Donna to deal with. Nursing rather bad headaches, chain smoking and with black coffee and a million nurophen in hand, The Girls arrived at The Beach Cottage. Getting stoned was crucial. The Buddha Company had already set the stage for Donna's lesson and the place looked like a New York Scratch club. The Girls loved the energy and soon woke up. Bloody Mary's all round.

"Well done guys. This place looks cool. Don't forget this could be your fifteen minutes."

"Donna wants to Scratch. Treat her like royalty."

"Now who's for another Bloody?"

The three scratch DJs, wearing white vests and those same baggy pants, could not believe their luck. Middle aged women smoking pot and mixing cocktails first thing? This was more like it. The Girls showed off and flirted with The Jailers work mates. Having young fresh rippling bodies to play with, made breaking the 11.30 rule a must. They needed to be fucked up before the assistant and her mate arrived at noon.

Donna arrived at The Beach Cottage looking adorable in faded denim jeans and a red woolen hat. Andrea, the partner was tall with super model looks. Her grunge urban outfit looked pretty butch for a chick but she was cute all the same.

"Welcome to the fabulous world of The Beach Cottage. We have drinks on the patio, scratch tables in the living room and lunch will be served in about one hour."

"Come in. Meet the guys. The Buddha Company. Best scratchers in town."

Dealing with almost complete strangers in opposite camps whom they collectively had to impress was very difficult for The Girls. They needed to work out the rules quickly, see how far they could go with either side. The Budda Company should be cool but Donna and her "mate"? Would they let their hair down?

"I noticed at lunch you had a packet of fags in your bag, yet you didn't step out for one?"

"You don't mind if we smoke?"

Perhaps they were just more Americans in denial? Donna produced some goodies from a purple velvet bag, including a packet of Cloves and The Girls were freshly optimistic. Ah ha! She did smoke, occasionally? However no one at work had any idea about her dark, terrible secret. It was pathetic. Bless her. She was indeed another of the aforementioned Americans. It was quite bizarre.

As the assembled gang sat down on the patio an Indian joss stick was lit and inhaled, then some very healthy looking green weed and a packet of skins emerged. The Budda Company's eyes lit up but on closer inspection the herb turned out to be chamomile, a diuretic for after lunch. No. The Girls were glad they hadn't jumped the gun, over enthusing about the pot. When the Church leaflets came out it was the final straw. What the hell was this? The born again herbalists reunion?

It turned out Donna and Andrea liked to smoke more than occasionally but only their specific brand. They inhaled the spirals of smoke from the burning incense at the same time as the cigarettes making the clove experience more healthy or something like that. Had everyone in LA LA Land completely lost the plot? The Girls needed to get back to Europe and sharpish. The television green light assistant and her possible lesbian lover were now chain smoking, God peddling, health fanatics? This was enough to make a Jew go on a shopping spree. The Beach Cottage was no place to preach particularly to three Mexican scratchers. There was only one thing for it. Get things hopping.

Taking control and making Donna feel at home was the right thing to do. The Girls would open the locked doors of "Big Brother is watching you" syndrome by diving straight into some controversial dialogue. Seeing how the relative strangers reacted to them and to each other was vital info to avoid any further embarrassment for everyone assembled. Within one hour the born again Christians were born again drinkers having the time of their lives with The Budda Company. Donna had a slight chip on her shoulder about being black. She sounded too heroic and judgmental about life as a woman in Television Land. Not another sad bastard with a hard luck story. L.A. was filled to the brim with people who had no idea how to have fun. Yet wasn't it fun that made the world go round. The Girls soon made her forget about all that shit and put a smile back on her face.

"We think you are fabulous. Now let's get you scratching."

Donna was a natural. She could scratch a mean scratch, as she scratched over a vinyl copy of Rock Around The Clock. The room was rocking like Elvis Presley on crack. Life to The Girls was so simple. One had to let ones hair down once in a while in order to realize that most people don't really give a fuck about anything. Donna was in heaven, her dream come true. As they watched her and her partner have uninhibited fun they knew they had done something wonderful.

The Girls never did manage to bring up the Lesbian question. It was more fun to watch and keep guessing. As they all said goodbye, The Girls told Donna their exciting news. Could she tell Jeff about Tommy and get them a meeting to pitch the show? Donna was impressed, The Girls could tell. She told them to call her on Monday morning and they could speak to her boss. It was fabulous news. They were in good shape and one thing they were sure of, as the party came to an end, Donna was now their number one fan.

It had been a pretty hectic week for two drunks from Yorkshire but now the future looked very rosy. Working over the weekend was a killer but well worth it. The How To Penetrate Hollywood Manual had been spot on once again. Making friends with the green light assistant was essential to reaching the next level in stalking celebrities. Thank God for Sunday, the day of rest. The Girls had a day of abstinence and an early night. Even these veterans needed a break some times. When Monday morning rolled around, the agenda was getting shit off one's chest.

"We've got two weeks before meeting Barbara and no pilot."

"We need the nod from Tommy."

"We still don't have pictures for Heff and I'm losing faith."

"Harvey needs a bollocking about dumping our Orchid."

"No word from Fran Curtis."

"I wonder what Elton would have to say about that? Those flowers were pricy."

"We have Donna smashed and on our side."

"I dreamt we pitched E! without a film. The whole place including Donna laughed us out of the building. Is it eleven thirty yet?"

Already the first day of the new week was looking like a right off. Focus was the order of the day it was decided. They now knew they could not, under any circumstances, rely on Challenge. As much as they loved him they had to find a new filmmaker once they had a date to shoot the pilot with Tommy. It made sense. Anyone with a camera and some kind of brain would see, having the opportunity to film Tommy Lee for E! Television with Miramax producing was a sweet deal. It would be easy to sell. Opening up hot mail produced a wonderful surprise.

Dear English Girls, Sorry about one liners but I get millions of emails everyday and if I answered them all, I would be writing a book. One world. Love T. XXXX

"Is that his idea of a solution? What the hell is wrong with this dude?"

"Hit him straight back. We need a call back from Carl the loser today."

Dear kinky@rockstar.com, Writing a book is probably not a good idea. One needs to be able to put words together for that but what you could do is remember you said you would help us. We have one week to get you on film or we are dead on arrival and all those poor kids in Afghanistan don't get our help. Please get Carl to call us. Love The Girls. XXXX Send.

They decided to send Harvey a fax about the Orchid. Sending flowers to men was generally a no no. Why inflate an already over inflated ego? But Harvey wasn't supposed to have an ego. He was a genius. They had never anticipated the possibility Harvey, their Harvey might not respond. The hard fact was that good manners were sadly lacking everywhere they ventured and it was beginning to piss them off. Alliance with a giant was imperative. What would it take to get Harvey's attention?

Dear Harvey,
We hope you received our Orchid. Maybe your thank you note is lost somewhere in the post. We have started working with Barbara and things are going well but it is you we really want to make contact with. We know you collect art and support emerging talent. We have the modern day Michelangelo in our hands. Please meet with us.
Love
The Girls

Some times they just wanted to be sensible. Surely selling fresco to the elusive celebrity, in the cultural vacuum known to the outside world as Los Angeles, had to be a piece of cake. The likes of Tommy Lee could definitely use the heightened art profile. Harvey was someone they knew would help once he met them and got up to speed. How hard could it be? Getting to him had proved impossible thus far but Socrates had found Plato. It was half past eleven and time for some wine to accompany the philosophy. They had to sack Challenge and hire a new genius. That level of disappointment could only be delivered after a couple of bottles. The Girls loved him to death but he was about as much use as a chocolate fire guard when it came to producing anything tangible to close the greenlight executive. Challenge was a challenge that was for sure.

"I've an idea for the five mill. Tom Cruise. He has more money than God. Vanilla sky just blew out the box office."

"We tell him he gets free art in return for his help. If he takes the role of Patron to the Fresco School, wins all round."

"We get a superstar for exposure and he gets fabulous free art for his time."

Calling Tom's agent was completely pointless even with the correct number. They got nothing but a recorded message with instructions what to do. These people really did promote the ever popular fax machine. Three days and fifteen calls later they got through to Cassie, his assistants, assistant and after a spectacular pitch over the phone, a nice long begging fax faxed its way to Tom Cruise.

After guzzling the second bottle of delicious red, they checked hot mail. There in black and white for all the world to see. Dear English Girls AWESOME!!!!!! One world T XXXXX

"He might be famous and very sexy but the guy's a vegetable."

"We are dealing with someone who is definitely brain dead."

For once they did not hit him back. The Girls decided very quickly continuing a business dialog with Tommy Lee was pointless. They needed to make friends with "the brains" behind the man. They needed to make contact with the elusive Carl Stubner, once and for all. They dialed the number with fingers crossed.

Calling Deluxe Management after two bottles was just enough Dutch courage to disorientate Blaine and trick their way into Cory's earshot, the next man up the totem pole. They needed a firm date to meet Tommy even though they had no one to actually film the pilot. Oh well it all works out in the end as they say in fairy tales.

Cory got a mouthful. Tommy needed some good P.R. They insisted this was a hot project and Carl needed a kick up the arse. He immediately put The Girls on hold. Blaine with confused confusion and good assistant skills picked up and told the girl's Tommy's single was being released that day and things were crazy. Carl would be dealing with their project next on his busy agenda. If he liked the idea and Tommy said yes, there would be no problem, it was in the bag. Yeah right. They were fobbed off once again.

After a few hours the third bottle of the day was uncorked. Sacking Challenge would prove harder than they first thought. Although he was useless and had not managed to produce a single fucking thing to date, they liked hanging out with him. He made them feel good. Unable to execute him totally it was decided they would compromise. Someone new would take over the primary responsibility for the pilot but Challenge could help. He was demoted to the assistant, not a position he relished. He still insisted his film was a cosmic explosion and so close to being finished. The Girls didn't believe him. Even getting pictures off his computer for Heff was impossible. Those photographs never materialized to this day. Yet Challenge would not go down without a fight, vowing to follow The Girls wherever they led him.

By chance, another complete and utter coincidence, Jailer two had a use.

Maybe jailers had their positives after all. Oh no. Pigs can't fly. It turned out one of his biker mates was a professional film editor for ABC, the giant television network Channel Seven. His name was Brad Ross and he lived close to The Beach Cottage. Brad warmed very quickly over the phone as he saw their idea unfold. Working with E! Television, Miramax and Tommy Lee had success written all over it and the drunken pair invited him round for a chat to pick his brain about their pilot dilemma. He wanted in and would be there as soon as he could. Brad arrived on a motorbike one hour later wearing a yellow, leather cat suit and a helmet the size of goldfish bowl. He looked like a visitor from Mars and was probably an X-Files fanatic. Whatever happened to style? It soon materialized, after intense grilling this guy Ross had more contacts than an optician. Apparently every year he worked on editing the bloody Oscars for God sake. A Hollywood professional and just what The Girls needed to pull off their pilot. They pitched him for all they were worth.

"Miramax and E! need a sharp short film to seal this deal."

"For us this is not about being famous. It's about promoting art."

"We have some help from a talented photographer who has tons of extra footage if we need fillers. Can you help us?"

Brad was impressed how far The Girls had actually got with absolutely no experience. Being in the business, he knew how hard it was to sell anything to anybody. Their dedication to supporting art was admirable. He would help them. Brad had a mate called Spanish, an experienced network cameraman who loved art, the ideal man to get the ball rolling and start building a team. According to the How To Penetrate Hollywood Manual, putting a crew together was vital. Brad said he could edit the piece once filmed and potentially, if all went to plan The Girls, would have a professional pilot by the end of the week. This sounded too good to be true. Brad convinced them that Spanish was their man. He was coming to Jail for supper that evening to discuss who else he could bring on board.

Working in Hollywood was all about the credits the Girls discovered. No one ever got paid until the idea was sold so getting a full crew to work on the pilot for free was very normal. Yes people work for free in LA LA Land. The Girls mission was still about the art and then the money so things in the film arena were truly looking up. Cooking gourmet food after a skin full of booze was unthinkable. The Jailers ordered take out and Spanish would just have to lump it. They needed him but not that badly.

Spanish was a funky black guy with a European sense of humor and the chemistry gelled as he greedily tucked into the Mexican nosh and guzzled a glass of red. The Girls grilled him like a kipper. They wanted to know how good he was. What famous people he had filmed?

"Tom Cruise?"

"Any sniffs of an Oscar yet?"

Spanish told The Girls to clam down, relax and have a hit on his pipe? They offered him the job on the spot. Wow this was a first, an American stranger admitting to smoking pot? They loved him to death, simply for being so refreshingly truthful. They told him their tale of woe, how hard the struggle to help Ilia had been, then shared their idea for 'Celebrity Art Interiors' uniting Ilia with Hollywood and a culture hungry audience. Spanish loved it.

"The show is about the rock star collecting erotic art.'

"The Russian painter needing exposure to survive."

"Let's not forget the fabulous art consultants who bring the two together with European panache."

They were about to find out, moving in Hollywood circles was a new ball game, everyone was out for themselves and Spanish was no exception. He immediately went into sales mode. He wanted a piece of the action. With confidence he assured The Girls he could pull a whole film crew together for no pay but it would cost them. When the concept was sold he wanted twenty five percent of the deal, in first position. Brad jumped on his bandwagon and insisted on the same. This gig was now looking horribly less profitable for Art Interiors. Fifty percent was an awful lot to give away to two total strangers who had done nothing as yet except talk a good story and eat their food. The down side of saying no was quite simply, without a filmed pilot, they were fucked anyway. And so reluctantly it was agreed. The shoot would be done in two segments. Half the day, the morning would be spent in Ilia's studio choosing the erotic painting and the afternoon, placing the art in Tommy's Malibu pad. The Girls would be expected to provide refreshments and plenty of pot. The film crew Spanish had in mind liked to get high, just like The Girls. At least that was a bonus. Spanish said he could have a team together by the following Wednesday; they had nine days.

Brad would take over as director and coordinator. He suggested Challenge, Polly and Ilia all be roped in to help. The more hands on deck the quicker the filming would be finished. Extra free workers made for better television. It was settled. Everyone would meet at Ilia's downtown studio at eight o'clock on Wednesday morning and the deal was sealed with a handshake. The Girls bid farewell to their new partners somewhat nervous Tommy Lee couldn't even string a full sentence together let alone commit to a date to appear in the pilot. Facing the job of dealing with Deluxe in the morning was enough to make anyone open another bottle. "It never rains, it pours" was now their personal motto. They had a professional crew in place, no celebrity attached and they were doing it all for half the profit? This was the biggest fuck up ever.

"We have to pin Tommy down. At this point I'll try anything."

"Just leave him a really sexy message. Men always fall for that shit."

Calling Tommy late at night drunk was probably not the best plan but they were desperate and there was always the possibility he would pick up the phone. It was a sad state of affairs when the rock star had less personality than the automated operator.

"Hello there sexy, we had to tell you our news. We have secured the same film crew that do the Oscars every year for our show. It's all set up for next Wednesday. What time shall we be there? Call us darling we are dying to meet you. It's your lucky day, big kiss."

Both girls, drunk, high and feeling superficially positive, brought the evening to a crashing end with massive celebration. Tommy would call back and the film would be the cosmic explosion they had hoped for all along.

The following day was Hangover Alert! in its' truest and rarest form. Without Tommy they could not move forward. No word from him so calling Deluxe was first on the list. Blaine tried with all his might to get rid of them saying Carl was too busy to chat. Oh no. You don't get away that easily, particularly when the person paying the salaries had already agreed to the project weeks ago. They had him by the throat. Blaine got the message and put them through to Cory once again. Yikes.

"It was Tommy who said he would help us. We have a whole film crew booked next week and remember this project is all about saving struggling artists and a children's charity. We don't want to have to abort and make Tommy out to be the bad guy here. The media would have a field day."

"You have to be joking, there is too much riding on this and a promise is a promise. We need to film Tommy on Wednesday. Sort this mess out and call us back."

The Girls were hard but Cory was harder. He 'shared' Tommy should never have said yes to helping them in the first place. Apparently he had a reputation for over promising and under delivering. Oh no not another Challenge. The timing was wrong for Tommy. He had rehearsals to attend and a tour to get ready for. The Girls were gutted.

Thank God they had balls and did not take no for an answer. Telling off a rock star's management was not a great start to the day but they hated people who let them down. It was time to make the call to Donna. She had promised to put their call through to Jeff and help get them a meeting. They dialed her number and after a thank you sermon for the scratching day, she put them through. Fingers crossed under the desk the weekend's entertaining had worked. Maybe with E! attached to the project they could finally get Tommy pinned down.

"Jeff darling how are you. We thought about what you said over lunch and now we have a dynamite pilot featuring Tommy Lee."

"We are pitching to Miramax on Monday and hope to secure them as show producers. We are ready to come back to the table and blow your socks off."

Jeff was impressed. Of course he had no idea about the loose ends that needed sorting out and went ahead and agreed to a pitch meeting. Someone would be calling them back with a date and a time.

"This is great. We have nothing to worry about. It says in the 'How To Penetrate Hollywood Manual', one has to truly believe for the project to materialize, never give up. Tommy'll help us, he has to."

They sent one final email to kinky@rockstar.com. Dear Tommy, We have spoken to Cory. You are a naughty boy. You should not have offered to help us according to Pop. Who works for who in your company? Come on Tommy you're the rock star. The painting we have chosen is pretty erotic. It will take us two minutes to hang it. Give us one hour to film, please, please, please. E! TV are desperate for you and so are we. Love The English Girls.XXX Send.

As the days passed by no word came back from anyone. Sending expensive flowers, endless faxes and groveling emails to rock stars and still no one was interested in helping them. Getting drunk was the only plan. With money tighter than a jailer's skirt, Steve at Ashley's extended their tab and they went on a binge.

It was Tuesday morning at The Beach Cottage and the day before the big film shoot. The seven day countdown to the Miramax meeting had begun. The following Monday was blast off. There was still no word back from anyone at Deluxe. They had sent Cory so many faxes by now they hated him and in twenty four hours they had a film crew but no celebrity. It was dire. Challenge and Ilia had their instructions to be at the studio by eight am so The Girls agreed to get some fresh air and splurge on new outfits for their fifteen minutes of fame. A shopping excursion was great exercise for blowing off lingering cobwebs and took their minds off the impending disaster zone they were hurtling into. A small local boutique was selected. Large communal dressing rooms didn't work for them and being on the Russian Madonna's show taught them an invaluable lesson. The camera really does make you look fat, even in black, the outfits for 'Celebrity Art Interiors' had to make up for that.

The American Express bill had been paid and they were able to shop cautiously without the fear of the card being knocked back. Both lying diagonally across the small dressing room floor, they wiggled and squeezed into tight hipster jeans. Helping each other back into a vertical position they observed the visual in the large cruel mirror.

"I look like a sausage in a skin."

They went ahead and bought identical outfits before heading off for a French manicure. The white, Oscar de la Renta, frilly shirts and full length black coats were young enough to be hip but sharp enough to talk business. Never letting the assistant rest they phoned Blaine again from the mobile.

"Hello there, it's us again, any news on a time for Tommy tomorrow? We just picked out our outfits. It's going to be so much fun."

Blaine still had no word from Carl and Tommy was locked down in twenty four hour rehearsals. The film shoot would have to be very quick. That's if they could pull it off at all. The Girls had faith Tommy had said he wanted to help. Where they came from a man's word was his bond. They had to believe in that. It was all they had left. Working so hard for so long with no money was brutal for two middle-aged art dealers. They just didn't get it however giving in now was unthinkable. Their strong attitude induced a quick cosmopolitan back at The Beach Cottage. They had to steady the nerves. They had great outfits but the pilot reality was truly too grim to bear.

"Let's have another. If the worst comes to the worst and Tommy is too busy, we can film the studio thing first and get Tommy on Thursday. No big deal."

"Whatever happens we need some kind of pilot for Barbara and Jeff."

"Everything's in place don't panic."

A second cosmo was downed and three long drags inhaled. The pot made them feel unusually light headed. Always hopeful forever positive, they made a three bottle call on two shots of vodka. Cassie, Tom Cruise's gal needed a follow up. It was a long shot but maybe their destiny meant shooting a different Thomas. She coldly stated Tom never accepted anything he was sent whether it was a gift or not. His people were under strict instructions to return anything delivered to Tom Cruise straight back from whence it came. It was clear the only people they were shooting were themselves. Why didn't he give things to charity? Was this place, Hollywood, one big conspiracy after all?

God forbid he accept anything. That may prick his conscience sufficiently to feel obliged to listen to what someone had to say, particularly about art and charity.

"I don't get it. Tom Cruise sits on the box and tells Oprah, he doesn't give enough back to life."

"He needs to have a chat with Cassie, his assistant's, assistant's assistant. He does give back. He gives everything back."

Offering to raise five million dollars was beginning to look like their own mission impossible. They couldn't get a thick rock star to give five minutes, let alone five million. The contradictions and the lies were so depressing. All it would take was Tommy calling Deluxe to override the ridiculously busy and probably extremely expensive Carl. Just put your hand on it, touch it Tommy. That was all he had to do. He just didn't get it and neither did they. With Tommy, having a dog and barking oneself was crucial.

The brutal world of Hollywood was beginning to take its toll and they had a professional pilot to shoot. The dawn would rise before they knew it. All the praying in the land would not help these two sleep. Knockout drops were called for.

Milk was boiled and silky smooth Cabury's Hot Chocolate made. Don't panic, laced with brandy. They needed to sleep and forget about work for a few hours.

The following morning after a good nights kip, two headache pills and a hit on the joint they looked more fabulous than fabulous. They had a film to make. The long black coats covered a multitude of sins including the tight hipster jeans, now just a little too tight thanks to a bad attack of the munchies the night before. My God this was Hollywood and it was show time. Calling Blaine before leaving was essential. If they were up at six am why shouldn't he be? Without Tommy this journey was over and it hadn't even begun.

"Hi there it's us again. What time can we shoot Tommy this afternoon? Do tell us something good Blaine, we are counting on you."

"Fuck we're in trouble. Tommy is too busy rehearsing and Spanish has his team booked for the whole day. Shall we kill ourselves now or let Spanish do it later?"

"He'll be easy to pull the wool over, don't worry, leave it to me."

The Girls had to film their pilot with no celebrity. Oh well, not for the want of trying. It was the perfect moment to blow ones brains out really but with the truck loaded with more wine than a winery, more fags than a tobacconist, and the best pot money could buy, they set off to seek fame and fortune anyway. As they drove in silence the reality hit hard. Spanish would kill them.

The downtown Los Angeles art studio looked amazing. Ilia had been up all night scrubbing the floors. It was just like a set in Dreamworks. The expensive camera equipment and the bright lights were already perfectly positioned and ready for action. The sound man was hot, a cross between R. Kelly and Brad Pitt, tight dreadlocks and a tight um. Yummy. Yes. Make a mental note, good entry for the Pussy Galore Notebook. He was playful as he tested for sound, one, two, three, four. Spanish was stuffing his face with breakfast insisting Challenge stop interfering. Was he in a bad mood already? God help them when he realized that Tommy was just a celebrity flake.

Brad was in charge, causing more confusion than a terrorist attack. He was about as much use as a chocolate teapot. The Girls made their way into the small bathroom to freshen up and assess the situation. Ilia happily handed out coffee to anyone who would listen about Fresco. Everyone was losing their minds.

"Roll a quick joint. Acting is not my best subject and by the look of things out there, this is going to be the biggest fuck up yet."

"I think we should tell Spanish once we've finished filming the first half of the pilot. At least if he kills us we'll have something fabulous to leave behind."

It was decided the nicely high duo would act innocent and behave like professionals, dropping the bombshell at the end of the shoot. Spanish, immediately nicked named The Spanish Inquisition shone bright lights in their faces and demanded they sit behind a desk and answer some questions. Cautiously making their way on to the set, about to face their very own Pope Sixtus IV, for the first time ever they were delighted not to be Jewish.

What script were they using? What acting experience did they have? What was that joint doing on set? Put it out now? This was not the nice man they had stuffed full of enchiladas. The man who had insisted they bring pot because the crew liked to get high. It was pretty clear Spanish was in a bad mood and not remotely the chilled out dude they had met the other evening. He gave them a scenario to act out. The phone would suddenly ring and they would reenact the call from Tommy. This was work not pleasure. Being a little high would help create a more realistic atmosphere to pull it all off in one take but if Spanish wanted to take the hard road. Then so be it.

The Girls sat behind the large desk and smiled at the focused cameras. The lights were hot and far too harsh for over forty, skin. Spanish turned into Mel Gibson behind the camera as Brad emulated Spielberg. The crew fell silent and everyone was ready to start. The Girls never did establish whether their team was gob smacked by the "more than my job's worth" duo or was simply following correct protocol in Television Land.

ACTION. TAKE ONE

"Tommy Lee? Wow is that really you, thanks for the call. You like art? Great. You like Erotic art, wow. We can come over this afternoon and bring you a painting." CUT.

The acting was abominable. Spanish was bored? They sounded like crap soap stars from Sunset Beach. He wanted more passion, more feeling and lots more interesting dialog.

ACTION. TAKE TWO.

"Tommy wow thanks for the call. You like art? Great. You like erotic art. Dirty bastard."

CUT.

Spanish was getting really pissed off. The Girls could not act to save their lives. It was a disaster. Challenge reveled in the whole thing. He had always managed to make The Girls act naturally. He just couldn't make a bloody film to save his life, bless him but he did provide the much needed fags between takes. They gave it another shot.

ACTION. TAKE THREE

"Wow Jimmy how amazing a rock star calling first thing on a Monday morning. You like Erotic art how fabulous. We have just the piece for you."

CUT.

Spanish liked the take better but it still needed more passion and they needed to get Tommy's name right. He encouraged The Girls to carry on and after over what felt like hundreds of takes, they had half a pilot in the can. It was a wrap.

It was way past eleven thirty and Spanish was panicking about time. He would never make it to Malibu, set up equipment and be filming until at least four. Nobody wanted to work that late. They had run over preventing The Girls from having to admit to Tommy letting them down. It was perfect. They had a stay of execution. Another twenty four hours to close the deal. Spanish suggested finishing the film the next afternoon. Everyone agreed it was a good plan. Without the celebrity on camera the film would be useless, worthless and the deal dead. Challenge told The Girls he had some great cosmic footage and would be competing with Spanish. His pilot would win prizes, yes and pigs can fly. He insisted he didn't even need Tommy in the picture with his award winning footage. He was stark raving bonkers don't forget. Feeling defeated, deflated and desperate for a drink, The Girls stopped off for a Cosmopolitan, a pow wow and to formulate a Plan B. It was never about them becoming television stars or celebrities. It was always about helping a starving genius feed his kid and improve his life style. The Girls had to find the strength to keep going. They had loud voices and someone somewhere would eventually step up to the plate and help them, surely.

It was settled. They would have one more then head back into battle. Leaving the film to Challenge would be very silly and unthinkable. They needed to keep banging on doors and pray Tommy would come to the rescue. It was time to head back to The Beach Cottage and bollock a rock star.

The Beach Cottage was dead as a doughnut, no messages, no calls and no sign of Tommy Lee. The jobs in Ralph's grocery department looked more and more likely by the nano second. They sent the begging email of all emails. It was their final shot before their world fell apart. He had to have a heart.

Dear kinky@rockstar.com, Where the fuck did you get to today? We had to make our pilot with you missing in action. It was not perfect but we have the camera crew for one more day and need to be at your pad to film tomorrow afternoon. P.S. We are trying to raise five million dollars for children in Afghanistan as well as help a starving genius get some media attention. This show is going to get us enormous exposure and without you we lose our opportunity to appear on E! Television. Come on Tommy get real love, we don't have your kind of money. Peace. The English Girls. XXX Send.

Later that evening Brad made an unexpected visit to The Beach Cottage. He had the first part of the pilot on VHS tapes. This was more like it. Challenge had never really managed to impress them with any kind of visual aid. They all sat down for The Girls fabulous screen debut. The studio and the art made a huge statement but without Tommy Lee the pilot would never fly. It was professional but only half completed. Brad left the tapes and said he would edit once the second half was shot. He was now convinced the half hour pilot would blow E! to bits. He had no idea at this point Tommy was a moron. After he left they decided to give Carl a piece of their minds. Deluxe Management were turning out to be nothing more than a bunch of idiots. What was it going to take?

Blaine was protective, as they bugged him on his mobile once again. He told them Tommy just didn't have the time to help them after all. He was sorry for any mix up and wished them every success with their project. It was like being struck down by lightening in a swimming pool.

After all that effort the great Tommy Lee, now, at the very last second just didn't have time to help. He was just like Harvey. Nobody in Celebrity Land gave a fuck about Ilia or the art. This was Art Interiors biggest disaster to date, the meeting with Barbara, only days away. They immediately faxed a fuck off and die letter to Carl Stubner explaining the damage Tommy had caused them agreeing to help, then letting them down. It was a last ditch attempt to make everyone feel bad. Perhaps after a large dose of guilt someone would get with the program and come to the rescue.

"Celebrity Art Interiors without a celebrity would be like offering a hooker to a penniless John, Pointless."

"The Russian Madonna interview might work."

"We need a real celebrity not a geriatric Russian pop star. Jeff doesn't like us that much."

Back in the twilight zone the phone was ringing, Carrie from the Style network. Talk about it never rains it pours. She worked with Jeff and wanted them in to pitch the celebrity art show. Tommy was someone she really liked and maybe the project was a possibility. Her bubbly enthusiastic attitude about their show gave them the second wind they so badly needed. The pitch meeting was scheduled for the following Tuesday, the day after the meeting, with Barbara. They could pull it off.

"Someone up there wants this to happen. We have been chosen to get Ilia his rightful place in America. The show must go on"

"Tommy is not that important. We still have time to replace him before we pitch the show."

It was decided to come clean and tell Spanish the bad news about Tommy. Surely he would understand it was not their fault after all. They had done everything in good faith. Famous last words. Calling the filmmakers and telling them they had no way of finishing the pilot, was not the easiest job in the world and Spanish had a fucking bad temper. He ripped their world to shreds. Brad came charging round to The Beach Cottage in his yellow cat suit and humiliating helmet, demanding the Girls hand over the tapes. No wonder these two had to get high. Nothing ever ran smoothly. It was clear Brad needed some kind of explanation. He was hopping mad and behaving like a maniac.

"Calm down. Don't lose your mind. Tommy let us down let's not forget. This is our project, remember?"

"Brad, with all respect, you guys would only have been paid upon sale of the pilot anyway. That was already established."

"It's a chance you take with something like this. Some you win. Some you loose. It's life."

"The tapes are no use to anyone without a celebrity attached."

"Why don't we all pull together here and sort out a way to move forward. Remember the client is already at the table."

The client at the table didn't help. Brad was furious. Both he and Spanish thought The Girls had pulled a fast one, using Tommy's name to get the pilot made for free. Now it was take away. The psycho twins wanted a legal agreement regarding ownership of the tapes already made. Were they mad? Nothing was going to work. Brad insisted upon signing legal documents just a bit too much and The Girls got the feeling, maybe the guy was a lunatic after all. They tried to call Spanish and use their charms to find a Tommy Lee alternative but he was an even bigger lunatic with no celebrity contacts whatsoever, what a surprise. He rambled on about suing them, something totally unforgivable but typically American and all because that loser Tommy Lee let them down. The whole thing was really fucked up. It was looking like the Hollywood dream team was really just a big bad nightmare after all. The Girls had everything in place except the celebrity. They had invested so much time and money. Giving in now was unthinkable. They would just have to start again.

"Look Brad just take the tapes and do what you will with them. We don't care anymore."

"Our partnership was agreed with a gentleman's handshake but it appears you are clearly not a gentleman."

Begging Brad, face to face made them choke. Humility was not their best attribute at the best of times. Brad insisted there was no room for sentimental feelings. The Girls, only out of complete desperation gave it one more shot. The Psycho Twins were hard as nails and not budging. Brad left The Beach Cottage with their tapes and they never ever saw him or Spanish ever again.

No matter how hard they tried, after months of plotting, planning and strategic stalking, they still had nothing to show for it. With only four days to go before the meeting with Barbara, they needed a miracle.

"Maybe tomorrow Tommy will feel bad and come to the rescue."

"Maybe Tom Cruise will get the begging fax then phone up and accept the free piece of art."

"Maybe Aladdin's lamp really does exist."

Checking hot mail before ending the longest day in history, produced something more ridiculous than ridiculous, a reply from the rock star. Dear English Girls AWESOME!!!!! One world Love T XXXX.

"Tommy Lee has the brain capacity of a goldfish."

"That's generous. More like a dead goldfish. Open some more wine. Roll a big joint."

The following day was not a pretty sight. If there was ever a time too commit suicide, this was it. All their hard work to promote art was about to be flushed down the toilet. They needed to stay up all day and all night and get completely smashed; time for a large Bloody Mary.

They decided to take a break and have a rethink. That spring day was proudly declared National Get Drunk Day. The Girls stared at the bright yellow daffodils in a pottery jug precariously balanced on a stereo speaker below Marilyn Monroe's lips. The famed Wordsworth poem they both knew by heart was recited. Indeed every British baby boomer knew that poem by heart. The 14th March, became a tradition of Wine and Wordsworth they would uphold in years to come. The reasons for which will become blatantly obvious as one reads on.

"Let's take the American Express card out for a spin and have a nice expensive lunch somewhere."

"The Peninsula Hotel?"

No matter how low these girls sank, they always had lunch to look forward to and the table on the patio was booked for later that sunny Thursday in March. Given the couple of hour window to evaluate the damage and regroup with the geniuses they used it wisely before the feet were up and the phone was off the hook. They couldn't face the twilight zone that day. Anyone ringing them, fat chance would just have to leave a message. They spoke to Challenge and relayed the situation with Tommy. He couldn't help himself and used their terrible reality to make his point about Spanish and Brad.

"Told you so."

He said his pilot was a cosmic revolution that would change E! Television forever. They told him to shut up and listen. This was a fucking disaster. Poor old Challenge, he really was stark raving bonkers.

Just as they slammed down the phone and cut him dead, The Psycho Twins, Brad and Spanish were back like Norman Bates but twice as twisted. This was supposed to be National Get Drunk Day. They still insisted on a legally binding contract. In The Girls mind one had to at least bring something to the table to get a legally binding contract.

It was time to put the whole pilot episode to bed, without any supper, take out or not. A legal battle just didn't work for them. Hip fun people on board, was the only way to go for The Girls. Brad and Spanish were fired and told never to call again.

The Girls unplugged the phone and the wine, pouring two large glasses. They silently prayed. And something really peculiar happened. The fax machine almost malfunctioned as a fax from Deluxe Management appeared before their eyes. Weird, hadn't they just unplugged that? It appeared Carl was a real person after all finally acknowledging, in his mind, their two millionth request. It was a letter from Tommy Lee thanking them for the painting and apologizing he was too busy to help.

"Happy Bloody Easter."

"What bloody painting? He hasn't even seen it yet."

The letter went on to say the painting looked amazing in his house and that Tommy wished them the best for the future? This was real confirmation that Tommy had a team around him incapable of managing a tea bag in a cup, let alone a dim rock star with a thug for a best mate. How could they think it was about giving pretend art away? How would Ilia benefit from that? Tommy had no idea who the artist even was, let alone the value of his incredible genius. How could they have got it so wrong? It was really fucked up.

"I don't get it. What the fuck use is this letter? Let's put these people straight. I'm ready to kill Tommy Lee"

"Wait, hang on a second. Now he has to be given the art. Without the actual painting in his house, this letter just exposes him as a liar."

At last they had a chance to get to level five. It meant reluctantly playing the dirty card but these girls remember have the balls of a gorilla. They needed to get clever and dig at the rock stars conscience. He deserved it.

Dear kinky@rockstar.com Thanks for the letter, so glad you love the art. We are confused. Maybe your management didn't give you the right instructions. You haven't actually accepted the piece yet. We need to make that happen. Think about it Tommy. You're a collector of an artist whose name you can't recall whose invisible painting has disappeared. When can we meet? Love the English Girls. XXX . Send.

A similar fax was immediately sent to Carl Stubner. Before one could say Jack Robinson, Blaine called them back with a ridiculous and tragic compromise. They could film Tommy but not until after their pitch meeting? By then it would be too late. Always positive, forever hopeful if they could put E! and Miramax off for a while, they could still film Tommy Lee and make a pilot.

'The How To Penetrate Hollywood Manual' was pulled off the shelf. They needed to see what it said about canceling pitches.

"There's one golden rule. Do not cancel a green light executive, period."

The book had been spot on so far. The show would have to go on. What could they do to impress the green light mob without a film or a celebrity? They needed to think of something so amazing to blow Jeff and Barbara's minds and secure themselves a deal.

"We need to get the idea into some kind of visual. We take it to Style and just hope to God they finance it. With money we can pay Tommy to appear if we have to."

"We are so stupid. It's been there all along staring us in the face. We were so wrapped up and so obsessed with Hollywood and films, we forgot about Ilia. He is the best filmmaker of all. He can paint our story. Carrie gets an idea of the show potential. We "attach" Tommy Lee in art and suddenly we don't need him in person. We have three days to pull it off. What do you think?"

It was time to take on a new challenge and get back playing in the deal. The film in art was really pushing the boat out. Could they manage it? It seemed fighting with Hollywood had taken them too much off track. They needed to focus and pull something fabulous out of the hat. Ilia had no problem and agreed like a eager puppy happy to please his master. Painting the story-board and saving the day, would feed his ego for months.

"If we lock him in The Beach Cottage with fags and vodka, he should manage it."

"The whole thing will be painted by the genius, the back story to 'Celebrity Art Interiors.'"

"It is the perfect way to go back to the art and keep control of the project. Harvey'll love it. You watch. We don't need a film."

"No. We need a fucking miracle."

When the battery in ones vibrator dies just at the point of the orgasm of a lifetime it is always good to have a Plan B, the moral of the story being, be prepared and keep a spare battery close by. What would they do if the art storyboard didn't work?

'The How To Penetrate Hollywood Manual' was preaching the gospel once again. Keep focused, feel the pain and never give up. They had not been to lunch in ages. Having time to think would be a pleasure.

On arrival at the posh Peninsula Hotel they encountered a flurry of valet activity for a Thursday. They had to flash some thigh to get noticed. Something big was happening as the paparazzis' flashing cameras caught various extremely good looking folk going into the hotel. Had they hit the jackpot? Yes it seemed so. The hotel was hosting a pre Oscar luncheon that day for all the nominees and was heaving with Hollywood Royalty. It could not have been better planned. Powdering one's nose and a quick hit on a joint was essential before any battle could commence and the valets patiently held open the car doors waiting for The Girls to disembark. Moving quickly in such a fabulous situation was critical. Maybe Michael Caine was there or even better Harvey. A glimpse in the rear view mirror and life changed in a split second. One nearly lost an eye that afternoon thanks to an out of control Chanel lip gloss.

A white Rolls Royce, personal license plate Scott 1 had just pulled up behind them and at the wheel was the hottest director in town, Mr. Ridley Scott. They almost came in their pants. The Girls could not believe their luck. Not only was he more famous than Michael Caine, he was up for an Oscar, what a result. In this situation timing was everything. Being celebrity stalkers of the highest level, they had to act. There they were about ten feet away from a huge celebrity but engineering a meeting would not be simple. Before one could say Jack Robinson, Ridley had disappeared. How did that happen? Where had he gone? This called for stalking at its very finest. To let a gift like Ridley Scott through the net would mean pink slips all around. The Girls dashed inside the hotel, antennas up, instinctively working with team like precision that would make the SAS proud.

Ridders had been quickly ushered inside and away down a long hallway by a million different people when they spied him. Chasing after him was their only option. In a split second they were off. It was the chance of a lifetime. Ridley's pace quickened. So did The Girls, surprisingly unhampered by falling Victoria Secret Thing Highs. The gates to that special luncheon opened just like those of an embassy, waiting to embrace one of it's own into a safe haven away from foreign policemen in beaten up Citroens. After a horrific experience on the auto route with stinky cheese and an offensive hitchhiker they didn't buy French automobiles anymore however The Girls knew once Ridley was inside they had no hope of ever Penetrating his Hollywood. They could not fail.

"Hold on to your pouchette."

Being in the presence of an English art major, made pitching 'Celebrity Art Interiors' seem rather lame. This celebrity could buy Ilia's work one hundred times over. Ridders was the perfect celebrity collector. Within what seemed like seconds, they had poor Ridley up against the wall. Pitching a Hollywood film director about to get an Oscar was not that straightforward but if anyone could do it, they could. With pouting glossed lips and breathless words, they attacked him like a bout of the chicken pocks. Ridley was trapped and uncomfortable wishing both women would get to the point.

"Ridley darling, we love your movies."

"The moment we spotted you, we just had to say hello. You're English darling."

"We sell the rare work of a Russian Fresco master, a modern day Michelangelo and would love to have tea and discuss. Maybe show you some of his collection."

Ridley told The Girls he liked Oriental art before hotel security disentangled him from their clutches and escorted him forward. He had thrown them a bone. Was he their first client? They had information, freely given information at that and it was definitely something to go on. As they waved him goodbye, shouting assurances they would be in touch, he did not look back. It seemed a little uncanny. Oh well. Ridley was from Tyne and Wear. Spitting distance from the great William Wordsworth's stomping ground in The Lake District and a stones throw from where they grew up. Everything would be fine.

Sitting on the outside patio at their usual table, their poor waiter was subjected to the exciting news, Ridley Scott had said hello. He was their new client and champagne was called for. The elated Girls could truly celebrate National Get Drunk Day, share some poetry and eat some lunch.

"Is Michael Caine having lunch, will you check for me."

Michael was not up for an Oscar and was lunching elsewhere that day. It was sad but oh well. They would catch him eventually. It was just a matter of time.

The food was delicious as always but the place was dead, all the excitement going on in the other room. After a second bottle of pop their bill was heading toward a limit even they couldn't justify. They needed a victim in the void to pick up their tab.

They had stalking down to a fine art and caged the joint for a possible wallet.

These girls were experts at pulling blokes. All those years of practice were about to pay off. It was easy to spot money. A good watch and expensive shoes was always a clear indication the victim in question had plenty. Important information before trying to get the bill paid.

"There's a guy smiling at me over there. He's not attractive though. Wait a minute his mate's not bad. He is wearing good shoes."

"Get them over."

"Fancy a game of spoof before our friend Ridley comes out for a fag."

The two gentlemen aged like Dorian Gray as they approached. In reality The Girls had only just got them in focus. Taking money off old age pensioners was a little hard to justify and having to have sex with one for a bottle of pop was an equally unthinkable option. This situation would take skill and charm to abort cleanly. No hard feelings. By now, their bottle was well and truly empty, and ordering another on Grandpa's tab was the plan. Teaching spoof to ugly Americans with hands everywhere was about as low as it could go but at least lunch would be paid for. Let the battle commence.

"Oh dear we seem to have finished this. Shall we get another?"

"Don't worry Ridley will be dying for a fag by now, no smoking inside remember?"

"We'll invite him to join us. He'll pay the bill. He's very rich."

Ridley had obviously quit as there was no sign of him anywhere. With the celebrity MIA, getting rat arsed before facing a weekend with Ilia was justifiable and The Girls gave the pensioners the ride of a lifetime. The older gentlemen paid the bill no questions asked. They did try to cop a feel but The Girls couldn't blame them for that. Always positive, forever hopeful the attempted grope was forgiven. Confidence on that level had to be respected.

Back at The Beach Cottage later that day, it was decided to strike while the iron was still hot. Being unbelievable Hollywood researchers, pulling out vital information was a piece of piss. They got out The List. Of course he was on it, right at the top of page 3. With no cigarette papers having a bong hit made calling Ridley less daunting. Jordan his personal assistant and right hand man laughed her head off at the story about attacking her boss over lunch. She explained Ridley was out for the rest of the day but told them to fax over details about their art business and she would put it on his desk. They followed the instructions and wrote him a note.

Dear Ridley,
It was a pleasure to bump into you this morning. We are sending you details about Art Interiors. We have a whole collection of work from the Orient and deal directly with a fabulous gallery in Sydney. We would love the chance to come in and meet with you. We are already working with other celebrities on an art show and can assure of our complete discretion.
Regards,
The Girls.

So another begging letter winged its way to the Land of Celebrity with all the hope in that land, Ridley Scott would be their man. When checking hot mail, they did have a reply from kinky@rockstar.com

Dear English Girls, Sorry. !!!! PS. Swing by rehearsals next Wednesday at four and drop off the painting. One world Love T XXX .

Creating ones own destiny was something these girls worked towards everyday. At last Tommy Lee had finally got with the program and made a date to meet with them. It was just a question of pitching the story before it actually happened, predicting the future yet again. Face to face Tommy would be fly food and the story-board would save the day with the Greenlight Gang. Having Ilia in ones space for a couple of hours was bad enough but having him painting the whole weekend? That was scary. Life coaching a genius was not a simple task but if anyone could make it happen, they could.

The following day Ilia settled in The Beach Cottage with a change of undies, some clean socks and his paintbrushes. He would be out of action for three days and under their supervision. The Girls had a plan and were secretly delighted they got to escape Jail for the weekend too. Who needed a Hollywood film crew? After The Psycho Twins performance it was no wonder the Oscars lost ratings.

"We have to concentrate on the story-board. What does Tommy Lee look like? Ilia will need to make this look as real as possible. We have E! Television executives to impress."

"We have to be strong with him, get him focused. Remember Ilia has a huge ego. Once he realizes his art will save the day and close this deal, he'll paint like an angel."

The plan was simple. They instructed him to paint ten, five inch by five inch, side by side frames, telling the story from choosing the erotic art to hanging it in Tommy's house. Ilia sat outside on the sunny patio, arms folded and terribly

SHIRLEY & HOLLY YANEZ

relaxed, savoring a glass of red wine, unusual for him. This was respite. He was in heaven.

"OK we have to paint Tommy Lee accepting a piece of your erotic art and make it look like a reality. What piece are you prepared to give away to this loser who completely let us down?"

It was crucial to let Ilia make the choice. They wanted to see some commitment from the Russian genius. True artists very rarely give anything away for free. Ilia, being one step ahead of the game, had already chosen the piece. Something so fabulous The Girls were jealous. The selected oil on canvas, about three feet by three feet, was beautiful in an odd sort of way; an abstract pink nude with massive thighs and no face. The Girls adored it. It was perfect for Tommy. This painting was one of the few remaining from his Russian museum exhibited collection. Only a fraction of those works had escaped Russia with Ilia bearing the official stamp from behind The Iron Curtain. The piece was priceless. Now the storyboard could really come to life. One thing The Girls and their genius did agree on, life was not just about going with the flow. Giving back and sharing wealth in any form was essential for humanity.

Ilia promised them a masterpiece. Time would be tight but by Monday morning they would have their painted film for Miramax. They would be ready to close the deal, finally even though The Illusive Celebrity had let them down badly.

All the fine detail gradually appeared on a black card pitching the story of 'Celebrity Art Interiors.' Watching Ilia work was like sitting in the Sistine Chapel regarding the great Michelangelo. His hand, moving swiftly and deftly created a story from nowhere. It was spectacular. They decided to leave him alone and tie up some final loose ends. Next week would be tough. They had three big meetings to prepare for, Miramax, Style then Tommy Lee. Was leaving Ilia outside with a two bottles of red and six packets of fags a good plan?

"Order some weed. We are meeting with a rock star next week. We must be prepared for such a wild occasion."

With their database to die for, they made some calls. Two bags of high quality weed and some rolling skins were requested and promised by ten. Ilia would get a treat only when he had done some work.

So many things had happened during the battle with Deluxe, The Girls' work load was mounting. Dr. King needed a call. His five million was no where in sight. Tom Cruise was obviously still thinking about things. They had heard nothing back from Cassie. The Russian Madonna's show had not aired and Harvey had still said nothing about the art or the orchid. The time had come to send out some letters acknowledging failure to all the people counting on them. It was disappointing but sadly true, Hollywood didn't give a fuck about art.

The Girls promised Dr. King they would continue the fight and keep the five million in mind but for now they had to stop themselves sinking. It was every man for him self. They emailed Tommy and accepted his invitation. They would be at BAG Studios with the erotic art on Wednesday at four. Get the wine open. When the Girls called it a night Ilia was redefining the word multitasking. He never ceased to amaze them simultaneously eating, drinking, smoking and painting all while watching Moulin Rouge on television. He wasn't tired.

In the morning, after an injection of expresso, Harvey got another roasting by fax even though it was Saturday. Sholem. Somehow they didn't imagine him to be a regular at Temple. The Girls prepared for the next twenty four hours with Ilia. An around the clock vigil was put into place to make sure he finished the story-board. Baby sitting a Russian lunatic was about as appealing as having a tooth pulled out. Thank God for the strong weed and lashings of red wine, the invaluable tools to get through it.

By Monday the storyboard was finished and fabulous as promised, more real than anything they had produced so far. The painting of The Girls dressed in long black coats and Oscar de la Renta frilly shirts, just like the day of the Spanish film shoot, were of photographic quality, produced from memory. Ilia captured the pitch perfectly and the storyboard itself was a work of art. The Girls were over the moon. The pure genius was mesmerizing and Ilia had saved the day. The erotic painting was identical except the size of a postage stamp and Tommy Lee looked so alive, it was scary. Unconventional as the storyboard may be, they now had their pilot to take to Television Land and impress the shit out of Harvey. Their dream was about to become their reality. Ilia went home to sleep.

Pitching Miramax television first thing on a Monday morning wasn't so unrealistic anymore. Everything was in place. It was just a question of bluffing their way through and closing a deal. They set out to impress Barbara dressed in matching black suits, white Chanel Ts, Gucci gold sandals and the ever-present pouchettes. A huge joint was rolled and ready for the ride to Television Land as they embarked to seek fame and fortune for the art, once again. Pulling into the small underground car park off Sunset Boulevard, the nicely high duo went over the plan. They had a potential battle axe to win over.

"She thinks Harvey already likes us. That's a plus."

"We just need to focus and get her to come with us to Style"

"We have no idea what this woman is like."

"I've told you before, short, fat and Jewish. All the top people are Jewish. Just pray she loves us and signs the check."

The Girls entered the small elevator and pressed the button up to Television Land, level six. They used the ascension time to slap on more tart kit. Looking hot for Barbara was essential. Their first observation when entering the huge reception area of the executive offices hit them like a brick. This was as high as they'd ever been.

"My God a big film company like Miramax and there's no art on the walls? Make a mental note. Send Harvey a fax. Barren walls urgently need Ilia's art."

The young blonde receptionist beamed a perfect white smile of welcome as The Girls stepped off the lift. She was a beauty, wearing not a scrap of make up. Those were the days. The Girls longed to be twenty every day and flattered her to death, name dropping for England. It was necessary to make a good first impression. They didn't know when they might need her. The young girl was blown to bits by the over friendly approach and was a huge fan of Tommy Lee.

"Good morning, Art Interiors we have an appointment."

"Harvey knows a pretty face when he sees one. You're lovely, far too good to stuck behind a desk. Ever thought about acting? We should take your number."

Her name was added to the Pussy Galore Notebook. If Tommy wanted to get laid, this chick had the job. Barbara arrived just in the nick of time as numbers were exchanged. She was short and Jewish but not fat and very young. Far too young to be head of Miramax Television for that matter. She swiftly escorted the two middle aged art dealers into her office diverting anymore trouble causing with her employees. Had they been fobbed off with a secretary?

"Thank you for giving us the opportunity to pitch our idea. We have been writing to Harvey for months"

"We noticed on the way in here you have no art on the walls. Surely you wouldn't object to us selling Harvey a painting?"

Barbara wasted no time at all telling The Girls to back off and leave Harvey alone. If she liked their project, it was her decision whether Miramax would pursue it or not, Harvey's instructions apparently. Was she the right person to form an alliance with? Feeling somewhat deflated, their quest to get to Harvey having been temporarily thwarted, it was time to get the upper hand. Barbara made it clear once again. Harvey was out of bounds unless they had a movie project. Anything to do with television was her patch. There was nothing for it. Standing side by side holding out their storyboard, giving the pitch of all pitches The Girls gave it their best shot. They had no choice. If the truth be known, it was pretty impressive for first time out the gate.

"Celebrity Art Interiors, a colorful art show with a celebrity twist."

"We explore the world of the celebrity collector, choose a piece from our struggling artist's collection, place the piece in their home and ask a few double entendre questions."

"You know, double meaning."

"The viewer gets a sneak peek at their favorite celebrity and the artist gets massive exposure."

"We have a meeting set up with Carrie over at Style and need someone with your clout and experience to help us pull it off."

They had now reached Level Six per 'The How To Penetrate Hollywood Manual.' Barbara loved the idea and concurred Style was the obvious forum. Ilia's art intrigued her. They could tell by her face. It was a phenomenal feeling. Anything was truly possible. She agreed to go with The Girls to Style as a Good Will Ambassador and help get them a deal. Having Babs along for the ride was worth sacrificing the orgasm.

They all arranged to meet the following morning at the offices of E! Television on Wilshire Boulevard in midtown and The Girls promised to leave Harvey alone. They tried really hard to get her out to celebrate (more intense grilling about Harvey) but like all busy green light executives, lunch was for wimps. She had work to do.

The meeting left The Girls flabbergasted. On the one hand they were delighted about the "Good Will Ambassador" bit whatever that meant yet being told off for trying to get to Harvey. Never call him again? The prospect of not being able to stalk their hero ever again, was enough to make a nun start masturbating. All future correspondence had to be funneled through Barbara. Was she a jealous ex lover or just a control freak?

"I have an idea. She said Harvey was only available if we had a film script. Perhaps we should get stoned and write one. How hard could it be?"

Although their ties to Harvey had been temporarily severed, Barbara was helping them so a quick celebration lunch was in order. The Peninsula Hotel was on the way home so stopping off there made complete sense. After ordering a moderately priced red and some Marlboro lights, they checked their messages.

Back in the twilight zone of the Beach Cottage they had one new message from Jordon, calling in response to their fax. She said Ridley needed some help with Middle Eastern art between the seventeenth and eighteenth century, a research project for his up coming blockbuster about Napoleon.

"What the fuck do we know about Egyptian art from that period? We're not really art dealers for God sake."

"Oh yes we are. Bad ones but we can do this. Call Ilia and send him to the library. Shall we share the crab cakes?"

Always get your priorities right. Getting a mandate from a famous Hollywood movie director was what they had wanted all along and it suddenly sent their business into a whole new arena. The plan was staring them in the face. Help Ridley with his art then attach him to their invisible movie for Harvey.

"Ridley has a production company and he directs. With him attached Harvey would have no choice."

"The Cannes Film festival is just around the corner. It shouldn't take long to write a movie. Let's plan a small get away."

They called Ilia before the food arrived and told him about the request, instructing him to do some research and come back with something fabulous. It was a chance in a lifetime to work with Ridley Scott and he was the academic after all. After a delicious lunch and some rather interesting cheese, they spotted a nice looking man sporting black Gucci loafers and a red rose. Was it James Bond? He was slick and sexy, possibly European. They needed their bill sorting and started to flirt. More than a few nods and a couple of winks lulled the nice shoes into a false sense of security. He immediately joined their table for drinks. With the subtly of a praying mantis they established he was English, from London, the City in fact. There was a God after all. His name was Robert Stone. His Pinks shirt and Tiffany cuff links made him appear debonair and boyish, just their type. This would be a battle. They both wanted him.

"So, what brings a fellow Brit to a dump like L.A?"

He agreed with their assessment of LA LA Land but didn't mind it in small doses. He'd been sunbathing earlier and was happy about that. Robert was an investment banker with an Arabic bank well known to them, an old client in fact. With the Englishman, name dropping meant sharing who they knew in the banking world. Robert was verifiably connected. The Girls were impressed. He was in Los Angeles to offer finance for a Hollywood cable network deal with Time Warner or some other huge conglomerate. He was extremely powerful and so English, they just had to make friends. Bad timing. They had found him but alas were to lose him. Robert was off back to London after lunch. Shit. The Lord giveth but be damn sure he'll taketh away if one doesn't keep on top of things. Oh well a drink and a flirt was better than falling out with anyone.

"It's not often we come across one so sexy. Fancy a quick snog before you go?"

"We're celebrity stalkers. We sell art and write movies."

"We must swap numbers."

"We are coming home soon."

"Let's meet up in Cannes."

Once again predicting their future Robert adored them and insisted on picking up the tab. Heaven. Boys in Yorkshire always paid and Robert just kept the home fires burning. They said their good byes and headed back to The Beach Cottage. Before too long the handsome stranger would be back.

Back at base camp things were still dead as a doughnut. No messages, no emails and no reason to carry on really. Getting pumped up for the meeting with

Style was tricky although Nigella Lawson was the latest craze on the network and they still had Tommy Lee to look forward to. Another early night paved the way for the big meeting in Television Land. Once again The Girls were determined to pull something off and finally get Ilia's art noticed. They had so much at stake. The swiftly becoming ever more essential Plan B was to write a movie and convince Ridley to direct it. How hard could it be?

They awoke refreshed and raring to go. A large Bloody Mary and a massive joint kicked off the day. Today would be the day of all days. Style would go for their concept.

Both dressed identically again in the story-board uniforms, they packed the truck and set out to meet Barbara. The receptionist at E! recognized them immediately and pointed to their Good Will Ambassador waiting on a sofa. Donna was on her way down. When Donna arrived her first piece of bad news came as a blow. Jeff would not be attending the pitch meeting? Shit. Carrie had to decide if Celebrity Art Interiors would reach the air. It was a small set back, but having Barbara along would surely close the deal. She was a big wig. They had nothing to worry about.

The meeting room was like the first Class Virgin Lounge at Heathrow Airport. A pot smoker's paradise filled with free goodies. The small glass table surrounded by soft comfy armchairs was covered with candy jars, a mirage in a desert, when a bad attack of the munchies was imminent.

No gin and tonics being served but oh well, water would have to do. It was LA. Carrie and her sidekick, the rather large Cheryl made a grand entrance. The Girls thought both, a little lower key than one would have expected from The "Style" Network. Carrie's corkscrew curls and Cheryl's titian tent translated to game set and match for them. This would be easy to pull off. They all introduced themselves and The Girls began the pitch. Time was short. That was clear. Barbara looked positive as the bubbly high girls kicked off their routine. They stood proudly holding up the work of art, their storyboard.

"Celebrity Art Interiors, the show where art meets celebrity to discuss taste."

"We are taking Tommy's painting to his rehearsal tomorrow."
"He likes erotic art you know."

The two executives from Style warmed to the idea as they drooled over the storyboard. Carrie laughed. That was good. She loved Tommy Lee, what a surprise. Ilia made him look very sexy. Thank God. The Girls worked the room like starving hookers at a business convention. The excitement was building by the second. They had everyone's attention. All things looked very positive as the pitch drew to a close. The general consensus was 'Celebrity Art Interiors' looked like a winner. Carrie would be in touch. Barbara being the real expert had one cautionary observation, art and Tommy Lee might be too high brow for a Mid- American audience. Too high brow eh? It's amazing what a big penis can do in Los Angeles when one wants to elevate oneself. Maybe that was where Ilia needed to focus with the media?

You have to be joking right? Tommy fucking Lee, too high brow? The poor man can barely string a sentence together."

Barbara not wanting to dampen their spirits played down the comment. Maybe she got it wrong. The Girls tried to get her out to lunch yet again but as always she was too busy and happily trotted back to Television Land. They decided to not waste time looking for somewhere with outside seating. They were on unfamiliar territory. Instead they headed straight back to The Beach Cottage. They had a rock star to prepare for and a movie to write.

Back in the twilight zone, they had two messages. Was it their birthday? Ilia called to say he was back in the land of the living after the "Art Marathon" at the weekend. He had some information on Ridley's research project but needed more time. Erase. The second message was from Jailer One. He had the credit card bill and wanted to know how one dress could possibly cost three hundred dollars? Oops. Definitely erase.

Even though they had not made one single penny from their business, they still had some mileage left on the good old American Express card. After opening a nice little red and having a hit on a joint writing a movie made sense. Meeting Tommy meant closing the art deal was only days away and mentally spending the profit before it was made was something they reveled in. They called the Carlton International in Cannes. They needed to go to the film festival to sell their imaginary script and sought somewhere to stay. Stalking Harvey to the South of France would be a breath of fresh air after such a bad year in Hollywood. Aga was still not in. They left their number. If they couldn't crash in his room then perhaps he'd have some pull and get them a discount at the hotel.

A quick look on the Internet at properties for sale in Europe provided a little escapism before slumber. No harm in just looking. If they were going to France they could view a few places while they were there.

Having an early night was crucial yet they stumbled across Villa Pera, the house that would become their house and both girls were touched with a bizarre sense of destiny. They didn't feel sleepy at all. It was strange with these two. A 52 roomed, thirteenth century house in Lucca, Italy filled to the brim with eighteenth and nineteenth century frescoes. Was this really happening? Few homes in Italy are frescoed at all and even fewer have frescoes in every room. Never in a million years would the Girls have expected to find a property on the planet with that number of frescoes, that old for that price. They felt an immediate affinity with the magical house perched high on a hillside overlooking the sweet scented Tuscan countryside down to the valley of Fir Enzi's sister city.

Like them the villa needed major structural restoration work doing. Although the ancient Frescoes had been beautifully preserved by, now peeling, elaborate Victorian wallpapers they needed a lot of work by an expert. Villa Pera had her story in art. Safe. The current owner, Donatella Pera, was forced to sell this ancestral home. The Pera family fortune had dwindled in the Italian casinos but the frescoes were set in stone, literally. Immovable. The place had a history and now a future. The restoration of Villa Pera was Ilia's dream project for his school and a steal at four hundred thousand dollars.

"This is a gift. All we need is the money."

Sleeping at The Beach Cottage once in a while was a treat and not having to face The Jailers, the perfect opportunity to get completely fucked up. On this occasion coming face to face with a sexy famous rock star would take much camouflage, so moderation on the drinking front was called for.

"We need to meet Tommy fresh and without the camera. We don't want to freak him out now we are this far down the road."

"What does one wear to meet a rock star?"

"Looking young is the key. The outfit will just be another decoy. Take his mind off the fact we're old."

The alarm was set and the make up spread out, ready for application. The expensive wrinkle cream now used only in extreme emergencies, as the pot was almost empty, was plastered on both faces, thick and plentiful. Tommy was sexy and they wanted to flirt, the cream was absolutely necessary. The following morning came all too quickly for the restless girls. Neither had slept very well. Both dressed in a little black leather for Tommy, a little too sexy for them it was a good job they were at The Beach Cottage. Leather always made The Jailers nervous. The storyboard, the erotic painting and some cool sounds filled the truck as they set off to meet Mr. Lee. The fridge at The Beach Cottage was on the blink so the bottle of champagne for Tommy was not chilled. They planned to stop on the way and pick up ice but forgot the ice bucket and needed to think fast. Warm champagne was not an option.

BAG studios somewhere in the back of beyond took bloody hours to find. Two hours in the car and a couple of joints were miraculously transformed into roaches. The conversation was creative as dreams were shared.

"You won't believe it. I found myself in Villa Pera with loads of people staying. It was beautiful, full of life, music, loads of banter. The manager got murdered at midnight and everyone was a suspect."

"Wow that's hot, a murder mystery for Harvey. Villa Pera the movie, Check in if you dare."

"All the experience you've had with villains it'll be finished by teatime."

A strip mall half way to Tommy's provided a rest stop. A child, preparing for a day at the beach, provided the perfect solution to the warm champers dilemma. Martha Stewart may be old fashioned but she did come up with a corker now and again. They offered the kid ten dollars in exchange for his green plastic bucket. For them it was always about making a fabulous impression. The ten bucks did the trick. Tommy was just a kid at heart according to Maxim. He would love it. They finally arrived at the out of the way studios desperate for a piss, dying for a drink and dreading meeting Tommy. The only up swing, the mental treatment for Villa Pera, the movie was drafted. It was three fifty pm. Coming up with a plot for a film script was hard work. They needed a fag.

It was time to meet the rock star who had let them down so badly and allow him the opportunity to redeem himself. As they approached the large metal framed doors Vignola, the thug, stood guard outside, smoking an enormous cigar. He was Tommy's right hand man covered in horrible tattoos and the friend of Mike from Challenge's studio. Their first encounter was hostile. The erotic painting didn't impress him. It wasn't Pamela Anderson. No really? He gruffly told them to go inside and wait for Cory. Tommy was busy but someone would deal with them. What was his problem? He gave The Girls the creeps.

The interior of the studio was worse than the exterior, if you can get your head around that. It was awful, grey vast and industrial. Not remotely the luxurious surroundings The Girls expected from the glamorous world of rock and roll, more like being in a youth club. The Girls sat back on a worn black sofa, housed in a corridor opposite a vending machine. Thoughts of the sweaty men who preceded them were dispelled. Smoking a much needed fag and thinking about the champagne, they were glad they were wearing leather. At least they wouldn't be covered in bits when they stood up.

Patience was not The Girls' strong suit even when waiting for a Hollywood rock star. They stopped two passing strangers for information about Tommy, one the boy next door trying to be a rock star and his sidekick a yellow haired punk. A silver safety pin pulled through his nose and a body too thin for words? What was he wearing? How old was he? Bless him. He looked like Billy Idol on crack.

"Excuse me do you work here?"

The young boys were members of Tommy's band and really quite interesting and polite for teenagers. Tommy went straight up in The Girls' estimations. They made friends with the intelligent pair and shared their story about art. As

The Girls proudly hoisted the heavy abstract nude into the air for the musician's approval the nonchalant comment was, Tommy preferred blondes and art wasn't really his gig. He got his kicks from trashing hotel rooms and shagging groupies. Oh? Maybe Tommy was the wrong choice for the show about art and culture. Things went from bad to worse when Cory from Deluxe appeared. He was furious. He had no idea The Girls were even coming to see Tommy and for him, this was a management nightmare. It was more than they could stand. Cory needed a telling off. Tommy Lee was not wasting anymore of their time.

"Let me get this straight. You're telling me Tommy asks us to come and visit and now we can't see him? The drive here was long and as you know Cory, time is money."

"We have champagne, free art and a storyboard."

"More importantly, a letter from Tommy accepting a painting which, at the moment, is by your feet. Now is Tommy available?"

Cory had no choice but to let them in. They knew their pitch needed to be fast and furious as the huge studio door swung open and The Girls walked into the vast, dark void. They had ten minutes before Tommy had to be back at work. As their eyes adjusted to the darkness of the huge, equipment filled space they focused on the wiry shy form of the rock star. Was that him? He was gorgeous. Coming face to face with Tommy Lee was electric for both girls. It was just like meeting the Rolling Stones, pure sex and rock and roll, the perfect combination.

"At last we finally meet. Glass of champagne darling?"

The green bucket was eagerly presented. The familiar orange label of the pop faced the star. Tommy smiled. It was his favorite, what luck. He liked them, they could tell. With that established they confidently instructed the sulky Vignola to find glasses.

The room was busy, filled with people trying to catch Tommy's eye before the rehearsal commenced. He was pulled by his team from pillar to post giving his nod of approval on everything from training shoes to half a guitar.

In an attempt to divert his attention back to them, The Girls suggested marketing the Rock Star's guitar shaped chopping board signed by Tommy. It would sell millions and Martha would be impressed. The diversion worked and before one could say "Insider Trading" they brokered their art like merchants from Venice and pitched the show, much to the outward annoyance of the entourage. Ilia's interpretation of Tommy showed an uncanny resemblance considering he had no idea who he was. Tommy could not believe his eyes. There he was in his orange house and he was an art collector. It was him

"Here is the painting. It's worth fifteen thousand dollars."

"It came from behind The Iron Curtain. It has the official stamp on the back. The artist is giving this to you as a gift, in the hope your mates will see it, love it and collect his work."

"We have already pitched the idea to Style and E! Television and they're excited."

Tommy laughed his head off. Their show sounded funky. He said he was sorry for all the confusion but with his tour in Japan looming, he had to practice. He couldn't commit to anything just at that moment however he did generously suggest The Girls hang out and listen to a couple of songs. The offer was punctuated with a rock star's flick of the hair and a rock star's twinkle of the eye. They could stay as long as they liked.

When Viggy, to his mates, came back with paper cups, the champagne was uncorked in celebration. The Girls grabbed their drinks and made them selves comfy on the huge studio sofa. Tommy emptied his cup in one gulp. The threatening Vignola, loomed silently demanding he be handed back the cup. The fun was over as Vignola forced the star back to work. One was all Tommy was having poor bastard.

With their mission accomplished The Girls relaxed and sipped their champagne. Maybe they could find some one with pot. Tommy was a rock star after all, the ashtray overflowing with roaches was somewhat of a giveaway. Scanning the huge dark box they spied someone else in black leather, standing alone in front of the stage. He was Tommy's personal chef and promptly offered them a slice of homemade cheesecake, his specialty. He was smoking a Dutch and was happy to share his high too. There was God again in the most unlikely of places and always so great to have around in a crisis. The celebrity chef had his own catering company and promoted his product whenever he could. What could be more perfect? The chef insisted Tommy played a mean guitar and advised The Girls to insert the ear plugs being doled out by one of the grips. Tommy picked his guitar as the style conscious pick shoes, carefully. In truth the guitar attendant made sure he got the right one. Yes that is a real job in LA LA Land. Not much was left to chance.

The huge studio door was closed firmly. Tommy was locked down. Positioned at the foot of the stage unable to hear a thing The Girls were ready to rock and roll. This was one jail they had no desire to escape from. The Girls were smitten. They would get to him after all.

Tommy stepped up to the single mike, center stage and The Girls were extremely wobbly to say the least. A red padded bra, apparently a symbol of good fortune from Tommy's last world tour, dangled below his large mouth as his right arm carved a full circle through the air in what seemed like slow motion. His whole body was torte. Mocha with chocolate ganache. Irresistible. And if the truth be known the sexual energy this man oozed was infectious to any female within a twenty mile radius.

Tommy struck his first chord with skilled precision and the noise was deafening. The song was superb and the high Girls danced like teenagers, the atmosphere electric. Tommy loved their enthusiasm and showed off in response. For middle aged housewives married to Jailers living in "Stepford" this was women behaving badly and The Girls loved every second of it.

After lots of shouting and too many bravos, Tommy dedicated the second song just to them. The classic David Bowie hit, Fame. It was fabulous. Both girls knew all the words and sang along like real pros. It was a magical moment for two friends from Yorkshire. For one split second it made all their hard work seem worthwhile.

Of course the intense euphoria could not last. Vignola was having a melt down. It was so blatantly obvious he hated Tommy getting all the praise. The guy was jealous and needed putting in his place.

"We're all here having fun, please smile."

His come back was so cutting and rude it floored The Girls momentarily. Maybe if they took their kit off he would have something to smile about? Was he joking? This was the insult of all insults. The party was over and they had to leave. Who did he think he was dealing with? The Girls were out of there.

The thought of getting naked with Tommy Lee was quite flattering but being thrown out by a thug? That was terrible. Tommy tried to make it better by offering a goodbye hug and thanking them for the art but it was too late. He was sweaty and his sidekick was obnoxious. Holly told Tommy they would be in touch by email once Style gave them the heads up. Dealing with the filming issue was best left for another time.

Shirley, horrified, didn't even say goodbye.

Once outside Cory thanked them for coming but "Don't call us we'll call you" was clearly written all over his stern face. The chef embarrassed gave them a card and a couple of reconciliatory cheesecakes to eat on the way home. He was a nice bloke. Always hopeful forever positive, The Girls prayed they had made a big enough impression on the star to assure them of his appearance in their pilot. They had taken him a fabulous painting and a bottle of Verve Cliquot. Would that be enough to seal the deal?

The week had been long and tiring. They had a feeling of achievement but no sense of success. With not a single penny to show for their efforts they were still financially desperate. The drive back to jail was brutal.

"OK you snooze, you loose. Tomorrow we call Style and close the deal. With a green light, Tommy will have to appear. We can make it happen."

The next day was a little dull really. Hanging with Tommy Lee was pretty tough to top. All their meetings were done and dusted, all their follow up, complete. They just had to sit and wait for a call back from Style. With the afternoon free to concentrate on writing Villa Pera the movie, a copy of Final Draft was dusted off from a pile of old software belonging to Jailer One and the script began to emerge. It was not long before they realized writing a movie was not easy. They needed a better outline than the one devised in the car stoned; a plot, a plan, a story with an ending.

A little pot was all it took to build some structure for the play. After hours of continuous dialog, they had the plot and a motley crew of characters based on people they knew from the past. Villa Pera, a murder mystery set in Italy with more twists and turns than the Monaco Grand Prix, would be the perfect production for Harvey.

Writing was a great way to pass the days and play emerged pretty quickly for two complete novices. They used every spare moment to weave the story and type the manuscript from there on. As the cast of characters grew and the script really began to take shape it was decided to call France again. If they had a movie script they had to go to Cannes to sell it. Back on home turf selling Villa Pera would be easy. It made sense.

Aga was still not at home according to the curt Frenchman who answered the phone at The Carlton. Did he really live there? So much for The Illusive Celebrity. They would try again later. They had heard nothing from their rock star in over two weeks. Just because the fat sidekick had thrown them out, they couldn't give up on Tommy.

Dear kinky@rockstar.com, We loved meeting you and hope the art is close to your bed. You should release Fame as a single. It would hit the charts like a rocket. Everyone loves that song. When can we come hang out, eat cheesecake, smoke pot and make this fucking film? Love The Girls. PS Do you have any rock star mates who might consider appearing in the show? You did let us down and you do have a free painting. Come on Tommy help us. XXXX Send.

Their business now hanging in the balance, they decided to call Carrie from Style completely sober. They had already left several three bottle messages but still no word. Donna was happy to hear from her bubbly chums, thanked them for coming in but not a dickie bird about Celebrity Art Interiors.

"Did they love it? Should we celebrate? Are we about to hit the big time?"

"Yes? No?"

"What is there to think about? It's what Jeff told us you guys were on the look out for. Help us here, please."

"We've put everything we have into this project. It's not just about selling a show. It's about supporting art."

Donna said it would take weeks to get an answer. Weeks they just didn't have.

The next development meeting was planned for three days hence and after The Girls desperate pleas for a quick response Donna assured them of some kind of feed back.

The advice that ended the call, Carrie might give them the green light they needed if more celebrity names were attached. OK they needed more celebrities. They called Jordon to talk about the art research and ask if Ridley might consider being in their show. Send over a detailed fax and she would ask him. That old chestnut again. The fax was sent to Ridley.

The Girls had a reply from Kinky. They assumed he was replying collectively and unilaterally to their multi dimensional request, releasing Fame, making the film, hanging out smoking pot, eating cheesecake and recommending celebrity friends.

Dear English Girls, No Sorry!!!!!!!!!!!!! One world. T xxx.

"So, Tommy won't help and won't ask his mates to help either, no problem."

"Call Blaine and make him feel guilty about letting us down. We need some rock star recommendations."

Blaine was an angel from heaven and immediately came to the rescue. The Girls genuinely sensed he felt sorry for them and handed over two telephone numbers, Mr Gene Simmons, the lead singer with rock hell raisers, Kiss and the legendary satanically inclined devil worshiper himself, Mr Ozzy Osbourne. He said the Osbournes loved art and may feature The Girls on their reality show. The Girls could not believe their luck and thanked poor Blaine to death. This was great news.

They called Gene first and got Malissa, his assistant, nothing new about that. She told them to put it in a fax and she would get back to them, nothing new about that either. A wonderfully funny letter was immediately faxed to Gene about their art show with Tommy Lee. They had no idea what Gene looked like. On stage, he always wore full make up, covering his face like a mask. They flirted in ink all the same assuming under all the cake, he would be just another gorgeous rock star.

Calling the Osbournes was tricky to say the least. They had the number one reality show on MTV and had just taken Hollywood by storm. It just goes to show how ridiculous the business can be. Sharon, Ozzy's wife of twenty five years, was the brains behind the exceptional marketing of the unusual family and made all the business decisions. Although they were the hottest thing in Hollywood they were English and from very modest beginnings. There was a good chance they would still be normal, hopefully having resisted all the temptations of the ego enhancer, Los Angeles.

'The How To Penetrate Hollywood Manual', out once again, (network, name drop and keep focused) The Girls planned their attack on their fellow Brit, Sharon but even she had an assistant Eddie, who told them to fax over their request and some one would get back to them. Another begging letter faxed its way across to the Osbournes, asking for help with Ilia's art. It was the first of many.

"Considering we drink, smoke and have no idea what the fuck we are do-ing, we have come along way from the days with Dullarse."

"I have no idea how we got this far but we have. I suggest we tie this up then head off into the sunset for a while. Take a bloody rest."

They called Aga for a millionth time but the dirty stop out was still not around and the bill for the international phone calls was mounting. They left another message before heading back to jail. The following morning, with all the hope in the land, they prayed for news from their celebrity mates. As always, there were no messages, no emails and the postman was definitely now a figment of their imagination.

"What now Sherlock?"

"The film script is almost done. We have an art restoration project. We have an Italian villa as the film set. We have no money."

"We should find some film producers and get the script out there. Project Dynamite."

"We'll need someone to bypass Barbara and get the thing straight to Harvey if we don't catch up with him in Cannes."

As you know by now, to talk to anyone in Hollywood Royalty, even pro-ducers is impossible. One would assume them open to projects that being their job. In reality it is completely the opposite. Although that didn't stop them try-ing. And before one could blink an eye, they had a producer, in Santa Monica, on the phone, Mr Robert Enrigues. Was he a Spaniard? They needed a champion for their own sinking Armada. Regardless of his nationality Robert was a star and invited them out to lunch. He would be paying. Life was fabulous. Always pre-pared for Plan B, they had a script to polish.

Outside The Beach Cottage, later that day, a badly wrapped box from the Style network sat on the step. Was it a parcel bomb? The Girls could not contain their excitement as they ripped the thing open. This was potentially the answer to all their prayers. Remember they had not had any good news in ages.

The package was stuffed to the brim with tasteless cheap marketing gadgets. Two baseball caps, some tiny scented candles and a couple of T shirts, all embossed with the Style logo. The accompanying letter was sweet but short. So much for dreams.

Dear Girls,
Thanks for the scratching.
Love Donna. XXXXXX

Although the gifts from Donna were not aptly chosen for The Girls, far too commercial, it was seen as a triumph. It's always the thought that counts. At the very least someone was thinking about them for a change. Sealing the deal with the Greenlight man's right hand woman was on the horizon. Making friends with the assistant always worked according to 'The How to Penetrate Hollywood Manual.'

"Let's put on the T shirts and go somewhere happening. We are celebrity stalkers for God sake. We need to get out more. Maybe we can track down Brad Pitt."

"It would really get us out of the shit. What do you think the odds are?"

They decided upon Jerry's Deli in Studio City. Brad liked Jerry's pickled gherkins according to People Magazine. The paparazzi were always in there lured by the better than average odds, the exclusive shot of the illusive celebrity, having a hot dog and French fries, was possible. The American media would buy anything with a celebrity attached. Thank the lord for the BBC.

On arrival, Jerry's Deli was empty. Brad obviously didn't feel like gherkins that day. Oh well it was still early and anything was possible. Ordering some drinks and a big plate of onion rings, a house specialty, took the edge off. Was that someone famous in the corner? Cameras were being shoved in his face. There was quite a commotion going on. Whomever it was had to be some variety of celebrity. What a coo.

Eyesight failing, it happens after forty, they strained to bring the man being fussed over into focus. He was tall, dark and rather "Red Indian" looking. His shoulder length hair, coarse and curly hair covered the collar around his cloak of leather. The bubbly waitress could not contain her excitement as The Girls casually inquired as to what was going on. She told them the man being filmed was Gene Simmons and The Girls were launched back into the twilight zone once again. What the fuck was he doing there? Following them? Come on, was this for real? It was only a matter of hours since their letter had gone to Malissa. This was certainly the ultimate in the twilight zone experience to date. Without thinking they chugged their wine then, like old timers on Broadway, danced over to meet the man behind the mask. They were creating their own destiny and that of the art, sober.

"Gene, it's so strange to find you here."

"Mallisa your lovely assistant said she would tell you all about us."

"What are you filming?"

Dropping Malissa's name made him a little less startled by their attack. He recalled seeing their fax. That was a gift. They had their chance to really connect face to face with a huge celebrity and pitch him their idea for the art show in person. Coincidentally the marketing genius behind the Kiss branding was on the reality bandwagon himself, filming a segment of his own for the NBC hit Extra. Again, it was another excerpt from the twilight zone.

"We would love you to appear in our show on Style."

"We already have Tommy Lee on board, that's how we got to you."

Gene turned out to be quite the ladies man. He flirted ferociously and demanded they rub their breasts together. Snogging each other was next on his list. The lesbian act performed at lunchtime, in Jerry's Deli? Must I? Oh well anything for the art. Lulu, the field producer from Extra, was rushing around like a chicken with its head chopped off, insisting The Girls sign disclosure forms and other rigmarole. Would they be on television? This was better than sex.

Gene wanted an eyeful and a handful. Is that what it was going to take? Let's put it this way he wasn't shy. He was no way as hot as Tommy in the looks department but celibacy was beginning to take its toll on The Girls staunch principles. They obliged performing their once in a while pretend lesbian act, their one goal in mind, to pin him down and secure a positive response. They had had years of practice and were pretty convincing all things considered. Rock star meets English art dealers in Jerry's Deli. Who needs Brad Pitt?

Touch touch touch, Kiss Kiss Kiss and Gene said he would be in touch, lolloping out of sight. Lulu dropped her card in their hands, as she waved goodbye. The Girls had to stay for one more drink and reflect. They had pitched another huge rock star and once again it was all by chance, the price having one's breasts fondled on national television. Dirt cheap considering everything else they had been through to date.

On the drive back they decided to give Carrie a shout from the mobile and tell her about Gene and Ozzy. Surely that would seal the deal? She had to be impressed. Donna confirmed she would relay the message but Carrie was in a meeting. Not to worry at least she would be up to speed before the proposed development meeting.

The next call was to Sharon Osbourne in the hope of getting hold of Ozzy. They left a message suggesting afternoon tea sometime to discuss art. Being English they assumed she would jump at the chance of a strong cup of Tetleys and a Rich Tea biscuit. She never did.

Back in the more familiar twilight zone of The Beach Cottage the phone was ringing. It was Donna with horrific news. What the hell was going on? She had said three days. The pilot was not flying, well and truly grounded was more accurate. Barbara was spot on. Their show was too high brow for Mid America. Style Entertainment Television was passing on 'Celebrity Art Interiors.'

What? How could that be? It was tragic. They finally had the celebrities saying yes but now the buyer was saying no. The blow was so below the belt. The news, so unthinkable, they were crushed. They were catapulted back in time, faster than one could say Orsen Wells. Having defined the word pass in the 'How to Penetrate Hollywood Manual' gutted now there's a word.

"This is not good news. In short we are fucked. It's not possible to go back to Style and re pitch the show. A pass means a pass. Over. Finito. Goodnight Sooty."

"It would really help me out now, if you would just kill me and put me out of my misery, once and for all. I have no preference just make it quick."

"For Gods sake, now we need a whole new concept or a new buyer. I say we drink more wine."

A few days later after some intense brooding and wound licking the azure blue Californian sky, the only thing Mediterranean about the place, pulled them back up by their boot laces. They had flogged the art show to death and now it was time to bury it. Looking up at the expansive palette of color was always better than looking down in the dirt so the sooner they did that the better. Having the assistant pass on their show had really upset them, especially someone they had given scratching lessons to but they were over it. They had to move forward. Starting all over again was simply not an option.

The next few hours were spent tying up all the necessary loose ends. Without Celebrity Art Interiors, they had nothing to talk to Barbara about. Ridley didn't seem that impressed with Ilia's research. There had been no response what so ever to all the information they forwarded. The Oriental art project that never was. They decided to send Ridley flowers, in the hope that may just spark some kind of reaction. While congratulating him on his recent Emmy swoop for 'The Gathering Storm', staring another of the Girls' heroes Albert Finney, a mention of Villa Pera, their script, was slipped in. Maybe he would consider directing? Ilia had come across a wonderful book during his research for Scott Free Productions and The Girls threw that in too, with the faint hope it might help Ridley with his new movie "Tripoli." A lovely note of praise was hand written inside the cover next to a sketch of a hangman mouthing the word "HELP". It was a long shot but he might feel sorry for them and just say yes.

Choosing a piece of art for Ozzy was simple. Ilia selected a rare satanic painting entitled 'The Cat and the Mouse'. Ilia believed it would be worth millions one day. They wrapped the precious canvas in expensive polka dotted paper, tied a huge red ribbon around the parcel and lugged it all the way to Divine recordings in Beverly Hills.

151

The rarest painting of all was just for Ozzy. Ilia loved him, how sweet.

"Hopefully we'll bump into Sharon, tell her off for not calling back, give Ozzy the art and mission accomplished."

"I cannot believe we did all that work with nothing to show for it."

"We do have something to show for it. We have stuck to our side of the bargain and got the art before the eyes of those who can help. Just because we don't have anything to show financially, we should still be proud of ourselves."

"We have the American Express Bill."

The office at Divine Recordings, Beverly Hills was closed up and uninviting. A note was pinned on the door. The Osbournes had left for England, that morning. Lady luck was no where in sight that day. The painting was placed back in the truck and with no emotion, other than complete defeat, they drove off. They needed to get it together mentally. Lunch was scheduled with their new producer Robert Enriques, the Spaniard. They had a movie to pitch. Project Dynamite. Going out with a bang was all they had left. They would give him the play and impress the fuck out of him.

Robert was not only very handsome and very charming, but also a smoker and drinker. Things were looking up. If they could sell the story of Villa Pera, (Check in if you Dare), a murder mystery set in a fresco haven, Robert would finally get them to Harvey. He was blown to bits by their pitch. Red Baron films, his production company often worked with new writers and would help them if the work mirrored the sell. He would read the script and then decide on a course of action.

It was the first time someone had actually understood what they were trying to achieve. The rushed piece of work was triumphantly handed over with more confidence than a charging elephant. Robert left the restaurant with Villa Pera neatly tucked under his arm. The Girls had no doubt he would be on the phone with offers from Hollywood, within days. Remember, in their world anything was possible.

Elated they returned to The Beach Cottage to give Ilia one last almighty push. They would stalk the biggest celebrity of them all, besides Harvey of course, The President of The United States. In a state of euphoria a letter was composed to Mr George W. Bush himself. Bless him. He seemed more home on the range than cultural attaché but the USA had welcomed Ilia and his art with open opens then left him to rot in Inglewood. The Girls asked the President to accept a piece of Ilia's soul, a painting, and consider hanging it in the White House to give the genius the recognition he deserved. It was the least he could do after giving Ilia genius status to reside in the US as an artist, then totally forgetting about him. The letter was signed, sealed and posted with fingers tightly crossed it would be the President who saved the day.

After a couple of days rest and some drunken calls to Tommy Lee's message machine, they waited on tender hooks for feedback from Robert Enriques and the President of The United States of America. The call from Robert was rotten when it came. He said their pitch was magnificent but their script, well terrible. It was like being dropped from a great height. He told them quite categorically they needed to start acting like writers if they ever wanted to impress the likes of Harvey Weinstein, time to stop dreaming and start listening. Poor Robert was driven mad by two women who just believed so much in their dream, they forgot about taking advice from an expert.

I won't go into why they were sacked by Robert but, let's put it this way they don't like being criticized, especially when drunk. When you think about, offering Ridley Scott as the director and Harvey Weinstein as the buyer when the script is toilet, it was really no wonder he wanted rid of them. They took the news well considering. They still believed their film was fabulous even if the script did need a bit of work. Hollywood was not going to beat them. They were going it alone once again.

The fatal blow from the top dog came a few days later.

Dear Mesdames Yanez.

The President asked me to thank you for your letter requesting to present him with a painting by Ilia Annosov. We appreciate your interest in arranging such a presentation. Although the President would very much enjoy having the opportunity to accept such gifts, I regret to write that due to many requests of the same nature, in fairness to all, we are unable to schedule appointments. If you still wish to forward your gift send to blar blar blar.

It seemed Mr. Bush had no interest in art either.

"Well that about says it all. They're all happy to take the art but not prepared to give anything back in return."

"George Bush should hook up with Tommy Lee. They have a lot in common."

Heads on the chopping block they decided to put away the bulging Rolodex and take a rest. The fight was not over but they needed a change of scenery if Art Interiors, with the huge task of supporting genius, was ever going to work in LA LA Land. A holiday first was essential. LA had finished them off, at least for a while. Hollywood was impossible to penetrate, even with a fucking manual.

Ilia was told to take a rest and recharge his batteries. Maybe paint something. Challenge still at his computer editing the cosmic explosion, bless him said he might go to Dallas with Polly for a short break, maybe do a little celebrity stalking himself and finish off the film. Yeah right, dream on. For the Girls, Celebrity Stalking had beaten them down. They were knackered. The time was right to say goodbye to Los Angeles for a little while and do some Dirty Rotten Scoundreling at the most bourgeois film festival in Europe. The Girls had to go and find Harvey in Cannes and pitch him their movie. It was now or never. Long live the French.

DIRTY ROTTEN SCOUNDRELING

"I'm a big-headed sod who thinks he's really good."
ELVIS COSTELLO

IT WAS TWO WEEKS BEFORE THE CANNES FILM FESTIVAL AND THE LURE OF THE Cote D'Azur was strong but with no clients and no outstanding invoices, justifying a trip was difficult at best.

"How do we get round The Jailers?"

"Research? They have loads of art there!"

"We can't afford it."

"That's why we have the Gold Card."

"No."

A couple of days later they received a rather unusual telephone call, a commission. A large exclusive property developer needed a commercial mural painting. Wow, they had a client. Coupled with the good news that the rent check for The Beach Cottage had cleared, much to their surprise, what better reason to knock off early and celebrate. Looking back perhaps Café Pierre, the local chic French brasserie in Manhattan Beach, was a bad choice. After guzzling an over priced eighty seven, Chateau Neuf Du Pape because they simply could not resist it and savoring truffles and fois gras, they returned home for a digestive and cheese. Coincidentally one of The Jailers had gone to the supermarket the day before, the only reason there was anything edible in the fridge that rarely housed anything of nutritional value. One of the reasons The Girls liked Roquefort so much was its unbelievably long fridge life in a fridge with no food.

After polishing off half a bottle of very fine grappa between the two of them, phoning Air France and booking two first class flights to Paris seemed like a solid plan. They could use The Jailers American Express points, one hundred thousand per ticket. By the time they were found out they would already be back in the U.S. Cannes was definitely the place to, find the celebrity client that had eluded them up until now, sell Villa Pera and a quick call to Ali Khan to get the information on his brother Aga, gave them the ever important Plan B.

"We're confirmed from LAX to Paris then connecting on to Nice this Friday."

They decided not to tell The Jailers of the planned trip. It was only four days, really anyway. It would take that long to broker it to them and they were leaving that Friday. There wasn't enough time. It would have been nice to have T-shirts printed for marketing purposes for the film, 'Villa Pera' Check In If You Dare, but of course the budget was limited. So they left for France two days later, The Jailers having no knowledge of their wives impending departure. The Louis Vuitton luggage was taken out and dusted off. The Girls had no idea what had happened to two of the pieces in the set. They were probably still sitting at the airport after the last trip overseas. Getting luggage back in ones' possession after a 12 hour flight, where the alcohol is expensive, unlimited and free, was always a challenge for these two, and I believe will remain one. Oh well, it was only a six day trip, two of which were traveling so four cases should be enough. They would just have to pack light.

With their bags packed and stacked on the curb, as many copies of the script as the poor Canon inkjet could churn out in 2 days, notes to The Jailers penned detailing where they were staying and 2 hours to go before their flight, they stood outside The Beach Cottage waiting for the taxi.

"What did you say to him in your letter?"

"Oh, that a big opportunity had come up and we had to pop over to France. I said we'd be back in a few days. He'll get over it.

"That's him coming now. I thought you said he wouldn't be here until five. Where the fuck is the taxi? We are going to get busted."

The taxi arrived in the nick of time. The Kenyan cabbie was startled by The Girls' frantic sense of urgency. He wasn't that late. Five minutes maybe. Were they trying to get away from the law? What was going on?

"Hurry man, hurry, we've got to go."

They sped off, just as a confused Jailer One pulled up. The Girls were hanging out the window, waving madly as they escaped into the distance. They were on their way.

Within seventy two hours of getting pissed and booking the flights, they landed in Nice dressed identically in white pin striped trouser suits and Stars and Stripes T-shirts. The designer accessories were copious and ostentatious but the look was always flawless. Gucci, Chanel, Dior, Givenchy, Jean Paul Gaultier. Well they were in France, it was simply out of respect.

"Darling, new sunglasses?"

"Yes, I bought every designer pair they had."

"Was that not a little excessive?"

"Well if Andie McDowell is wearing Chanel then so shall I. She's here to promote The Crush. If it's Gucci I'm ready"

As they headed towards the Sortie of the small but extremely busy Nice terminal building they took out cigarettes and lighters. They were in France and yes, yes, yes everyone smokes.

"Did you know if you ask for a non-smoking table in France they seat you next to the bathroom."

"So hence everyone smokes in France, just to get a good table."

Six days free from scathing stares and violent coughing attacks from ones' fellow co- habitants of earth, free flowing wine from the cellars of the wine gods, unlimited shopping in arguably the finest stores in the world and of course the food, the cheese, the plat de jour, ah the food was irresistible. As they hurried out of the airport and flagged down a taxi The Girls were elated. They had totally forgotten they were supposed to be in France for the art and to find an investor for their movie.

"Let's check in get a drink, do some shopping, get a little nibbly thing, wear something Chanel"

"Don't you think we should check out some art?"

"Oh Manet, Monet, Mona Lisa, the Louvre. I'm better when I'm a bit pissed."

As the taxi pulled up outside the famed, Carlton International Hotel, Boulevard de la Croissette, the most prestigious hotel in Cannes, The Girls let out a heavy sigh. When they checked in they already had two messages from The Jailers. They decided they would get settled in and deal with them a little later. They compromised on the room, booking the cheapest available at seven hundred dollars per night. Well they didn't need an overpriced super deluxe suite with a swimming pool in it. Whomever they made friends with would have one. After a massive flirt with the concierge,("ménage a trois" and "je t'adore" had come in handy from the phrase book) to secure VIP reservations at the hottest club in Cannes that evening and a baggie of top quality marijuana, a quick change and a fresh coat of lipstick were in order. Within an hour of arriving they were enjoying their first cocktail, a record. Well they do say practice makes perfect.

The smart hotel restaurant was busy as The Girls made their entry. The crowd was a mixture of chic euro trash doing the French equivalent of a power lunch, taking the afternoon off and getting trashed with ones mates, and "pareod" beautiful people having spent the morning perfecting an already flawless tan, now in need of libation, shade and a petit gastronomic treat. Soon after finding perches on exquisitely upholstered bar stools, they spied their victim, sorry host, for lunch. They had not yet spoken to him, but he was perfect. Showy, probably American.

It was always interesting to them. Put a European man in Gucci he is chic and debonair, while an American in the same "vetements" is considered flashy or even worse, puffy. This chap was confident however. His hair was uniformly black for a man of his age, obviously out of a bottle and his moustache was terribly eighties. Apart from his basic all round sliminess, he was tall and quite good-looking, alone and they guessed in his 60's. He probably lied about his age hence the bad dye job, making him an easy target. The plan was simple. Flatter him, ask him to join them for lunch and inevitably get him to pick up the tab. A lovely thing that happens not just in Yorkshire but all over Europe, men pay the bill. It was straightforward and The Girls were experts, certainly on this side of the Atlantic.

Luring the selected victim over was easier than even they had imagined. One smile, goodness they'd forgotten how easy it was to get someone's attention, in France of all places. Weren't people supposed to be aloof here, even at his age? It was true they had, indeed, been married to The Jailers for too long.

His name, he said was Vincent St. Clair. Was he French? His accent was unusual, broken English punctuated with the occasional "merci beaucoup" and "ciao". Hardly bilingual, and he told them he worked in Hollywood. It was a good job neither fancied him because the geography could prove a tad too close for comfort. Of course he was there for the parties and the food, the same as them, but as he described the film festival and all his important commitments, they spewed verbal ramblings about the world of fine art and the restoration project in Italy. Four bottles of mediocre overly priced vin de table later he was sold. Thank goodness they had already kicked off with a good bottle. They had had their quick aperitif, a bottle of Cristal, deftly added to his bill within moments of him extending his linguistic repertoire. "Garcon!" Mr. St Clair had shouted across that sophisticated restaurant to obtain the bill. Uh how gauche. Yes, he was a phony with a wallet and his name was Sinclair not St Clair. Everyone knows no one says garcon anymore, particularly in France.

"Oh well, he could lead to bigger and better things. He is staying at the hotel"

"I'm a bit wobbly, how much wine did we have? I need to rest a minute"

"We haven't had that much, have a cigarette and you'll feel better."

They stood up, a little shaky and made their way over to 2 empty loungers by the large weeping willow on a May afternoon during the Film Festival. The only week when the Cote D'Azur becomes a jet set playground for the who's who on the international scene. Fab. A young boy, about 17 and gorgeous, wearing a crisp white shirt and black dickie bow, on that scorcher of a day, brought them stripy deep, blue and white cushions for their chaises and moved a matching umbrella over to give The Girls maximum shade. They were already in heaven.

"Bonjour."

"Oh leave the boy alone, he's a baby, a gardener and far too young for us."

Within moments, before they could say "Two cosmopolitans please" they were asleep.

Several hours had gone by before The Girls were being awakened by a large Frenchman in a good suit. They had passed out, it was midnight and the gentleman, in broken English, kindly suggested they might be more comfortable in their suite. Disheveled and still a bit pissed they got to their feet. It was not pretty. Eyeliner smudged, clothes crumpled, shoes missing, they left the hotel garden with their polite but irritated escort. A lonely pair of Chanel sunglasses floated gently on the clear blue crystal water of a nearby fountain. The sunglasses went to a good home. The young boy's girlfriend was proudly sporting them the next day.

The Girls went to bed for a couple of hours, to catch up on some much needed shut eye. They were jet lagged when they awoke at two am. Shit, they had fucked up the reservation for the evening. Well it was only five in Los Angeles, and they had been asleep for hours if you counted the time in the garden. They decided to get up and go out anyway.

"We'll try and get in, it'll be a piece of cake, we'll just name drop. Sylvester Stallone or Tom Cruise is bound to be here"

"Lead the way."

Beaming madly at the ever polite nighttime hoteliers who obviously thought this pair was stark raving bonkers, The Girls emerged in the hotel lobby dressed from head to foot in marginally too tight Dolce and Gabbana hipsters and matching sparkly t-shirts. Not bad for forty at two thirty in the morning, after a transatlantic flight.

Not surprisingly the night proved to be a disaster. They could not get into the club and ended up at a not so chic lesbian bar in the only not so chic area of Cannes. As if that was not bad enough, who should be there but the ever present Vincent Sinclair, the Cad. What was he doing there? Probably trying to pick up a prostitute.

He settled for The Girls instead and was easily talked into going back to the hotel for a night-cap, thinking he was going to get lucky most likely. Had they known then, it would prove so terribly difficult to escape his amorous advances when they got back to the hotel, they would definitely have sought an alternative mode of transport but money was tight and he did pay for the cab.

"Thank god you got me away from him. Uh! His aftershave was so cheap and he needs to clean his teeth."

"Sorry but I didn't fancy thumbing a ride with a butch lesbian having a bad hair day, not after tonight anyway."

And so they went to bed. It was quarter to seven in the morning. The Girls snuggled down into the crisp white Ferguson Irish linens, the very best sheets money could buy and dreamed of doing a deal, meeting a celebrity and selling their script. They would call The Jailers in the morning. Facing those two after the night they'd had? No thanks.

They had to be up by noon the next day, as they had finally arranged to meet Mr Aga Khan in the hotel lobby at one o'clock on the dot, a potential client, an art buyer and rich. Fortunately the events of the previous day and night had not left them too incapacitated.

"Always start with Cristal, it's like Alka Seltzer but before you drink."

They were ready to charm him, impress him, humor him and help Aga with his art. Maybe he would have an investor or a producer for the film. When they had asked Ali how they would recognize Aga he had simply replied,

"He is my brother and he wears a gold Rolex."

This was the South of France where everyone wore a gold Rolex so The Girls were left looking for Ali Khan's brother.

As they sat patiently in the opulent lobby of the hotel, very smart people, young and old, meandered, glided and ambled by. Nobody rushed here. Gosh how lovely. The Girls scrutinized the crowd of people milling in and out. It was busy, it was one o'clock, France, Cannes no less, in the busiest week of the year and a good lunch table was as rare as a canary diamond. At one minute past one, by the matching Cartier Tanks strapped to The Girls' wrists, one real the other fake, they spied him. He was a younger version of Ali, not quite so bald and not quite so fat but still extremely short.

"Not so short when he stands on his wallet."

They stifled their giggles as they approached him across the vast marble floor of the lobby to say hello. They all shook hands. He seemed a little grumpy. Maybe he was hung over. There were some fabulous parties the night before. Was he a player? They didn't know. He suggested they eat at a small, terribly expensive eatery close to the hotel. Wow he'd got a reservation? It transpired he knew the owner, and once again The Girls were back on top frequenting the impossible to frequent. Who cared if he wasn't attractive. The Maitre D' showed the trio to a small private table outside. It had a small sign on it saying Reserve, which he removed with a magician's touch as he simultaneously pulled out both The Girls' chairs, placed napkins on their knees and offered them all a cool aperitif. How in hell's name those guys do all that at the same time is still a mystery. And they say American waiters give good service. French waiters will perform sexual favors as well and tipping is still discretionary. (Isn't compulsory tipping an oxymoron?)

The restaurant was crowded and the conversation difficult at first. Although Aga spoke perfect English, educated at Oxford and all that, he seemed shy at best. He had a warm smile that lit up his face and The Girls worked hard to coax it out of him. Compliments, jokes, humor, intellect, they played all their cards and after some fine faire, two bottles of extremely expensive wine and 3 rounds of cognacs, Aga was ready to talk business. He told them he was showing some art in his suite that afternoon and would like them to join him and some friends. OK, well how bad could it be?

When they arrived back at the hotel, The Girls followed Aga to an elevator away from the main ones normal guests paying a mere seven hundred a night would use. Immediately they could tell these lifts took you higher than the other lifts would ever go and let's remember The Girls like to get high. They had not had an opportunity to surreptitiously smoke the neatly rolled joint that had been carefully stashed in one of the pouchettes. They still had to source the appropriate time and place. The only difficulty might be finding it after a couple of bottles of wine. Hopefully they'd have sobered a little by then.

As the attendant stepped out of the elevator and into the welcoming space, The Girls were naturally high. They were in the penthouse suite at the Carlton International, Cannes during the film festival. Fuck. Ten or so people were already mingling. The tray passed drinks were simple, Cristal and Orange or Citron presse, with or without vodka. Evian was available but nobody ever asked for it. The Girls were thirsty and already quite buzzed so the water was a blessing. The crowd was a group of multi cultural, well dressed socialites and business men but sadly no celebrities. The only boys who stood out were two casually dressed, very good looking thirty somethings with orthodontically perfect, white straight teeth. They were obviously Americans. The Girls made a mental note, English from America in France, massive appeal. Must Use Later.

The Girls allowed Aga to introduce them as Fine Art Consultants from Los Angeles, they got the plug and he got the kudos. Aga ushered the pair of them into a private room, like a cheetah hiding its kill. The Girls feared a threesome. Fortunately his plan was quite different. He had a rare work he wanted them to see. Having been offered a large amount of money by a private collector he needed their opinion. Shit. They were fine art dealers. The artist, Henri Rousseau, neither of them had ever heard of.

"May we use your ladies before we view the piece properly?"

"Well it looks like something a 2 year old would paint, all those bright colors and animals. Maybe we can get him a gig at Sea World."

"Shit, fuck, shit, what now?"

"Nine hundred grand for that and the guy is definitely dead. Let's tell him we'll do some research, were staying in the hotel, talk to our people blah blah blah and we'll call him tomorrow. Great way to get back in touch if nothing better turns up"

"Or he doesn't call us back."

The art business works in mysterious ways sometimes. Aga was delighted. Their ignorance was construed as the seemingly casual shot with a distinct lack of interest chaser. The approach worked. A million dollar deal was a small deal for them. Yeah right.

A happy host made for a great party and The Girls were free to mingle. The afternoon had provoked several scary questions about art forcing The Girls to rely on their three, pre planned desperation responses, only to be used under absolute duress.

"I'm not that familiar with his work."

"Didn't he just finish a show in New York."

"Would you excuse me, I see Tom Cruise, I must say hello."

The Girls made a beeline for the totty, chatting quietly in a corner drinking beers. Where did they get those from? Thirsty work this art business. They were, indeed, American but nothing like The Jailers. These boys were snobby, funny, cocky, cute and young, a result. The token sports jocks, from well connected East Coast families, invited The Girls to go sailing with them later that afternoon. That was quick. They had barely said hello. It sounded fab. They all arranged to meet at the private hotel marina at five, passed out a handful of business cards to the array of art entourage, blew kisses and left.

A lot of people were left talking about the New York art scene after that soiree but who cared really, nobody. The phone at The Beach Cottage was living proof. Let's be truthful. It had been fun and would soon be forgotten by all. Sadly this gathering had been too small for the Tom Cruise line. That would be put away and saved for another day. The happy Girls retired with a client and they were going sailing with the American East Coast elite to celebrate. How ironic.

"Sailing? Is navy and white still in"

"Military darling, Mondi. He's French isn't he, minor designer but his couture is alright."

The Girls were excited at the prospect of spending a few relaxing hours on a beautiful boat, enjoying the perfect vista, the men and sipping cool, icy cocktails. They wondered if there would be food, probably some delicious hors d'oeurves. All the boats in the marina had staff. It was the done thing in the South of France.

Both girls wore denim. One, long shorts, Valentino, no French shorts were available in the suitcase, the other was comfortable in jeans. Ornate military blazers, now vintage couture, completed the ensemble. The shoes selected were wedged and wobbly sandals, where the amount of leather used, is inversely proportional to the price. It wasn't far to the private yacht access for the hotel. It was a good job as neither Girl was going very far in those shoes. When they arrived at the boat the boys greeted them with somewhat cautionary and puzzled looks. The Girls should have realized then, they were totally inappropriately dressed for their excursion, but the sexy smiles of the sun tanned thirty somethings and the draw 42 feet of sleek, fast, expensive sailing boat caused them, excusably, to be a little distracted.

There were 9 men in total, and The Girls were not restricted to Americans only. An international selection was always a bonus. There was Andre, a Frenchman with an attitude, OK a Frenchman. He was smoking a cigarette. Well that was one important question answered. Good. Paulo, from Brazil. No one spoke Portuguese, but he was definitely a laborer of some description as he needed a manicure in the worst possible way. Len and Sven were Swedish twins in their early twenties with big muscles and broad smiles. They spoke English well, which was a plus as The Girls' French was limited to wine, designers and the odd sexual epithet. The red head with a fine bone structure and bedroom eyes would not give his name. Was he a mute? Even better. French was definitely not his first language. Maybe he was Russian. They mentioned the name Ilia, but it didn't seem to help. He just walked away smiling surreptitiously and started messing about with some ropes. John the captain was an Englishman, an aspiring gentleman and sailor in his late forties, never married with a son at one of the lesser known public schools somewhere in Suffolk. He had a tummy that only too many pints, down the local pub, could produce and a rugged complexion one would attribute to his passion for sailing. The second important question was answered. The man in charge was a drinker. The only thing left to establish, who was the drug dealer in this motley crew and The Girls were set. Douglas was a charming Scottish blaggard with a receding hairline that somehow didn't matter on a sailing outing. However he was a player. That was obvious. He was extremely courteous to the captain, maintaining the upper class bravado of the sport, speaking in sailor language, performing his tasks one handedly, his other permanently preoccupied with the ever present gin and tonic. Douglas the drinker but Douglas the dealer? It didn't really sound right. He was a friend of John's from school although he looked and certainly acted a lot younger. Maybe Douglas had been John's lad. The English aristocracy, well that's a whole other book in itself. The last two to make up the stable were the thirty somethings from Aga's suite earlier that day. Their names were Johnny and Chuck. Jonathon Hogan Churchill III, was obviously very well to do by American standards. Only in America could the English and the Irish join together to create the contemporary aristocracy. Chuck was actually Charles McClean, brought up a catholic but definitely trying to become a protestant. The appeal of the WASP sorority girls and the catholic churches molestation scandal was enough to put any self respecting social climber over the edge. Including The Girls, it was The Reality Ocean's 11. Maybe there was hope in the film world after all. All they needed was the right director.

The Girls stepped aboard, helped to steady themselves by the Swedish twins, they mutually concluded perhaps the sandals had been a bad idea. With their poise and grace temporarily disrupted, they went into "joie de vivre" overdrive.

"Anyone got a light? Andre darling assistance s'il vous plaît."

"Thank you so much for having us. Terribly hospitable. Darling would you get me a drink? Anything is fine, champagne, whatever you've got."

Douglas gestured to The Girls it might be prudent to take off their sandals and put their larger than usual LV, (restoration/make up otherwise known as tart kit just in case) safely in the cabin. He was smiling and being helpful so they accepted his advice. They carefully handed him their sandals leaning down into the cabin. He took them with the necessary respect one shows for shoes that cost more than a good lunch for four, grabbed a quick glance at dual cleavage leaning precariously into the hold then casually tossed the expensive footwear into a cupboard with a cheeky smirk. Indignantly The Girls decided to stow the Louis Vuitton themselves. Unless he had drugs he was history.

They came aboard to find the captain, John doling out jobs faster than The Jailers at their recent garage sale. The sails, the ropes, the wind, the race, it all sounded marvelously complex. Then it hit them, the race, now that sounded scary. Many roles had been allocated, and it was now obvious not one of the oceans' nine crew was there to serve drinks.

What kind of sailing trip was this? The Girls made it clear to John that giving them responsibilities would be terribly foolish. After all there were eleven people aboard. The Captain had to look out for everyone's safety. Perhaps The Girls could get drinks and light cigarettes. It would surely make the trip more enjoyable for everyone. John smiled and suggested they get comfortable, take off their jewelry, and find a place to sit. Shit the jewelry might get ripped off. Yikes! Find a place to sit? There weren't any seats. Enjoy the ride? OK, they were open. It was going to be a beautiful evening after all.

So where should they sit on this magnificent vessel to obtain the best late afternoon sun? The induction had been intense, but they were prepared to step this trip up a notch and have some sport with their boys. They were sailing on the Cote D'Azur, with a nine to two boy girl ratio, for Christ's sake.

The Mute, was sitting up on one side of the boat, his legs dangling over the side. He looked sulky. With the Swedish twins already in the bag, The Girls had held hands with them, he was next on the list to be made friends with. Bare footed they approached. Nobody spoke. The Girls loved 'One flew over the Cuckoos Nest' the Jack Nicholson triumph, especially the scene in the film where the giant Indian mad mute had spoken. They had learnt to occasionally use the power of silence. On this occasion it worked. The Mute did speak first but his serious message not what they had expected. He firmly told them to sit down next to him, to listen for the word tacking from the captain and to make sure they were holding on tightly.

"He's very serious."

"I'm making friends with him. I expect your support."

"I'm not really concerned about your love making rocking this ocean."

Things started out fairly serenely on that Sunday night in May somewhere off the Southern French coast. With John at the helm everyone joked and chatted as they motored out to the start of the race. The crew's common denominator was a passion for World Cup racing and equal levels of aptitude that made the team a force to be reckoned with in the sailing world. They were so good, having two total imbeciles, when it came to sailing, aboard was not viewed as too much of a hindrance and the weight would be a bonus. One of the few times in life carrying one or two extra pounds as a girl is not a problem.

The Americans found The Girls hysterically funny and surprisingly attractive regardless of how credible their ties to the Royal Family were. Jonathon had used his dashing good looks and perfect smile to charm a rather tiddly Sarah Ferguson at a party apparently two nights prior and thought perhaps the connection with The Girls and Gerry Casenove her US publicist could somehow help him impress her. Yes rich but sadly stupid. Ah Sarah, the Libran that loved to love. Perhaps he'd at least get to kiss her feet. She was a duchess after all. For him the appeal was the title. What a coup taking Sarah home to meet Mummy would be. Well if he was telling the truth she was single for goodness sake and allowed to go out to lunch with a very handsome American. Even when you're a Duchess promoting Weight Watchers one still has to eat.

The banter on the boat was fast and furious between all those who spoke English. Andre didn't say much, Paulo spoke Portuguese here and there and The Mute not surprisingly was silent. The Girls kept their audience's attention with tales from Cowes Week. Even though neither of The Girls had ever been to the regatta, they were familiar with it as part of the Season and had enough information to confuse and amuse. Of course they knew about the Whitbread Cup, it was sponsored by a brewery and on a wild night out a few months back they had gleaned some now useful information from a pair of drunk but very sexy Kiwis. New Zealand had won the America's Cup twice. Sailing added to the New Zealander's world class accomplishments: sheep farming, rugby and cricket had the assembled group howling. The Girls appeared knowledgeable and relaxed. All was well. As they approached the buoy that marked the start of the race, the motor was turned off and the crew fell silent. The coastline was a thin line on the horizon, and The Girls realized they were stranded. The boat came into line and suddenly they were off. The activity was frenetic, shouting, hauling, pushing, pulling, jibbing, jabbing, bobbing, jobbing, The Girls hung on for dear life. Within 10 seconds two more pairs of designer sunglasses were history and within 15 seconds The Girls streaming eyes were so thick with black mascara they could barely see. "Stand by to tack," John shouted and then the most terrible of all terrible things happened.

"No I can't, you don't understand, No, I can't get across to the other side on my belly, No, Oh my god. Ahhhhhhhhh!"

The command was called, three, two, one, tacking and the boat started to tip. Pulling themselves commando style across the width of the vessel was a terrifying and strenuous exercise but had The Girls not made a move the choppy blue waters of the Mediterranean beckoned. The Girls were not known for their physical prowess and their strength training had been limited to a lifetime of opening wine so once again Swen came to the rescue with one. Swedish muscles come in handy. Paulo and Douglas yanked the other across, simply as they were the closest.

"My god, what was that. I can't do that again. No you don't understand. No."

Men who went sailing were looking less and less appealing by the nano second. The Girls were dripping wet, soaked to the skin. There was nothing they hated more than being wet. Even when they bathed or swam in the pool they never got their hair wet. It just did not look good, period. Then it happened again,

"Getting ready to tack" came the command and O my god, they were having to repeat the exercise. As the boom swang across The Girls had no choice but to move, and as quickly as possible.

By the end of the race they had no idea how many times they had gone from side to side but my God it had been a lot. Their knees were skinned, their arms, shoulders and upper bodies ached, in short they were miserable. Their boat had come in, in second place, much to the delight of the crew. They had beaten some world class competition, even with their unusual guests aboard. The Girls could not have cared less.

They went down below in search of a mirror and the repair kit in the Louis Vuitton bag as wine was poured on deck. The crew toasted to their success as they motored back in to shore. The Girls, a little shaky, accepted the glasses of wine gratefully. They needed it to steady their nerves.

After several large gulps, The Girls found a mirror and assessed the damage. On reflection it was a good thing the mirror was tiny, the shock of viewing a full length version of their battered and beaten selves, too much to bear. They needed major restoration work doing just like Villa Pera. It was obvious the portable repair kit was unable to cut the cake.

They decided to patch themselves up and skulk down below pretending not to feel very well, which wasn't that far from the truth. When the boat docked, it was decided, they could make a fast but polite getaway. They could not be seen in this condition, even by sailors. It was worse than being blotto.

The Girls left the boat so quickly that evening they forgot to retrieve yet another pair of shoes. The last Jonathon saw of them, two wet silhouettes as they sped away, bare foot up the jetty. Damn he had wanted them to join him for lunch with Sarah.

Once back at the hotel, The Girls soaked their aching bones in piping hot bubble baths, fragranced with expensive perfume, opposite one another in matching marble tubs. Even in the cheap rooms one still got two tubs. They puffed on individual joints. They were too far from one another to share one, each girl needing her own unless they were going to resort to the emergency illegal class "A" pharmaceuticals they carried. Pills were something they rarely did, after a bad experience some years ago at a Rugby sevens match, when they had both had a bad trip on a dodgy acid tab. They had made a pact to try and steer clear of anything that had resembled a tablet nevertheless keeping them handy in case of emergency. It was one principle to which they had little trouble sticking unless in extreme physical discomfort. Only if the joint didn't work, would they revisit the pain medicine option.

Comfortably buzzed, they chatted about their plans for the next couple of days. The deal had to take priority and so the unappealing task of doing some homework on the Henri Rousseau became a necessary evil, regardless of how bad they felt.

"We'll order some room service, have one very good bottle of wine, watch a movie and have an early night. We'll go to St Paul de Vence, art capital of the

Cote D'Azur, talk to some gallery owners and find out what we need to know about Henry. I've hired a car so no drinking until we get back."

"Who's driving?"

"Well it's not you is it? We can't afford a driver and a chauffeur in a Renault 5, I can't see it myself"

"We're looking at a few homes for sale after siesta, around 4pm, nothing too expensive, but nice, like Villa Pera."

"Are you mad?"

Estate agents always know who's in town, where the hot parties are and they generally love to show off, particularly if they think they are about to rake in a commission on that Mediterranean gem, villa of all villas, that just came on the market.

"We can barely afford this room and now we're looking at villas. I'm getting out, I'm all wrinkly and my head is spinning."

They watched Russell Crowe in Ridley Scott's Gladiator, on pay per view. Looking at lots of great bodies, researching and admiring yet another of Ridley's epics, they felt a little closer to him. All their attempts to get to him at Scott Free Productions had proved fruitless, but the amount of trying put them on a first name basis with Ridley. Watching one of his movies was the only way to execute one more of their ever so important principles, always mix business and pleasure.

The calls down to reception always started with a polite Parlez vous Anglais, Monsieur?, another handy phrase from the already battered phrase book. It was Cannes and everyone spoke close to perfect English, but The Girls hated to be confused with the uneducated bourgeoisie who only spoke one language. When in Rome and all that.

The chap on the other end of the phone jotted done their order. Coques San Jacques, scallops in white wine sauce with melted cheese on top, a house salad, the ever present beaucoup du pan and a moderately priced Chablis at the order taker's recommendation to compliment. Only in France can the chap who answers the room service phone successfully suggest the wine. He also suggested the cured beef, a French variation on Braciola and half a bottle of young claret from a local vineyard. This bloke knew his wine and was not afraid to promote the family business in anyway possible. Perhaps his current employment was entrepreneurial strategizing at its finest. The Girls made a mental note to tip him handsomely before they left. The food arrived within half an hour, unusually quick for a packed to the gills hotel in the craziest week of the year; however, The Girls were grateful as the pot high was mellowing and the munchies were setting in. The young waitress pushing in the trolley looked ridiculously formal in her immaculate, yet dated get up. All the platters were covered with highly polished, shining, silver domes. The wine with a white starched napkin around its neck, tied like an expensive silk cravat stood proudly in a crystal ice bucket, stacked to the brim with ice. The only other things on the trolley were the half bottle of local red already opened downstairs to give it maximum breathing time before it was poured and a single freshly cut pink rose in a fine porcelain bud vase that matched the china. This was the life. The check was signed. Fuck. Two hundred quid just for that. Oh well they were hungry.

"Mucho gracias."

"Sorry, ...Merci."

They settled back on the huge beds, propped up by pillows, so stuffed with goose down it was not surprising fois gras, the expensive delicacy in the States was so readily available here. They had to do something with all those livers.

The food was to die for and the red wine surprisingly delicious. It did indeed go very finely with the beef. As they polished off the last 2 ice cold glasses of Chablis, they were satiated and extremely tired. Snuggling down into the decadence of those exquisite sheets once again, slumber was not far away.

"Do you mind if I watch a little porno?"

"I need earplugs and eye mask. Good Night."

The Girls awoke feeling refreshed. The early night was just what the doctor ordered as the morning sun shone in through the crepe de chine, puddling, curtains creating the perfect grand entrance to a spacious balcony over looking the promenade and the packed marina. The sky was indeed azure blue, and the gentle breeze gave the illusion of cool, on a soon to be, scorcher of a day. The continental breakfast, pre ordered the night before for eight am, arrived semi promptly at eight fifteen giving The Girls time to clean their teeth, brush their hair and put on a much needed coat of lipstick. They were not twenty five anymore let's remember. The waitress this time was rotund, in her fifties, but once again starched and pressed in her, larger sized identical uniform. She was jolly and blabbering in French, bonjour, bonjour, mais oui, ca va, ca va. The Girls just nodded graciously, exchanging puzzled glances at one another. With a tilting motion of the head to the balcony, the waitress set up the table outside. As she chatted to herself, "Ah, la mer, c'est jolie, aujourd hui." The Girls pulled on t shirts and wrapped around sarongs. "Ah oui, est les bateaux." Les Bateaux was enough to bring The Girls back to the events of the previous day. Their new friend was dismissed with an overly generous tip. She was very sweet and appreciative and left the room without any further utterances. Their sea legs had been lost, possibly never to return, ever again. It was a shame, as they had, in the past, been on much larger yachts and had a perfectly pleasant time.

The Girls wanted to get off the subject of boats and have breakfast. They were starving. They sat down to enjoy an array of freshly baked pastries and breads topped with homemade preserves and piping hot, aromatic Columbian black coffee. Once again they were in heaven as they gazed out into the clear blue yonder and planned their day. It was work after all.

The clothes were important for an outing like this. Expensive enough to impress art gallery owners in the South of France, no small task in itself, yet comfortable enough to sustain an hour, possibly two in a frightfully small automobile and allow one to emerge, not looking like one had just been dragged through a hedge backwards. Definitely not linen, too stiff and creases far too easily. They settled for well-cut summer shift dresses, Armani. Sorry but no one cuts a shift dress better than the famous Italian. Flat slip on Gucci mules and lots of carats were chosen to compliment, for individual reasons. Walking more than a few steps always meant one would have to take one's shoes off at some point. If the shoe designer was to be promoted, better make sure it's a good one, especially in France. The jewelry they sported was enough of the real thing so as not to raise a question as to its or their authenticity. No one suspects when the cubic zirconias are carefully mixed with one or two pieces of the real thing. Sparkly gems were always a necessity when practicality meant the clothes were unable to stand alone. Making a fashion statement in a small piece of Lycra was the perfect example.

They would have liked to have had the option of different handbags that day, something a little larger than the pouchettes and more tote like but the limited packing space had forced an agreement between the two that only one handbag was required on this trip.

The keys to the tiny red Renault were waiting as promised with the now overly flirtatious concierge. Obviously all he'd been thinking about for the last 48 hours was ménage a trios, ménage a trios, ménage a trios. He must have been dreaming, kissing an overly sweaty, overly anxious, concierge with a nose bigger than Julius Caesar, no thanks. They smiled gingerly, so as not to encourage him anymore, took the keys and waved to him without looking back. It didn't deter him from bellowing "Bon Voyage" at the top of his lungs as they escaped through the grand revolving front door of the hotel.

The Girls bundled themselves into the car assigned to them parked outside. It was easy to spot theirs. It was the only one that wasn't black and wasn't a Mercedes. The small red Renault stood amongst an array of BMWs and other super expensive, European variety sports car, rarely seen outside the seaside resort towns that make up the exclusive Cote. Undeterred they got in and buckled up, with fewer complaints than one would usually expect from either of them. They had a job to do, research the painting and hell they were good in a crisis. The plan was straightforward. The car didn't do it for them. No one, of any influence must see them in it or close to it. There would be no flirting on the way, and they would park sufficiently far away from any gallery owners or their places of business so as not to be connected with a vehicle of such low stature. This caused a little dissention in the ranks as neither of them liked walking, it was right up there behind queuing, as an activity to avoid, but they knew this was the only way and so it was agreed.

The ride up to St Paul de Vence was quiet and uneventful. They had chosen several CD's for the road trip before they left, surprisingly organized for them but sadly the car had no CD player. Not excited by poor reception of the crackling French radio they decided to enjoy the exquisite panorama in silence, before they had to go in search of gallery owners and find out more about Henri Rousseau. The heather of the Cote D'Azur and bordering Provence filled the car with a natural aromatherapy one cannot purchase at the spa, The Girls had tried, and the vista of lavender, acres and acres of pale purple supplying the nearby perfumery capital, Grasse with its harvest, was breathtaking. The scent reminded them both of Amanda and more importantly her tarot card reading. Maybe she was right? There was definitely sometimes more to life than champagne and caviar. This was delightfully therapeutic, but life without champagne and caviar ever again? Now that would be tragic. They imagined other modes of transport as they sat back, in silence and soaked up that magical day. One sat against soft, café au lait calf skin, the upholstery in her dark blue Bentley, with a young stud, scantily clad making dirty martinis. Andrew up front, straight and tall always making sure she got where she needed to go. The other chose a convertible Lamborghini, Jackie Kennedyd out, her Hermes scarf tightly knotted under her chin and her Gucci sunglasses perched on her nose. Her good looking, silent companion managing hair pin turns at a hundred miles an hour on a never ending windy road while running one hand through her hair that fluttered at the nape of her neck. What bliss.

After just over an hour of fantasy cooped up in the car, they arrived in the small ancient town home to aspiring artists for centuries. Paul Cezanne was amongst many famous names in the world of art who had found refuge in this quiet spot not far from the coast. The reality was they had to find out about Henri Rousseau here. They at least hoped they could find a gallery owner who had some experience with his work and could give them some legitimate value of the piece in Aga's suite back in Cannes. The Girls had been together enough at the afternoon art shindig the day before to snap a couple of digital photographs of the painting. It was important they had something tangible to show, as their French could not be trusted for delicate business negotiations of this nature. The

Girls set off on the walk up to the fortress-like port-cullis that welcomed residents and visitors alike to the old Roman citadel.

The surrounding large stone wall once occupied by gallant protectors of the land from onslaught an age ago was a great vantage point from which to peruse the maze of cobbled streets that made up the city and the rolling green, fragrant countryside of the valley on the other side, 25 feet down. Eager and able bodied visitors could now embark on the 2 and 3 quarter mile walk, perched up high over looking the valley. Not a walk for the faint hearted or anyone suffering from vertigo.

A guided walk with a tourist's map was hardly The Girls' cup of tea, far too conspicuous and they had work to do. So instead they made their way up the winding cobbled main street, to the Place de Vence. Flanked by remarkably stylish, art galleries on either side, the town square would be a good place from which to start. Old men in berets, with three day old stubble and hunched over stances, were playing Boules before lunch, olives, tomatoes, bread and pastis, an aperitif, similar to Pernod in flavor but double the strength. Poor mans rocket fuel in the South of France. One would have to be a veteran drinker to take on any one of those old fellows in a one for one, so no fun to be had in that corner.

The café on the square was filling up nicely, for a Monday lunchtime, just before 11.30am. The clientele was a mixture of urban moderne, obviously the gallery set, tourists, well enough said about them and upper middle class locals who could afford to eat out on a Monday. The prix fixe or plat de jour was more expensive than the décor warranted, but the owner obviously didn't give a shit as his restaurant was 1 of only 2 in the center of town. The Girls needed somewhere to sit down, have a drink, a cigarette, and ask a few questions about who may be able to help them. It was a possibility.

The other establishment on the square was a small exclusive 5 star hotel, the Columbus D'Or. It looked more up their alley. They crossed over and headed towards the discreet gated garden entrance into a lovely shaded patio restaurant. As they poked their heads in they spied intimate tables, draped in fine white linens, with large upholstered white canvas arm chairs, a little worn on the arms, from years and years of interesting guests' lunchtime conversations, propped up on elbows. Placed with the symmetrical precision of a pyramid builder, the white blooms of huge spring peonies spilled from the Cape di Monte vases in the exact center of each table. The tables were filling up with the upper echelon of society. How had The Girls never heard of this place? The ladies were graceful, slender beings who floated on cushions of air as they glided to their tables, seemingly nervous to allow the soles of their expensive shoes touch the ground. The men were all shapes, sizes, ages and nationalities. The one thing they all had in common was money. This was surely the place to meet the person to save the day.

The creeping jasmine scaling the brick wall around the patio was abundant and the sweet scent, heady and strong. The Girls did not notice a small discreet sign, half covered by the tiny white, waxy blooms of the fragrant flower. Roughly translated; Lunch reservations for hotel residents only. It was one way to keep out the riff raff.

The Girls looked at one another then without a word pushed open the wrought iron gate entering into the courtyard restaurant of the rich and famous. Maybe this place wasn't so bad after all. Within steps of setting foot over the threshold, the pair were headed off by a curt Frenchman who, annoyingly, spoke fluent English. He made it clear, those so lowly as not to be staying at the hotel, he was unable to accommodate for lunch. Even as The Girls eyes widened to proffer their best damsels in distress, he remained unmoved and unwavering. Was he gay? He didn't seem camp but probably a woman hater. Should they book a room just to show him? It had been done before. Not today, they had too much to do to get into a pissing competition with a French waiter, so they accepted defeat gracefully and left clutching a leaflet and a tariff. They had been out snobbed. If only they spoke fluent French, he would have been annihilated.

"I've been thrown out of better."

"Of course you have. It's not London is it, Darling?"

The higgledy piggeldy narrow cobbled streets left the town square without any arrangement or design. They chose a particularly enticing opening and followed its meandering path down a steep incline. The bottom of the street was a smaller place with four of five extremely sophisticated art galleries. Each had its own uniqueness, one white and minimalist, another all windows and frames. The gallery they chose belonged to Monsieur Jacques Dunez. He was a young, rich, avant garde art lover, with a business degree. The Girls told him they were holidaying with a rich client in Cannes, they were looking to find an Henri Rousseau, original, and the client was prepared to pay up to three million francs. Could he help? Personally no, however he did have a friend, another gallery owner who may be able to help, Giles. Giles had a wealthy reclusive client who collected Rousseau's art and hence was a great source of information on the most recent documented sales of his work. Many art deals are between private individuals, and information rarely released, making Giles knowledge all the more important.

His gallery was not far from Dunez's however it was much less impressive. Art was scattered around, unframed and dusty. It reminded The Girls of The Beach Cottage. That was a worry. Giles looked like he hadn't slept for days. He was grubby and crumpled although his clothes hung well on his slender body. He was French after all. He talked confidently about Rousseau but gave little pertinent detail. He was overly anxious to make a deal there and then making The Girls uncomfortable. When The Girls were not immediately forthcoming his eyes narrowed. He wasn't sure of these two. After finding out where they were staying, their client in the penthouse, he softened. The taste of a healthy commission check certainly loosened his lips. The Rousseaux had been going for between a quarter of a million for the smaller later pieces and up to six hundred thousand for his larger earlier work. What music to their ears. If Aga's potential buyer was legitimate, then he really wanted it badly.

They called Christies in Paris from the cellular. Thank goodness one of them had remembered the phone. They requested a fax to be sent to the hotel detailing as many Henri Rousseau sales as the young art historian intern had on record, dates, catalogue description and of course price. To their surprise he had record of five sales in the last 2 years. Before they told Aga anything, they wanted to be pretty sure that the information gleaned in 10 minutes from Giles the Chatterbox was close to being accurate. After all they were being paid a commission and truthfully had no idea. Some level of professionalism and service was required. Happy they had all they needed from Giles and Jacques they bid the two men farewell, kissing them both on each cheek. The small cream business card displaying their room number and the hotel monogram helped The Girls credibility and they said they would be in touch.

"We came all this way and we just found out what we needed by making a phone call."

"Looks like that but you saw some sites and Jacques was quite sweet."

The inside of the car was too hot to bear as The Girls embarked on the journey back to base camp, Cannes. Their unnecessary and far too warm for that time of year, pashminas were used to absorb the heat of the black vinyl interior, avoiding stripping their already sun burned shoulders of any remaining skin. The shoes were cast off. Holly had her feet firmly on the peddles as they drove out of town. Shirley's were plonked on the dashboard as she examined a rather large blister.

"The things I have to do to make a living."

"I told you those shoes were too tight. I brought the hip flask. Have a sip and your feet will be fine. We'll get a pedicure; after lunch."

The drive back was South of France slow during high season. Cars were so backed up on the main road they decided to venture off the selected route and take the Peage, or toll road, back. The scenery was especially a sacrifice but the hum of the engine doing a steady seventy five kilometers per hour, as they floored that little car on a straight road home, gave both Girls time to reflect on the information they had gleaned and decide how to best make use of it. By the time they pulled into the hotel it was almost four o'clock. The estate agent was meeting them in the lobby. Oh well he'd just have to wait. They couldn't go out without changing into something more comfortable and hip. House hunting was hard enough.

A quick fag, a quick change and they were on again. Who said this wasn't Broadway. For once they were not dressed alike. One was pretending to be a secretary in a 1950s movie with a pencil thin pale grey skirt, white starched, Carolina Herrera shirt that crossed over the bossom showing cleavage and tied neatly at the side. High heeled, calf shaping, sling back winkle pickers, the finishing touch. For Shirley, palomino suede loose-fitting trousers, flat fronted with a side zip, very flattering and a silky sleeveless tank, the only other thing not French in the suitcase, was her ensemble. They were smart, cool, expensive and comfortable. Perfect. French clothes, French shoes, French lingerie, French suitcases were quite an accomplishment for four nights, five days and two people.

Jules Dubois, estate agent, found them immediately in the crowded afternoon lobby. It was easy to spot reality AB FAB anywhere. The reception was busy with people checking in. Expensive valises and soft leather hanging bags were everywhere. The Girls obviously looked the part. Good. They were going for wealthy definitely, stylish certainly, conspicuous never or so they thought, and had pulled it off once again. Jules was smiling as he approached them with his hand outstretched. The Girls were comfortable immediately. Years of selling expensive homes on the Cote D'Azur had brought Jules success and the confidence to go with it, allowing him to put virtually anyone at ease, swiftly. It was imperative he connect with his client immediately as the competition in his line of work was fierce and cut-throat. He was handsome, with hazel eyes and fine, handmade shoes. The Girls always noticed things like that. The sleeves of his pale blue cotton shirt were rolled up to his elbows and a copper bracelet replaced his wristwatch. His tan line gave him away. Did have rheumatism? Arthritis perhaps?

When the pleasantries were over Jules shared details of three houses to view. The long string of English and French adjectives described the homes with passion one could only exude for ones childhood abode. Surely he hadn't lived in all three places, although he did seem able to recount the smallest detail about each of them. A true professional perhaps? That was a pleasant change. The only thing he neglected to mention were, the asking prices. Perhaps it was a tactic. They would only know how much, once they were safely trapped in his car, child locks on, with no means of escape.

Jules led the way out of the hotel once again to his awaiting car outside, parked precariously in a no waiting zone. He opened the front passenger door to the large silver BMW, and Shirley stepped in. Holly was left sorting and piling the pages of loose leaf file paper, magazines and newspapers strewn across the back seat in order to clear a place to sit.

"I thought I was buying the house."

"He's quite sexy."

The Girls had told him they were looking to spend no more than four hundred thousand Euros, give or take, depending on the exchange rate. They could only look at things in the same price range as Villa Pera. Even though they had never actually seen it, it was the leading contender for their European pied de terre. The favorable exchange rate against the dollar would make the house seem cheaper. The Girls' own unique logic. It seemed all property in Europe was sold in Euros now. Sounded like a Greek sandwich to The Girls but it made it easier to compare house prices in France and Italy. As they pulled up outside the first property it was obvious Jules had taken no notice whatsoever of the price cap. The villa could not be seen from the private road beyond the surrounding wall in no need of any repair, the first warning sign. Jules made a quick telephone call and as if by magic the grand, iron gate, denying them entry, began to open.

"This is far too expensive. I said 3 million francs not dollars."

Jules, able to avoid answering questions he considered inconvenient, irritating or irrelevant, didn't tell them how much the house was. The price remained a mystery and they moved on to house number two.

They later discovered, prix was never discussed until one had decided one wanted the property. It would be crass for one to talk about money without a connection to the house, a desire to eat there, drink there, rest there, love there. It was frightfully simple and terribly romantic. Money was the finale not the prelude and so they continued on their search.

The next house was smaller and seemingly more affordable but the subject of money was not mentioned again. The Girls regarded the possibilities. It was set back a way but was clearly visible from the road. The couple who owned it was English and they, like the house were, very Homes and Gardens. They had done a lot of renovation which sadly detracted from its original appeal to The Girls. Much to Jules' unconcealed dismay, they were definitely looking for something a little more authentic, roughly translated, cheaper.

The drive to the third and final property was stoical. Jules, doing his best to remain polite yet personally questioning if The Girls were wasting his time. A good looking, successful, Frenchman driving a big BMW in the South of France would not take kindly to that, and so the flirting and the situation turnaround tactics began.

"Jules, tell us about the next one."

"We know you're saving the best till last, does it come with a pool boy?"

Jules was amused. His mood softened. The house was an old grey, moderate manor long in need of some TLC. The ivy, creeping around the windows of the 2 storey home, was tired as it hung, heavy and overgrown. Terracotta pots standing outside the front door were worn and empty. This house had been vacant for a while. Downstairs were two large rooms, stretching the breadth of the house. Windows on either side and a grand fireplace against the wall in the middle, made the room look larger than it actually was. A large family style kitchen and an adjacent overgrown herb rockery just outside made up the other half of the floor plan.

The upstairs consisted of, six maybe seven rather small bedrooms and two bathrooms. The bathrooms could prove interesting with a full house. The nicest bedrooms were at the back of the house, the best part, everyone thought. Each had identical wrought iron balconies off true French windows and a view of the terrace, a pool yes, a pool and the splendid vista of tiers and tiers of French life right down to the ocean. The only thing missing was art.

"It's perfect."

Shame they had no money. Minor detail and Jules didn't need to know that. They were just about to close the deal of the century. All was well. Amanda was right. They were moving to France.

Jules was delighted. The Girls were buying the house. Ah, he would get the very best price for them. This was the house for these unusual English women. Jules insisted they join him for dinner that evening to celebrate. He was just locking them in but The Girls didn't mind. They did love the house, and they still hadn't talked about cash since their budget was discussed the day before. They were covered, so off they went to dinner at the home of their new estate agent. They were mentally half way to their house on the Cote D'Azur, by the time they reached his. All they needed now was the money. They needed a buyer for Villa Pera the movie. A friend of Jules, and dinner guest that evening was a film director and art buyer. What luck, they could pitch him the screenplay and he was a possible celebrity. That was certainly a reason to celebrate.

As they walked into the main room of the house, they were greeted by Lilian, wife De Jules. She was sophisticated and thin, ageless. Her face showed signs of the kind of wisdom one has when one has known hard work, and The Girls liked and respected her for that. She wore no bra and got away with it, difficult to do at her age. Difficult at any age for most, come to think of it. She was dressed in white, floating, fine linen flares with turn ups, very Dolce and Gabbana, and a halter neck roughly knitted sweater that showed her belly. They respected her more for that. The Gucci's on her feet were last year's but they still had some wear left. Two hundred and ninety five dollars of strappy Gucci should last at least two seasons if you don't try and run a marathon in them.

Jules kissed his wife playfully as he threw some papers and his pouchette on one of the comfy leather couches that divided the majestic room into 3 distinct living spaces, breakfast table, living room and formal, formal French dining space. That night, the outdoor circular table was set for eight and covered with a mixture of Provencal pottery and a variety of wine glasses in varying sizes. The outdoor stoves had been lit much earlier and as the fires roared, the light from the flames danced with the many lighted candles and lanterns over the casually laid table.

Not wanting to arrive empty handed, The Girls had insisted Jules stop to buy wine and flowers for their hostess, on the way to the house. The shop was a roadside shack with a dirty limited stock of everything except cigarettes, of which it had every variety imaginable. It was hardly Fortnum and Mason. They had swiftly put one bottle back when they found out the price. Three hundred dollars? How could that be? With Jules' help they arrived with a couple of very good and very reasonable bottles. That was more like it. Lillian glanced approvingly at the vintage then showed The Girls into the library.

One of the other guests, the only one as yet to have arrived, stood looking at the books in the library with a view, off the main room. She was an erotic French author according to Jules, not surprisingly dressed in fishnets, a beret and pearls. Some things never change. A friend of Lilian's from the Sorbonne, with aspirations to write and direct high quality porn, Claude Ravel was in Cannes for the festival, to get someone to look at her work.

Claude, usually a boy's name, suited her. She was classically beautiful in a boyish way, artsy and open, an attractive and obvious ally. The Girls told her of their association with Harvey Weinstein, of course Claude was impressed. He was the biggest name in independent film after all. She asked them if they knew Andre Stanesky, the polish film director. Andre, of course they knew him. Yikes, never heard of him. He was invited to dinner, an old pal of Jules apparently. An obscure European director was perfect for Villa Pera. The Girls could not believe their luck.

Andre was more than a hero according to Lilian and Claude, an idol; he was strange, mysterious and told stories of the sometimes not so pleasant truth. Over the years he had spent so much time in France people thought he was a Frenchman. Somehow erotic French director sounded better perhaps. The Girls thought he sounded surprisingly like Roman. Was this just another example of branding at its best. They had wanted Roman Polanski, even before he was nominated for The Pianist, a front runner to scoop the big prize. Cannes was the prominent Oscar Race primary, so they were not optimistic about getting to him. The media was all over him. This director Andre Stanesky sounded similar, just a lot less famous and a lot more accessible.

There was Claude thinking she could tell a good erotic story. Andre would sit there, amongst them, a reenactment of Da Vinci's Last Supper, only more sex and less Hollywood. This was going to be fun.

The air outside was close and balmy and the moon was high. The Girls wished they were. As more people arrived, sadly not Andre, The Girls helped themselves to more wine and moved outside for a mingle and a cigarette. Guests were smoking inside, but they had been well trained by The Jailers and couldn't seem to get out of the habit. Mr. and Mrs. Gorgeous People were laughing as they approached. She was your typical South Of France, 22 year old with devastating good looks, a rich boyfriend and not much else. He, it turned out, was an Argentine polo player, a horseman with a quick wit and quicker temper. Did he have a job? Not sure.

The Girls, too busy chatting voraciously about Polo, found out little else about him. Smith's Lawn, The Moet Chandon annual polo match the English aristocracy attend religiously? Of course he was familiar with it.

"A great excuse for splurging on a new hat."

Always hopeful, forever positive, The Girls had never actually been.

His name was Marco. The Girls had neglected to catch hers and so as not to appear rude they paid attention until she was introduced again. Julia. Jules and Julia, easy to remember should one get a little tipsy. The chef bobbed his head in and out from the kitchen trying to get Lilian to give the nod to start serving. If dinner was not served soon they'd be there all night. It was almost ten pm. A private, French supper, at home with a distinguished film director, guest. There was more than bread and cheese coming, but still no sign of Andre.

As the rest of the party wandered outside to take their seats, half a dozen or so bottles of wine were opened. The already chilled white placed in matte metal buckets around the table and the red, left on the side to breath. The Girls strategically waited until everyone was seated, before taking their places at the round table, leaving an empty seat between them for Andre, if he ever showed up.

By the time the first course was served it was already ten thirty and The Girls thought of The Jailers, at home, fast asleep in bed. Even a bender for them, two drinks, ended before ten.

A large bowl, filled to the brim with piping hot Moules Marinere, mussels steamed in white wine and veal stock, a delicious local dish, appeared on the table. Everyone greedily helped themselves, filling up the individual handmade bowls, with the gleaming black shellfish. The warm crusty French bread was passed for dipping and the smaller white wine goblets filled with the icy vintage. As the flavorful fish was washed down, with the crisp, dry burgundy the conversation was sparked. Much to The Girls' relief, most of the group spoke excellent English and as Shirley flirted ruthlessly with Marco, Holly chatted to Claude about Paris, strangely enough her youngest daughter's name, The Sorbonne and writing dirty books, sorry erotic literature. Jules was available for a flirt and seemed extremely open to offers of sexual innuendo from any corner of the room. Lilian had her eye on him and the 2 new ladies at her table. Lilian's mother had always said, never marry a drunk, a sloth, a gambler or a philanderer. Lilian always said 3 out of four wasn't that bad. Discovering Lilian kissing Claude secretly in the kitchen it was easy to work out where weakness lay in the Dubois household. The kiss, not on the cheek, was kind of a giveaway.

As the mussels were polished off everyone at the table pulled out their personal brand of cigarettes for an intercourse fag. Jules gallantly lit all the ladies smokes' and then his own. Marco pulled out his shiny Dupont lighter and took care of his own soft brown cigarillo. He was from Argentina let's remember.

The conversation focused mainly on the film festival. For this group, who definitely saw themselves as international, jet set socialites, it was the main event. The Girls gained information about who was in town, who was staying where and who was sleeping with whom. It was fascinating. Weren't they supposed to be the celebrity stalkers? These part timers had more information than the CIA. There was also talk about a huge extravaganza the following evening, rumored to have cost one point five million francs. The firework display alone was over twenty five thousand and tickets to this hoopla were scarcer than a penis in a convent. It was established the only person at the table who had entry was Marco, two complimentary tickets to be precise. Marco obviously moved in the right circles. Was he taking Julia? With Julia's attention elsewhere Marco was left sad, lonely and in need of a date the following evening, The Girls interpretation. The level of flirting was stepped up a notch particularly in Marco's direction.

The main course was brought out and the door-bell rang. The chef had his hands full. Jules occupied Julia, whispering French sweet nothings and giggling quite openly considering he was within slapping distance of his wife. The Girls, not sure they would risk such open displays of affection to another, in the presence of The Jailers, kept their heads down. Lilian jumped up with the enthusiasm of a small child getting to stay up late. Was this a lovers tryst right there in her home with her husband at the same table? Yes they are extremely liberal in France. It was certain to The Girls, whomever was at the door, Lilian was very excited to see. So were they.

Only one of The Girls could see the door from where she sat, and the other guests were too polite to crane their necks. Had the much anticipated Andre Stanesky finally arrived?

What? It wasn't Andre Stanesky. It was Andre the smoking sailor. Shit what was he doing there? The Girls excused themselves from the table for a much needed private board meeting.

"We went sailing with a pretty major film director and had no fucking idea."

"He might be a nobody, I've never heard of him."

"Smile, she's bringing him over."

"Bonsoir, vous etes un peut enretard"

"You speak French."

"Un peut."

"Ow ah your, how do you say, sea leggggs?"

The Girls nervously greeted Andre, movie director and person with whom they went sailing the day before. The group was flabbergasted The Girls already knew Andre, and he did nothing to dispel the mystery of how they had met, much to their delight. He enjoyed the intrigue like any great story teller would. And so The Girls basked in the glory of really and truly being connected to a celebrity even though they hadn't realized it at the time. Typical.

Andre was overtly sexual with Lilian and Claude and Jules didn't seem to care. Surely she wasn't doing Andre as well as Claude. As it turned out she was. The Girls rolling their eyes in amusement looked at one another shaking their heads. This was a first.

Jules chatted to Andre just like old mates while Andre fondled Julia. Everyone was into it. Marco and Shirley were dancing on the terrace, smoking and drinking, how old fashioned. Could she broker him into dumping Julia and taking both of them to the party the following evening? That was the challenge. While she danced, her partner in crime talked about art mainly, trying desperately to get Andre's attention away from the two skinny French lesbians/bi-sexuals, Lilian and Claude, but of course failing miserably.

It was a tall order for any woman. He was a wild man.

She could not believe it when he kissed her full on the mouth on the way to the bathroom for a pee, no less. Gosh he was forward. Well she had to talk to him somehow. He beckoned for her to join him. Wow. He was choosing her over the Lesbians. The secretarial outfit had worked. If this was her only opportunity to get him on his own, then reluctantly she must seize it. The Girls rarely split up on reconnaissance missions. They preferred the protection of having their partner close by, but this was an exception. Worse case scenario if things got too heavy in the bathroom with Andre, she would have to resort to screaming.

"Je reveins."

"No thanks. I'm enjoying the wine."

The bathroom was large and rustically ornate, a large free-standing tub, in the center of the room faced a white mantled fireplace. Local bright colored, hand painted tile surrounded the two large square pedestal sinks. On a small table next to a comfortable blue toile bedroom chair was a bowl filled up with tiny pink pills. Andre popped two, maybe three in his mouth and swilled them down with the mouthful of wine left in his goblet. He offered the bowl to her, but she politely shook her head. He shrugged his shoulders then peed in the bidet. Uh. Disgusted but still smiling, she entered the small separate room off the main bathroom that housed the loo. Desperate to go she moved to lift the lid without closing the door properly. Oh my god. There on the loo seat were three large lines of cocaine and a thousand franc noted already rolled up. She was desperate to go but not about to fuck up the drugs. What was one supposed to do?

Snort then shit. No, she would just have to piss in the bidet in front of Andre. Worse things had happened at sea.

Andre was rolling in the aisle as she pulled down her too tight skirt over her even more expensive G string. Amused, he took her by the arm to show her the cocaine and the paper money were nothing more than art, a joke to confuse first time visitors to the house. They were enameled onto the toilet seat and weren't going anywhere. Most people she later came to find out hurriedly tried to snort the cocaine before going, making peeing in the bibet seem quite resourceful and responsible.

Returning to the table they shared their private joke. She asked him for tickets to the party. Sadly the only two he had left were for Lilian and Jules. The reason for the dinner party that evening a gracious thank you from his blonde beautiful lover. He did know someone who maybe could help, a thousand each. They exchanged telephone numbers. He made no promises but would see what he could do.

Dessert was served, a tower of profiteroles and cream, Croque Bouche. Everyone waited politely before diving in but Andre and Lilian were nowhere to be found. One could only guess what they were up to. Jules insisted everyone eat without removing his hand from the top of Julia's thigh. He talked to The Girls about the house they had seen only hours before, always working the close, unperturbed his wife and the director had gone missing. His manner friendly, nonchalant and relaxed, he seemed to think nothing of publicly stroking Julia's vagina while his wife fucked the film director in the next room. Validation of the French infidelity theory, sex for pleasure not just marriage was The Girls clear and undisputed conclusion. After a while the novelty of his open amour wore off and The Girls stopped staring.

The dessert was to die for, a mixture of delicate textures and flavors that left one wanting more. The Girls had puffed on a joint with Marco and Claude earlier and the combination would take more than will power to resist. As the evening grew chilly and the fire became little more than a few glowing embers, the party moved inside. An array of cheeses was served, two more bottles of red wine opened and Jules pulled out an unopened bottle of brandy and half a bottle of Pastis. It was daybreak. The Girls were heady, and their speech, starting to slur. It had been a long day, not to mention the half a case of wine they had polished off between them.

"We really must go. It's late. Marco, can you drive?"

Jules reluctantly called his usual driver ensuring The Girls got back safely to the hotel. Lilian, energized from the "Tete a tete" with Andre, and back with the group, begged The Girls to stay for the games about to commence. In all honesty they were not sure what kind of games she had in mind but felt somewhat out of their depth. Car keys were already in a bowl on top of the coffee table and Claude was topless. The Girls had had more than enough good clean fun for one night, a rare occurrence but easily recognizable. They were veterans but swinging was a different story.

After what seemed like an unusually long wait The Girls getting antsy were about to abort. Marco and Claude were already at it. Feeling sure making a run for it was iminent, the driver appeared thank God. He wanted to have a drink and join the party but The Girls were having none of that. They escaped in the nick of time grabbing Andre's crotch as a final goodbye and hoping he would call. He never did.

How they made it up to their room was a vague memory. They awoke partially clad on top of the covers. The door to the mini bar hung on its hinges and there were sweet wrappers and clothes strewn across the floor.

"What time is it?"

"No idea."

"I bet he calls today with tickets."

"Let's be realistic, shall we. He was fucking Lilian, babe. I hate to tell you this, but I don't think you were number one on his list of priorities."

Four cans of coke and three large bottles of Vitel later they checked their messages on the hotel voice mail. There were seven new ones. Three from Giles, telling The Girls he had several suitable Henri Rousseaus for their client to see. Shame their client was selling not buying. Oh well. Jules had left a very nice courtesy message. He had obviously ended up sleeping with Julia and was in a good mood. The Jailers had called twice more. Shit. They really did have to make a call home but it was impossible to do so without a little Dutch courage. No call from Aga or Andre. Fuck. The final message was from the Hotel asking them to stop at the manager's office. There seemed to be a problem with their credit card. Fuck.

They had to talk to Aga that morning and impart their information. Avoiding the hotel staff like the plague until they had a moment to talk to American Express, a priority. Their advice to Aga, ask the buyer for no less than six million francs, just over a million dollars with the favorable exchange rate. What would their commission be on that? They had no desire to rip him off. Five percent? Fifty thousand. That seemed fair. He would still get considerably more than his buyer had originally offered. This way everyone would be happy.

A call back to Giles would keep him at bay for twenty four hours. They didn't want him turning up at the hotel, hungry for the sale and screwing up their plans. They got his voicemail, a bonus. Hopefully by the time he called them back they would be on a plane back to Los Angeles, fifty thousand dollars richer. They justified the lie to Giles as being absolutely necessary. He'd get over it. All he'd told them was market price for a Rousseau, something that was clearly verified by a free fax from Christies waiting for them at reception, nothing that wasn't already public record. They didn't feel bad. They would do the deal, have a celebratory lunch and quite possibly talk Aga into getting them into the party, the all important Plan B.

After trying unsuccessfully to get round a surly telephone operator and get put through to Aga's suite, they decided to shower and dress. They had to go downstairs to deal with the offending member of the hotel staff face to face. They hoped it would not be the same person who left the message about the credit card problem. Worst case scenario if American Express was mentioned The Girls would express shock, horror and vow heads would roll. They were in no mood to be shut down by a receptionist. They had dined with Andre Stanesky, for god sake, Aga was a "nobody" by comparison.

One donned the white pinstripe trouser suit back from the hotel dry cleaners; the other, a navy blue knee length skirt, twin set and Gucci loafers, power dressing at its finest. With a purpose and a plan they set off downstairs, attitudes out on show, to face the enemy, God help him, and get back in touch with Mr. Khan.

"Just call the room and ask him if he would like to talk to us, it's very simple."

"No. No. It's a tip. We live in America one tips there you know, for everything."

"We are working to sell a terribly expensive painting of his. He is going to be very annoyed you weren't able to help us."

Girls defeated, resorted to penning a hand written note to Aga. Ensuring Mr. Khan be handed the note personally when he came to pick up his messages was the most the surly receptionist was prepared to do. The only upside was nobody mentioned the maxed out credit card. Thank goodness.

Dear Aga,
We have some information about your marvelous painting that would be to your advantage. We have reservations in the restaurant at one o'clock. We'll hope to see you there.
Peace,
The Girls.

"He will get this, this morning?"

"Can you call his room and tell him he has a message from us? Thank you. That would be helpful."

"If he doesn't pick up his messages this morning, in "Le Matin" he's going to miss lunch. N'est pas?"

Deciding a little people watching was in order they took a cab to the main shopping area armed with two neatly bound copies of Villa Pera. The prices were lower than Rodeo Drive, Beverly Hills and once again the good exchange rate stretched the dollar a little further. Just not far enough. Four hundred each on another t shirt until they were positive they had done the deal with Aga, was an unrealistic luxury, much to the shirty shop assistant's annoyance. God forbid one ask for help then not buy anything. Still concerned about the card and the impending hotel bill they could not justify paying retail for T-shirts, not these days, anyway.

Happy to browse through the racks and racks of overly expensive clothes in each of the fabulously French boutiques they entered it didn't matter they couldn't buy anything. The sale racks only sported a few things from the spring collections and The Girls looked through them swiftly, not showing too much interest in last years' designs. It just wasn't cool. After waltzing in and out of four or five shops and not buying anything, they needed a buzz. All the assistants spoke in the same clipped, disinterested English. obviously trained at the same designer shop assistant training school somewhere in France. One could never perfect that level of snobbery without a committed professor and loads of practice. Chanel surprisingly wasn't doing it for them that day. There was always the possibility of a last minute attack on the duty free shops at the airport the next day to take care of the much needed shopping fix.

The Girls abandoned the search for the perfect little something and decided to have a quick aperitif instead before heading back to the hotel to meet Aga. It would be a lot cheaper and perhaps provide a back drop to meet some influential film people. Who knew they may even bump into Harvey. They chose a smart roadside restaurant/café, perfect for a drink, a cigarette and some pretty spectacular people watching. The aproned garcon showed them to the table they suggested, directly opposite a fancy, three storey gentlemen's clothing store, and offered them menus. They had spied two extremely good looking guys going in and wanted to catch them coming out. Perhaps get them over for a drink? They did have half an hour or so to kill, and the other people in the café didn't look too promising, mostly middle aged woman surrounded by expensive carrier bags.

As they sipped their gin and tonics and puffed on YSL cigarettes, they pondered getting into the festivities that evening. The pre party, being held at a hotel down the road from the Carlton, would be easy to crash. Worst case scenario, they would loiter nearby until someone who needed a beautiful, OK female, escort turned up. It had never been a problem before. It was the main event that posed the problem.

Sucking on a few remaining pieces of ice clinking in the bottom of the tall slim glasses, they decided whether or not they had time for another. The cute boys came out of the store but paid absolutely no attention to the coy pair sitting in the café, grinning like Cheshire cats. The Girls looked spectacular. What was the problem? Had to be gay, lovers of course although men with pouchettes, not necessarily the indicator in France.

"Let's go, there's nothing going on here."

"I want to talk to Aga sober."

"Just pace yourself and you'll be fine."

Flagging down a taxi on a Tuesday afternoon in the center of Cannes proved more difficult than usual and they feared they would be late to meet Aga back at the hotel. As they climbed in the grey Mercedes, one gave the driver their destination as the other kicked off her shoes. Vite, vite to the cabbie was not the best idea as he took off, literally at hair raising, break neck speed, closely missing a man on a bicycle and two pedestrians. The Girls pinned against the leather upholstery in the back seat felt like they'd just stepped onto Superman, The Ride.

"We're not in that much of a hurry."

"Never say faster to a Frenchman behind the wheel of a car."

Back in the room they checked their messages again; nothing. That was a relief. No news was good news. They decided to postpone calling The Jailers. The time difference was favorable but the mood was not.

Hot and sticky from the morning shopping, they showered off and changed before calling down to Surly, the receptionist, to make sure Aga had received their note. His shift was over and his effervescent replacement was no help whatsoever. She was a big improvement on him, much more pleasant but had no idea as to what, they were referring. They thanked her and made their way to the restaurant outside, fingers crossed, hoping Aga would be there.

It was déjà vu as they exited the elevator and strolled over to the restaurant podium that marked the entrance. They had a reservation but elected to wait at the bar for Aga. It seemed a tad rude to sit down before he arrived. More realistically they were unsure as to whether he was even coming and couldn't afford to pay for lunch themselves, not in there anyway.

"Yes Cristal would be lovely,"

"I thought you said you weren't drinking?"

"Don't worry, he will be. Relax, take the edge off."

After a couple of top ups, Pierre poured the remaining two glasses from the perfectly clear bottle into The Girls empty champagne flutes. They had been there almost an hour and still no sign of Aga. He wasn't coming. Fuck. Like Aga could afford to be so fussy. He was hardly a looker. With no deal and a four hundred dollar bill for their expensive champagne buzz it was yet another cock up. Not knowing quite what their next move was they tried to make the final glasses of champagne last, while lunching on breadsticks and cheesy things, courtesy of the bartender. They tried to come up with the ever important, Plan B. The well mannered barman was sympathetic to ladies with an obvious plight. He gave them drinks on the house, without mentioning the embarrassing situation they found themselves in. He was a pro. It was much cheaper champagne, poured by the glass, but better than nothing. He went out of his way to introduce The Girls to two Italian filmmakers, could it be Pupi Avati, dressed in leather, sitting at a nearby table. The young men were the consolation prize or so it seemed but The Girls were grateful for the gracious introduction and the four started chatting. There was no way the unsuccessful Italians would pay for the champers, but they may be very interested in Villa Pera, their huge international project based in Tuscany. Still reeling from the humiliation of being stood up by their client they needed to save face with the young Italians. Thank goodness they had their very own Michelangelo and knew a little about Pupi and the Di Laurentiises.

It was not long before the name dropping had reached a new level of ridiculousness. Before they knew it they were recounting stories of their vague business associations with everyone they had encountered in Los Angeles. Tom Cruise,

Ozzy Osbourne, Tommy Lee, Ridley Scott. They brought them all out for a spin. It was not until The Girls heard the film makers mention a certain American movie mogul, arriving for the festival celebration of the century that evening, their ears pricked up. Harvey Weinstein was in town? Apparently! They were elated. On cloud nine. Just as swiftly as one door closed another one had opened. Julie Andrews in the Sound of Music was right. What a stroke of luck. There was not a moment to waste. This was the opportunity of all opportunities and had to be capitalized on. The Girls sucked down their free champagne, signed their own tab for once, and headed back to their room for a sleep. If they were going to track down Harvey they needed to be rested.

Cannes was not a large town but finding a total stranger in arguably the busiest film week of the year was not going to be easy. The odds of him being at the party, at some point during the evening, were high and so they had to get in. It was as simple as that. It was fabulous to know, they were in the same city, at the same festival at the same time as their mentor. No surprise really on reflection but nevertheless actions stations were called for. It was going to be a night.

As they stepped out of the lift and into the hotel corridor, there was cause for concern, a man knocking on their door. Who was it? They couldn't tell. They were far enough away not to be seen so without thinking twice darted into a linen cupboard avoiding detection.

"Who is that?"

"I can't see a thing without my glasses on."

"Sush."

The Girls stood motionless in the tiny space surrounded by soap and towels. They stifled their giggles so as not to be discovered. One held her crotch to avoid peeing her pants. She should have gone before leaving the restaurant. After a few minutes they emerged, to see Giles getting into the lift. What was he doing there? How pushy can one be? Well at least he hadn't seen them. That was a good thing. They would just have to be extra careful to make sure he didn't track them down.

Safely inside their room with the door locked and the do not disturb sign displayed they listened to a message from Aga. Surprisingly there was no message from Giles. He was obviously trying to catch them off guard, hungry for his commission, greedy bastard. He had two hopes against this pair, Bob Hope and no hope. They were experts. Did he not realize that?

Aga's message was lovely. He explained he had sadly, got their note too late to join them for lunch but casually stated he would see them at the party that evening. Little did he know, they weren't invited. There were no details of how they would meet. No where, no when, no what time and still no suite number to call him back. Finding two short, fat, guys at a chic French film party would be a challenge. These two would hardly stand out. Small, fat Jews would be everywhere. Aga and Harvey, would be about as conspicuous as bald, Buddhist monks at a Nepalese retreat if they could gain admittance to the party at all. The Girls had their work cut out once again.

After a moment's reflection, one pulled out a newspaper cutting from one of the LV suitcases. They didn't even know if it was good of a likeness of Harvey Weinstein and his brother Bob on the front page of the Los Angeles Times business section. Of course they had never met him. He was in the background of the photograph, and the picture was a little blurry. Was that the photograph or the champagne? It wasn't clear. They committed his face to memory as best they could before settling down to get a couple of hours sleep.

They awoke hungry, some time later. Although they loved to eat, curves a testament to the fact, it was often low on the list of their priorities. The lack of food at lunchtime had left them feeling sluggish from the champagne. Oh well, they would order room service. The pre party wasn't due to start for at least another couple hours. Everyone would be fashionably late which gave them an extra thirty minute cushion. They were in good shape. They had mentally picked out the ensembles for the evening before nodding off, so it was easy to pull them out of the suitcase, put the chosen creations on hangers and hang them in the bathroom to steam while they bathed. The room service was ordered.

They had to eat before going out or they'd be off their heads by nine o'clock and that would never do. As they relaxed in the tubs one smoking, the other thumbed through a copy of French Vogue.

"I have to close something."

"I'm not going home tomorrow without a damn good try."

"Short, fat and balding, describes virtually the whole film community worldwide even most of the woman."

"Is Roman Polanski Jewish, maybe Harvey knows him?"

"You don't get to play the kind of games he likes in Church. Why do you think the Catholics are in so much trouble?"

It was just before nine when they both stood side by side admiring each other in the long heavily gilded mirror in the middle of their suite. Shirley wore white Chanel. She'd bought the full length, delightfully sleek gown long before the last market crash. It was a classic. Her golden hair was coiffed and her bronzed skin shone under the sparkly lights of the chandelier. She looked and felt great. The jewelry chosen, her wedding ring, surprisingly, real diamond studs and a 5 carat Suzanne Somers creation, a ring that made a statement. It was all the Chanel needed. That dress could take care of itself. It was going to be a long night. She hoped it would take care of her too.

Holly, remaining in the spirit of the French designers selected, Galliano, House of Dior, the dream dress. First and foremost because it made her look slim. A mystifying trick few dresses ever achieve, particularly after bearing two kids. It was the main reason she loved it so much. It was short and simple, floating yet fitted in dark grey micro-fiber that clung in the most sexy, yet flattering way. In short, the miracle dress, no wonder it was so bloody expensive. She looked younger, not much but a little, her pale skin glowing from the days away in the Mediterranean sun. They were as ready as they would ever be.

Picking up the pouchettes, the only true handbag that does, indeed go with everything, they headed out for the evening. They were on the look out for the persistent Giles but expected he'd given up the ghost and trotted off home. There was no way he was going to be at the party, didn't look the part, far too grubby.

The Girls walked into the lobby. There was a throng of activity. Good, less likely to be spotted by the hotel management. They could not face dealing with that unpleasantness tonight. They needed to focus on the task in hand. They walked directly and purposefully to the grand door that took them out into the evening. Once through it they were safe. They didn't look back even when The Girls heard someone behind them shouting urgently and scurrying to catch up. He was just another of those annoying little dogs yapping at their Yves St. Laurent, nude, strappy evening shoes. Mesdames, Mesdames. Yes. It was one of the higher up hoteliers. They had no choice but to face the enemy. He wore a suit not a uniform but his manner was certainly military. Shit they were in trouble. They cringed as he approached. Would it be better if he explained the problem in English of French? They prayed for a quiet talker. Both scanned the room to quickly address the odds as to which language would prove to be the least embarrassing. Yes they think like that in a crisis. The ego needed to be put aside and quickly. Humility and embarrassment were the only way to go.

Surprisingly he said nothing. Oh how even more humiliating, reduced to lowly women, who couldn't pay their bill. They thought they were done for but instead he proffered a beautiful cream monogrammed envelope. The hotel stationary didn't look like that. They knew, they had already used up the whole sheaf in the room. Short succinct notes to all the people they needed to impress, were essential. Was this just another tactic the hotel used to humble and label their bad-debtors? Were they being paranoid? They gingerly took the small envelope and the gentleman, after nodding his head politely, bid them bonsoir.

"That was subtle. I don't get it."

"It's not the bill, thank god. That would have been terrible."

"Aga has given us a restaurant, an address, a time and a cross.

"It's a kiss."

"It's a miracle, that's what it is."

After the terribly close shave they were more in need of a little fresh air than ever. They decided to walk along the promenade that evening instead of taking a taxi to the pre party. It was of course, totally strategic. They were bound to talk to someone along the way and secure their entry to the exclusive gathering of celebrities that awaited them. The venue was less than a five minute stroll away and The Girls felt good for the small amount of aerobic exertion. It gave them time to collect their thoughts and lower their heart rates from the interlude at the hotel. Surprisingly they didn't meet anyone along the way. If this was the party of the year there weren't very many people about at all. Strange?

The hotel hosting the party was also on the seafront. Flags of all nationalities flew proudly from its entrance, as The Girls, were ushered in by uniformed valets, to make theirs. Walking in evening gowns, perhaps lead to the misconception, they obviously belonged. The Girls were delighted to go with the flow and made their way up to the roof of the hotel where a cocktail party with potential was already kindling. Most of the men wore black tie or a derivative of and the women seemed to be primarily in black or white. They were obviously in the "in crowd" without even being aware of it. Once again the winds were blowing in their favor. Maybe that was the reason for their unhindered entrance. Eyes peeled for Harvey and Aga, they kept on trucking.

After circulating for about half an hour The Girls established the crowd, a group of B movies actors, directors and general hangers on were useless to them. Everyone likes a good piss up but the heavy hitters were obviously elsewhere. Maybe all the key players were at Aga's restaurant in the note. When one has money, one doesn't have to rely on the free booze for an early buzz. The sponsor Smirnoff, this time the vodka giant was a welcome guest. It was a relief to know Challenge's cat was not the beneficiary of an aging widow's fortune. The movie star fame had already gone to his head.

Four buzzards disguised as American 30 something sex goddesses were salivating over the soon to become available table and hovering nearby. They needed a seat. Manole Blaniks and a long evening ahead was no laughing matter when one is the wrong side of thirty five.

The Girls decided to finish their drinks and head off to meet Aga, forfeiting their valuable table. The Girls had got lucky they didn't need it and were happy to pass on their good fortune to the high heeled Buzzards. For once they were wearing sexy, strappy but certainly low heeled sandals. The night was going to be long and arduous, and both had the good sense not to attack it in heels. The risk of falling at an inopportune moment was already bad enough.

The kind gesture sparked conversation and within moments The Girls were entrenched in the brunette's divorce from the man she knew she should never have married, Stick Insect's abundant sex life with an artist, Buxom's search for the perfect man and Rich Daddy's Deep Voice. Wow. Fascinating. They were 4 girls, or should I say woman from varying parts of the United States. Stick Insect and Buxom were both from the Deep South and apparently had terribly high standards about practically everything. The Girls could teach them a thing or two in that department. Brunette was a Jewess from New York and Deep Voice, an heiress from Los Angeles. One learns something new everyday, as The Girls were unaware of any heiresses in L.A. Must get her card, her father might be a potential client.

Their clothes were stylish, expensive but a little too much gold and sequins for The Girls taste. The costumes reminded them of Las Vegas, glitzy and revealing. In the buzzards defense however their bodies were fabulous. Not one of them was larger than a size eight. It was difficult to tell how much of the sculptured toned frames and fine bone structure were down to many hours spent in the gym with a personal trainer.

Were they healthy eaters or were their fine forms down to the deft and able scalpel of a highly skilled plastic surgeon? It was irrelevant to the onlooker. Visually this quartet was formidable. The conversation, however, carried a large warning sign, Danger.

"I was in San Francisco with Ted."

"I had the best sex in San Francisco."

"I need to have sex."

"I screwed a waiter? My Dad would kill me."

Fucking Hell. It was easier to keep track of the center court at Wimbledon on finals day full up to the brim with champagne and strawberries than talk to these four. The Girls were unable to ascertain how The Buzzards were connected. Did they all see the same therapist?

Fortunately The Girls got a breather when Buxom went to the bathroom and Deep Voice and Brunette decided to follow. Brave Stick Insect stayed put with The Girls. She got points for that. When alone The Girls found out there was much more to this one than just sex, even though the artist she boasted of, was in fact an artiste, if you know what I mean. She was by far the best looking and funniest of the four and The Girls decided she would be a magnificent entry in the Pussy Galore notebook. Her hunger for wealth and power she wore on her sleeve. With a body like hers she could afford to be so refreshingly open.

With a seventeen year age gap between her and her young stud of the moment, she boldly and blatantly acknowledged dinner and sex were all he was good for. The Girls liked her, a liberated, honest American. They had found one? Did she own up to masturbating? That would be a hat trick. The Girls talked to her of great possibilities with wealthy European clients for fun and expensive treats, an all round fab lifestyle. They decided she would be great for Villa Pera. She seemed sold. Man that was easy. Stick Insect knew of the party and was eager to secure an invite so The Girls took a risk and briefed her on their freshly formulated plan. They brokered Aga, as a potential boyfriend. That was decidedly straightforward too as she was familiar with the restaurant name on the expensive stationary. Then came the tricky part, getting three girls into the party of all parties was a difficult enough task in itself, six was virtually impossible even with an ego maniac for a client. At some point during the evening, ties would have to be severed with the trio in the bathroom. She got it. Stick Insect assured The Girls to leave it up to her. Play it cool. She would give them the nod. What did that mean? Unsure, they decided to look on the bright side, pleased, for once, they had met someone who got it and left the execution, of the separation, to their new friend. It was a relief to hand off some responsibility for a change.

The American trio walked back from the bathroom and jaws dropped. It was a fantastic sight. If only the onlookers knew what they were really like. A couple of brave champions were obviously rejected as the three Americans swanned through the crowd of collected aspiring beautiful people. A wave of the hand and a polite "no thank you" with a southern drawl was as far as it went. Gosh. They were really fussy. It explained a lot. Why The Jailers were like they were for a start. No one in the United States of America being actually able to communicate with anyone else would be a revelation for Larry King. Maybe it was a national crisis. He needed some decent content.

As they took their seats a plan was made. With four eager trophies at the table The Girls could not catch a cold let alone a man so they paid the bill. Oh well it was business. They were surprised the heiress had not offered to pay, she was obviously lying. They quickly got over it and with their new entourage, moved on to the next venue to meet their hero of the day Aga. The Girls were in good shape. They had found the ultimate deal sweetener for Aga in Stick Insect and Harvey or at least someone from Miramax was bound to be at the party somewhere. It was going to be a night to remember. Was the Pianist a Miramax movie? Maybe Roman would be with Harvey. That combination would definitely mean a premature ejaculation for someone. The six women made their way downstairs and out into the clear, beautiful night. After a squabble about who was going with whom, everyone piled into two taxis. Long gone were the days when The

Girls would pack ten people in a taxi primarily for the sport. Legs out of the window at 40 was just no longer sexy. The Girls tried to orchestrate Stick Insect going with them but one of the remaining trio fought tooth and nail to leave them with Deep Voice. She was obviously the dead weight, along to pay the bill and didn't come up with the goods. The Girls were stuck with her. They needed to think about Plan "B". They would capitalize on a potentially disastrous scenario and get to the bottom of whether she was talking about silly, fuck off money or vacations in Europe, the occasional cigar and a holiday home in Mexico money. As you now know there is a dramatic difference between the two.

Deep Voice was somewhat sulky. She was childlike in her demeanor but her face had been round the block a few times. Rich Daddy's money had not extended to the plastic surgeon. Her sleek physique was down to hard work in the gym, which she apparently resented. A hard body could never provide enough allure for The Girls to warrant what one had to go through to get one. They didn't really understand. She was weak, with no lust for life, pissed off about it and completely sure the right man could provide it. How wrong could one be? She talked of not feeling well in the taxi and said she wanted to go home. That was a score. Bloody hell, they got the taxi paid for and got rid of her, without doing a thing. Thank you God. One down, two to go then on to Celebrity Ville. Things were looking up.

The taxi pulled up at the most prolific, happening restaurant and nightclub in Cannes and possibly the Cote D'Azur. The Girls were nervous Deep Voice would change her mind and stay but to their relief she stuck to her early night plan. Why go half way round the world to have an early night? Another unanswered question.

Without another thought, The Girls stepped out and made their impact. They were glad to be alone for this entry. The doorway was not glamorous but it was heavily guarded and a trail of hopeful entrants, extended farther than the eye could see. The wanna bes, eagerly waited, to drink at the bar. The restaurant was far too expensive for most to dine. The Girls could smell it was a great place to be and immediately they dropped down a gear and pumped up the revs. Walking confidently up to the gate keeper, heads up and shoulders back, they smiled seductively.

"Monsieur, nous sommes avec Monsieur Khan, Monsieur Aga Khan?"

Tonight, Holly was ready to go on with a pre rehearsed monologue but it wasn't necessary. The bouncer stepped to one side just as a bullfighter avoids the on coming bull and The Girls were in. Any worries of having to dump the other chicks were already over. If they could get into this joint without an invite, there needed to be further investigation. The jury had stepped out all too rapidly so

The Girls had a wager. One had her money on Stick Insect making it in alone: the other, Buxom leading the charge and getting all three of them in. The loser of the bet would pair the duty free bill at the Chanel counter on the way home. It was a deal.

194

Once inside, they feasted on visuals one rarely gets to experience individually, never mind collectively. Intimate booths, dimly lit, were lined by reproductions of erotic renaissance paintings above plush dark blue velvet upholstery. The floral arrangements were individual productions, each a swirling mass of fruits and flowers precariously stacked in huge vases for maximum effect and definitely maximum expense. The eyes were overwhelmed but these giants offered no scent. This was France. Nothing interferes with the food. Preliminarily, it was the food that touched the other human senses but The Girls were relying on the clientele for the dessert. The place was packed to the gills with gorgeous folk. The crowd was definitely older and there were more groups of 4 or 6 than one would normally expect. Usually the chic parties were couples or groups of men. It was much harder to penetrate a mixed table of more than four people. A minor concern though when The Girls were on fire. There were one or two additional possibilities to play with, a couple of possible tab picker uppers, but The Girls didn't want to commit too early, even if it meant being left with the bill again. The Maitre D' complimented them on their gowns assuming they were going to the party after dinner. That was always a confidence booster. He was sweet. After a couple of key questions they established he knew Aga rather well. He was expected momentarily. He showed them to a table, beautifully laid for six. The only table in the most prominent spot in the room that lay empty I might add. There was enough silver cutlery and stemware for a middle class wedding banquet. Again the reserve sign was removed. They sat down and the few people watchers in the room returned to their delicious cuisine. Fuck. Aga had some pull. It was already close to eleven, The Girls were an hour late and no one in his party had arrived. This was the best table, at the best restaurant, on the best night during the Cannes Film Festival and everyone was over an hour late. Now that was taking the piss.

Unperturbed The Girls asked for the wine list. It was a safe bet Aga was paying but they decided upon the cheaper Tattinger, just in case. They were feeling terribly Gauche but it was a quarter of the price of Cristal and the English always drank Tattinger.

Shortly after the first bottle was poured, Aga arrived. The Girls underlying good manners and sense of etiquette took over as he approached. They had made sure to order a couple of extra glasses so as not to appear selfish or unprepared to be hospitable, however he was alone. They arose. He seemed enamored with the gesture and proceeded to kiss them each generously on both cheeks, before plonking down in one of the heavily worn dining chairs and slugging back a full glass of pop. Was he drunk? The evening could not be going any better. This was going to be a piece of cake. The guy was in a great mood. He had just come from Monaco, gambling in Monte Carlo and had won. He wore a beautiful Armani tuxedo that fitted him well and made him look younger. The future could not seem brighter and then all of a sudden it was. Cat, formally Stick Insect walked in. She had changed and got rid of Buxom and Brunette, all in forty five minutes. Fuck. How had she done that? She definitely needed to be in the Pussy Galore notebook. Cat was now dressed in a black shiny tube, posing as a dress. It showed every curve but she could get away with it. She said she was thirty-eight. How could that be possible? She slinked in, in the same high- heeled sandals carrying a black Gucci pouchette, similar theme, equally stylish. The Girls liked it. She joined the table with a flounce that indicated she had known somebody for years. No one was just quite sure whom. Cat certainly bought something to the party and before The Girls could say "Jack Robinson" the tables were turned. It was Aga getting the plug and them getting the kudos. A two day turn around with their new client was not bad work. Aga gallantly ordered more wine. He was trying to impress the sweet smelling Cat. She was playing him like her old mothers piano and he was lapping it up. This was working out perfectly.

Dinner came and went and it was time to talk business. The Girls were still relatively sober compared to their co huddling cohorts. This evening was definitely going on record. They were poised and ready for the kill. Aga, bless him, was in a hopeless mess, he was in love with Cat.

"Is she a hooker?"

"An American tourist with a great body and a free spirit."

"You don't think changing your clothes halfway through the evening to suit the occasion is a tad unusual. Dress in the pouchette? Let's be realistic."

The evening could not have been more perfect had it been produced as a West End play. The dinner divine and the Maitre D' attentive but not overly so. The buzz was absolutely on their table. The Girls talked intelligently about the Rousseau and Aga showed off. Cat contributed when it was appropriate but mainly listened. Well mannered and gracious, she really was a lady. They did exist in America. As the cheese arrived it was time. The Girls might not get another opportunity.

"It's all about what the buyer will pay."

"Test the water. The market can stand it."

"No less than six million, he'll pay it. Trust me."

No more was said on the subject. It had been a long day for Aga and a busy one at that, the casino, then Cat. It was not surprising the chap was whipped cream. The Girls made Aga some creamy cheese on a minute cracker and offered it to him in a protective and warm way. He took the energy booster and smiled broadly as he got up to leave. He placed the jacket of his suit about Cat's shoulders with a seducer's flair. Reaching into his trouser pocket he pulled out a crumpled envelope. Triumph. In the folded envelope were two complimentary tickets to the Marques party on the beach.

And with that, his parting gesture, Aga said goodnight. A paired of stunned Girls kissed Cat, one quickly penning their contact numbers on a random business card. She was a great girl. Was Aga their first client in the escort business? They owed Cat. They had her number so that was cool. They must call her in the morning and make sure all was well. They all said their goodbyes. Aga could not have been happier. They would all be friends for life? After all isn't that what it was all about.

"We need to regroup."

"Well, we just did the deal of all deals, I think we should celebrate. This one is on Aga."

Relaxing with cognac, coffee and a cigarette they contemplated their next move. They were in to the party, thanks to Aga and with official tickets there was no hurry to get there. The party was sure to be an all nighter. It was the first time that evening they allowed themselves a breather. They needed it. They scanned the room to see if they could find something worth playing with. Fuck was that Harvey? It was him. Wasn't it? Yes they were sure. Blow me down with a feather, Harvey Weinstein himself, the man, lord and master was sitting not five tables away finishing his dinner with a few friends.

"Pitch Harvey and probably the Miramax board without an appointment, sure great idea"

"He's probably not with work people. She's probably somebody's sister."

"Ask him to join us?"

"No we charge a drink to him."

So the tab for coffee and cognacs was sent to the Weinstein table courtesy of the obliging Maitre D'.

"Is he looking over?"

"No."

The Maitre D' informed The Girls the gentleman at the table had no problem accepting their bill. He had had no opportunity to mention Art Interiors, scribbled on a napkin and tucked in his pocket. The obliging gentleman didn't even inquire as to whose it was. He had simply paid cash then dismissed him. He obviously did this all the time. Generous. Harvey was generous? Had Harvey

Weinstein accepted their bill without even thinking about it? Was he a generous Jew? In truth they were not even sure if it was, in fact, him.

He didn't come over and they could hardly approach him after that. Mr Weinstein, if it was actually him walked by their table as he left with his party that evening without giving The Girls a second glance. He had paid their bill and he didn't even know it was them. Should they chase after him? They had done it successfully with Ridley but he was alone. It was a shame Barbara wasn't there. Fuck. Wouldn't that have been perfect?

It was time to justify their failure and to land the Big Kahuna was in fact, remarkably straight forward. Off they went again trying to see the positive in the face of adversity.

"Let's not worry about Harvey. The bloke's on holiday. Being pitched is probably the last thing he wants."

"He looked fatter in person and that never happens."

"I need to look at the picture again; with my glasses on."

"What about Aga?"

"Oh babe, that's a done deal."

After emptying another two brandy balloons, compliments of the house The Girls were relaxed. They had done a deal, had some interaction with Harvey and were going to the international party of the year. Not to mention the additions to the Pussy Galore notebook and the fruits that might bring later. Not bad for two girls from the North of England. They had been busy and now it was time to take their old expensive dresses out for a spin. They had a few hundred dollars in Amex travelers checks left over from a previous holiday, emergency fund and agreed to blow it on a car and driver for the rest of the evening. It was their last night. Once again the Maitre D' of the restaurant came in handy. They were to have a drink in the bar and the car would be brought round. This was more like it.

By the time they arrived at the main event the party was in full swing. Major celebrities were everywhere. It was magical. It was splendid. It was the best party they had ever had the good fortune to find themselves at and that was quite an investiture. The magical red carpeted entrance, opened into a huge white tent, pitched on the beach. Gossamer curtains fluttered against the sand and filtered the moonlight. The diaphanous shifts gave the impression of openness but the security was tighter than Fort Knox. A funky French band, with a gorgeous lead singer, serenaded the crowded space. Everyone was into the singer's groove. He had to be a somebody. The Girls didn't recognize him but that didn't mean anything. They were not really into the international music scene. Well it was all rap and scratching, hardly David Bowie. You will see their appreciation for rap and scratching develops significantly but during this trip they were without question still Rap Virgins.

In one corner, several tables were roped off with exquisite sashes of silky purple cord, how perfectly ecclesiastical. The VIP quadrangle was subtly guarded but obviously impenetrable. The Girls got a good clear face to face look at Tom Cruise. There was no eye contact but this was definitely the place to be. As they milled about it was not long before they each had a score card going. How many of the elusive celebrities had each of them spotted? Nicole Kidman was there, so was Kim Basinger. Arnold Schwarzenegger was seemingly very friendly with someone who was definitely not a Kennedy. Neither spied Ridley Scott or Andre for that matter. Maybe all the directors had already retired. It was after one.

The Girls were high on life and needed to make a plan. A quick trip to the powder room, a board meeting and a much needed coat of lipstick was required. Neither had touched up their make up all night. Yikes. They were sure they were in need of repair work. They'd been out since nine. The bathroom lady was spraying Chanel number five with reckless abandon. They emerged pooffed and refreshed. It had been a long time since either had worn Coco's signature fragrance but it suited them both, heady and sexy, just like them tonight at least. It also masked the stale smell of too many cigarettes that had already been smoked, one of The Jailers many pet peeves.

There were celebrities at every turn and on every corner, brushing elbows as one ordered a drink. They were in Celebrity Stalkers paradise. This evening was to be the pieces de resistance, the Jeux sans Frontier, the evening that would go down is history.

"Where shall we start?"

The Girls agreed before doing anything they should get a drink. The champagne was complimentary. All the tables were occupied so they made their way to the crowded bar. Attempting to push their way to the front with a few polite "excuse mes", they found themselves face to face with Rich and Randy from Montana. What was this payback to the Yanks for Cat? Hardly fair. Each was holding a beer in one hand a glass of champagne in the other. Shit they had made eye contact. Oh no the champagne was coming in their direction. They had to take it. Fuck. They were trapped.

Rich and Randy were not rich but very randy. Within moments of meeting they had The Girls committed to dancing and all kinds of things. For cowboys they talked a good story. The Girls could not take their eyes off the boots. They were so shiny. Oh dear this was a scene and they did not want to been seen with Howdy Lil lady and his best friend from the Ho Down. They left America to escape people like this for Christ's sake. And how did they get in to the party anyway. It was another unexplainable phenomenon. The Girls downed their drinks and as Rich the consummate gentleman cowboy made his way to replenish them, the two Girls silently concurred, they had to get away.

"Oh I see Tom Cruise over there."

Well it was true and desperate measures were called for. The Girls were released from the clutches of Rich and Randy on the firm promise they would be back to two-step before the end of the night, fat chance.

Back in the throng they looked around as to who might be next. They had to talk to someone. Now they wished Aga had been with them. Damn. He was bound to have known people and the introductions would have been invaluable. Oh well. One couldn't blame him, I suppose. The toss up? It was not surprising the balance had tipped as it had. Getting laid by Cat or going to yet another pretentious celebrity party. Aga could not use his wealth to pull at the party. He wasn't good looking enough. Sometimes money just wasn't enough, he was the perfect example.

After using all kinds of dirty tactics to gain access to the hot celebs like Tom, The Girls had to accept they were not getting into the celebrity enclosure. They made there way over to two handsome chaps standing alone nearby. Sparking up a conversation with somebody soon was a necessity. They were starting to look conspicuous. They made an unfortunate choice. Fuck.

The handsome chaps couldn't speak English. The Girls struggled with the little French they had at their fingertips but these dudes didn't speak French either. What now. They had no choice. They had to dance and oh no it was a slow song. This was turning out to be a nightmare. As the Faces led their selected Girl onto the dance floor, arms slid tightly round each waist and both Girls were pulled tightly to their respective partners. The Faces were strong and even though The Girls upper bodies remained somewhat mobile, their hips were held firmly in place against two tight black panted erections. Oh God, what was happening? This just wasn't fair. The Faces smelled of garlic and as they danced The Girls urgently signaled to each other, their immediate plan to escape once again. When the dance was over, they made their getaway to the bathroom. Not very original but with the limited language resource The Girls were in a bind. Reluctant to throw themselves headlong into anything else, they stepped outside for a cigarette and a breath of fresh air.

The party crowd was thinning out and it was growing increasing more difficult to avoid people. It was stressful. They needed to connect with someone useful. Where was Harvey? The one person they needed to bump into was Harvey. This was the closest they had ever been to him. They could thank him for the cognacs and the coffee, they could be frightfully gracious. He would adore them but no sign of the fucker. Wasn't he supposed to be the guest of honor at this stupid party filled with famous people that the likes of The Girls were still denied access to. It was just not easy.

"Let's go back in and give it one last shot. I'm not ready to call it a night."

"What time is it?"

"Quarter to five."

"Most of the big knobs have already gone home."

"OK finish your drink and let's have one last look around."

They emerged back through the floating sheer drapes, to be stopped by security.

They were in no mood to deal with a brainless ape in a black suit and pushed passed him straight into Jules and Julia. No. This wasn't happening. Where the hell was Lilian?

"Do get a life mate."

"Hi! We are not leaving until tomorrow afternoon, let's talk in the morning."

"OK, now if that works better."

"We need to get out of here."

Quickly scanning the area, with military precision, for an exit strategy, Rich and Randy were close to the only official exit from the tent, so that was not an option. It was simple to get onto the beach through the many airy openings to tables outside but that didn't help them as the high perimeter fence, keeping any undesirables out was now stopping anyone leaving by an unorthodox route. There was no way they were scaling an eight foot fence in three thousand dollar dresses. They saw the Faces had spied them and were coming over. They had to act and quickly. Jules and Julia were also closing in. They had to go, but how? Where?

Through the kitchen, it was the only clear path to the outside world and the getaway car waiting patiently to scoop them away to safety. Without saying a word to one another they were off again except this time it was more exciting than the Olympic final of the one hundred meters. They pushed passed bemused servers who were now in the throws of trying to clear up without appearing to do so. Must not make the guests feel it was time to go home and they were being forced to leave. That would be extremely rude and unhost like.

The Girls made it into the makeshift kitchen, their shoes already off, they could feel sand between their toes. They clutched them with the same determination a relay runner holds his baton. Losing the shoes meant certain disqualification. As they flew past a line of surprised men and woman in chef hats and blue stripy trousers, The Girls offered their profound apologies. They didn't stick around to hear their response. It was irrelevant. They had to get out of there. To the shock and disbelief of the catering staff The Girls couldn't resist grabbing some leftover Hors D'oeurves before waving goodbye disappearing out into the night. Well they were just sitting there all lonely on that silver platter and in all fairness they were starving. They piled out of the tent through a grungy passage way of trash cans, empty bottles and card board boxes and emerged on the street around the corner from the looming and impressive grand entrance. Now where was their car? It found them thank goodness. They piled in one after the other and for the first time, in several hours The Girls were able to relax.

The next morning the suite at the Carlton International was still and seemingly void of any life form. There were two empty wine bottles on the side. One was half full of cigarette butts. Nice. Clothes, shoes and lingerie were strewn everywhere and the bathroom was a war zone. The white linens on the bed showed signs of wear and tear. The black smudges of mascara on the pillows were a dead giveaway. Holly was unconscious on the pullout when the other awoke to the sound of knocking at the door and emerged from under a sheet.

"I hear you. I'm coming."

"Get up, we have to be out of here in 15 minutes."

"Get up now, get in the shower you'll feel better."

"I remember guys in our car. What was I thinking?"

"There were guys?"

"I feel rough, I need aspirins?"

The details of what had exactly happened that night are still a mystery. It was one of those evenings one just chooses to forget because however open one thinks one is there will always be things one just doesn't understand. It's life.

It was back to Los Angeles that afternoon. They had to pack up their life from that room. It had been their home for almost a week and it was easy to become attached. All in all it had been a good trip.

Moving slowly it took them both forever to get cases packed and dress for the journey home. Both wore flared hipster jeans, with low heeled pointed boots, one pair were scarlet suede, the other black snake skin but identical in every other respect. White t shirts and soft leather jackets completed the perfect combination of style and comfort, the ideal traveling clothes for a long journey with the most magnificent hangover. They also needed to play down the designer angle and play up the struggling artist. They were still nervous about the bill, but had just decided to come clean, get terribly told off and then work out some way to pay it off. What other choice did they have? They could try and escape, never to be seen or heard from again. But that would mean they could never come back. That would be a shame as the service had been frightfully good. Thank the Lord they were flying first class. With those monumental hangovers it was questionable either would have boarded the plane, had they been forced to travel Economy.

They were hoping for a little sympathy as they prepared to take it on the wrist from the hotel management for being unable to immediately take care of their bill. There were a few bottles of Cristal on it. Shit. Was that really taking the piss? No! They decided it showed the management that this had been a terrible mistake. How could anyone with their good manners, order the most expensive Champagne on the list without any intention of paying. They were sure it would not be a problem. It was not as if the hotel would not get their money. In fact The Girls justified to themselves, it probably happened all the time, Jailers stopping credit cards when wives escape to South of France for a break. It was definitely more common than one would imagine. They would, most likely, have a form for it. Yes. It would be fine.

A young sexy valet came to get their suitcases and for a moment The Girls were sad to be leaving. It had been worth it. They now had a massive client who would be feeling very happy that morning, after his encounter with Cat. Not to mention they had done the deal of the century and all in four days. It was not surprising they were knackered. The valet handed them a blue ticket for the luggage and a twenty dollar bill was exchanged in thanks. He was glowing. Ah it was nice to see such joy in one with such an awful job to do. Lugging suitcases up and down stairs all day, and smiling while you do it? He got rewarded by The Girls big time for that. The Girls were pleased they had kept money back for tipping, they weren't always that organized. They had been given 5-star service and tons of freebies, jams, expensive soaps and bath oils, delicious chocolates. It was true to say they had been very well looked after and it made them feel good to leave generous amounts in American currency for all their attendants that week. The Girls appreciated nothing more than good service. They signed all their hand jotted thank you notes, The Girls, and left the room without checking under the bed where an abandoned pair of loafers, a pair of tweezers and a Rigby and Peller bra sadly lay.

On the way down in the lift, they started to feel unwell. It was after two and all they'd eaten so far that day were two aspirins each and three cups of Listerine. Stepping up to the reception desk counter, they were greeted by Surly, being smiley. Was this just to confuse them? Butterflies fluttered. Fear of the impending fraud investigation over the hotel bill reached an all time high but somehow they managed to hold it together. As The Girls waited for him to address them, he fiddled on the computer. He handed them a long itemized bill and indicated where he needed a signature. What was going on? They were apparently paying the tab some how.

As it happened, American Express had not actually covered the hotel bill. Smiley informed them their bill had been paid for by Mr. Khan. He had taken care of it the night before. Their client had paid their bill. It was over five thousand dollars. Wow. The result of all possible results and another miracle.

This, their first true back hander in over two years, they were delighted to accept it graciously. Now this was a man with style. Once The Girls, much to their relief, had signed off on the rather scary, perfectly itemized bill, Smiley had another lovely surprise for them. Mr. Khan had also taken the liberty of arranging their transportation to the airport. Their luggage was already on board and the captain was waiting for them. On board? Captain?

The Girls followed Smiley to the private elevator and were passed on to Lifeless the Liftman. Like prisoners to the next guard, the man who operated the elevator, was there to make sure The Girls were seen, safely off the premises. Lifeless pressed the button with purpose and up they went, straight to the top. This time when the doors opened they were on the roof of the building. It was unbelievable. A Helipad on top of the hotel with a helicopter, yes a helicopter, just like the one the President of the United States rides in waiting for them to get in to it. My God, they had seen this done in the movies (where the girl runs out to the helicopter jumps in and flies away) but real life? Not 2 hours before they had imagined themselves, worst case scenario, washing up in the hotel kitchen. Oh how things can change.

"I've got it. I can do that."

"It just lifted up a little bit, is that normal?"

"They have our suitcases loaded. OK Here we go. Au Revoir."

And with that they were gone. Getting into a helicopter was surprisingly easy, although a word of warning. It does mess up ones' hair a little.

THE REVELATION

'Great spirit s have always encountered violent opposition from mediocre minds.'
ALBERT EINSTEIN

THE MONUMENTAL, FUN FILLED TRIP TO THE SOUTH OF FRANCE ALREADY SEEMED like a distant memory, as the Jailer reality hit home hard. Even though Aga had paid the hotel bill, putting the expensive trip on the over worked American Express card had not been a good plan. Things looked pretty grim for the future of Art Interiors. After escaping for a while and having a good old dose of European life, they were now well and truly locked back in jail, with no hope of escape. It was impossible for them to fathom. The Jailers did not remotely share their dream for life, their passion for saving the art or for Ilia and his family for that matter. The concept of doing something worthwhile and fulfilling being the key to life, (not going to the same boring job everyday, for a pittance of a salary, worrying about paying the rent and waiting to die) seemed lost on them. Was that really living? Surely not? Their secret to life was working hard at what you loved and The Girls were hanging onto it for all they were worth.

It was Sunday morning and The Girls really wanted to stretch the French experience to the limit, before going back to work on Monday. The plan was to prepare a traditional French breakfast out in the garden and send The Jailers for chilled champagne and fags, optimistic but, as usual unrealistic, where the cigarettes were concerned. Fortunately they had a few left over from the trip.

"We can relax, make some plans, then back to work first thing.'

Creating a little of the South of France in ones American back yard required just the right touch, and it was still fresh in their minds. It was a way to gain a twenty four hour reprieve, Esperanza had the kids, before some monumental decisions had to be made. A white vintage table cloth was placed on the wooden table outside. It looked splendid and provided a fabulous blank canvas for their brightly colored Tuscan pottery. The food was simple. The delicious smell of homemade walnut bread and Brazilian coffee filled the air. It made one want to smoke a French cigarette, much to The Jailers chagrin. For one fleeting second, it was like being back in France. The Jailers complained for America about the smoking and The Girls, not impressed by the one bottle of cheap sparkling wine, envisioned the commencement of the Battle of Waterloo. Closing the deal with Aga would certainly get The Jailers off the warpath. Would he pay them a commission from the sale of the painting? They didn't actually have anything in writing.

Going back to work at The Beach Cottage now had new meaning. They would close Aga and not have to worry about penny pinching, something unthinkable to both. As soon as The Jailers had eaten, they disappeared to be "constructive" leaving The Girls free to chat. Planting a few colored pots in their own attempt to be "constructive" they stumbled across a couple of roaches which were swiftly re rolled with a little French tobacco. Another miracle, they thought, as the tiny but welcome buzz steered the conversation.

With The Jailers out of the way the rest of the day was spent in total euphoria enjoying the positive and creative dialogue. Maybe now they could really concentrate on selling their art. Ralph's checkout counter had to be avoided at all costs.

Chasing Harvey around Cannes had been fun but it was time to buckle down and get busy. Monday morning at The Beach Cottage came all too quickly and did not start well. They had one message in the twilight zone. Barbara, from Miramax had called to tell them off, yet again. The voice was calm however the fury behind the words, unmistakable. Neither spoke. When it was over Shirley hit delete and Holly put the kettle on.

Whatever it was about stalking Harvey Weinstein, they could not escape it. His energy followed them everywhere and before they had left for Cannes, proved no exception. The article and photograph that had accompanied them on the trip had been spied in the local paper, actually by one of The Jailers. According to the writer of the article, Harvey Weinstein was creating a new life style network cable channel. The headline read as follows,

"Miramax chief puts energies into network cable deal."

As always anything about Harvey shifted the gears of their brains down to third, giving them additional necessary revs. Getting his attention had always been a priority. Now they had a real reason to talk to him. Undaunted by his major flop with Talk magazine, it seemed Harvey was looking for a new challenge, just like The Girls. He was looking to raise two hundred million dollars in finance. Harvey had a dream too and The Girls hated defeat.

Immediately their brains started silently processing. They had met the Englishman, Robert Stone wearing cufflinks and Churches shoes, very unusual. Even more so was the fact he had just done a deal with Ted Turner or was it Rupert Murdoch. It didn't matter. Venture capital for cable deals was his business. Did they still have his card? Yes. And that was that. Anything was possible in their world let's not forget. They now truly believed this would get them everything they desired and Harvey would finally acknowledge them. As they had dialed his number the ever present Ben answered the call.

"He wants to produce independent edgy films, great news stories and stylish travel."

"We'll raise the cash."

"Yeah yeah yeah, we know the drill."

It was always about giving the client what he wanted or so they thought. If Harvey wasn't prepared to recognize their creative genius maybe money would talk. They faxed the banker their ridiculous idea, which after a prompt email back turned out to be not so ridiculous after all, then set out to impress Harvey with another well written fax.

"What do we do if he calls back and says OK?"

"We tell him off for not saying thank you for the Orchid. That was just rude."

The Beach Cottage had been filled with all kinds of business possibilities and excitement that afternoon. Their company could be so versatile, selling art would be the end result but life without planning was going nowhere, they were leaving for France and The Girls needed income. Plan B was to potentially get jobs with Miramax at the very least. At least if nothing happened in Cannes they would have something to come back to, or so they thought. Bursting with newfound energy and confidence they had followed up their fax with a message about possible finance for the new Miramax cable channel. They produced new resumes to impress the pants off Harvey and hire them if all else failed. It was the only way to go.

GOAL: To work for the best in television, movie or media in a development role.

OFFERING: Outstanding, driven, articulate sales people with a true understanding of what it takes to be the very best.

The new resumes had sounded spectacular as they winged their way over to Harvey in New York. Working for Miramax would really be a great achievement. It would certainly go down much better with The Jailers than chasing a dying dream of saving fresco and maybe this way they would get to meet Dino De Laurentiis regarding Villa Pera.

The phone at The Beach Cottage had only rung twice before The Girls left Los Angeles. Within hours of the message regarding money for Harvey's cable deal. Charles Layton, Chief Executive Officer of Miramax and Harvey's number two was on the phone. What did he want?

He wanted their guts for garters. He was astounded and completely bewildered by The Girls' offer of financial assistance. He reminded them curtly who exactly they were dealing with, told them Harvey had countless revenue sources available and intimated The Girls were a little out of their depth. So Harvey could borrow from God if he needed to. Big deal. Charles had shown a glimmer of playfulness and The Girls, now coming from behind had needed to capitalize on the moment. Momentarily he softened and inquired as to whether or not they were sisters. Did he want a threesome?

Despite all their efforts Charles informed them getting to Harvey would be impossible, he thanked them for their interest in the company and hung up. The second call that day was from Dino De Laurentiis' wife and manager, Martha, saying he was too busy to participate in the fresco dream. The Girls had anticipated it would be Barbara so the De Laurentiis call was a blessing, even if it was to say no. It was true to say the call from Charles was the most monumental in Art Interiors long and laborious history but once again The Girls had put a cat amongst the pigeons with Miramax. On reflection it was a good job they were off to France. One thing they did know by now, without a shadow of a doubt, Barbara would be calling for sure.

First day back and The Girls had Barbara's extremely cross message to deal with. Their whole future hung in the balance. They had to be clever and keep her happy. It had been days and potentially a week since she had called them. That was in their favor. She could have got laid since. Barbara was the one light at the end of what would be a miserably dark tunnel if something didn't happen soon.

They called Barbara and said sorry, like naughty school girls, about the message to Harvey and the subsequent conversation with Charles. She told them she would now be their only point of contact at Miramax and under no circumstances were they to try and contact Harvey directly again. If they really wanted to impress him, they needed to come up with something "unique and salable". Celebrity Art Interiors had been really salable. Why else would Barbara have gone to the meeting with Style. It didn't make sense for a top Miramax executive to act as a 'Good will Ambassador' on a project she didn't believe was 'unique and saleable'.

No more stalking for a while, it was time to concentrate on getting their business back on track. Going down the Celebrity stalking route and dealing with useless losers like Tommy Lee, was now not an option. They couldn't afford the necessary three bottle antics, until Aga sent them a check. They called the Carlton International to try and reach him but as always, he was out. He was probably shagging Cat to death, having too much of a good time to even think about them. They left him a bubbly message asking him to call them back.

They needed to talk to Ilia to bring him up to speed on what or more correctly wasn't happening with Villa Pera, the art restoration and Tommy Lee. He had agreed to give a valuable piece of the collection in return for profile let's not forget. Maybe he had some good news. So far The Girls had accomplished nothing with Tommy to help Ilia. Raising money to buy the house or even getting anyone interested in the project had been impossible. Trying to find a Patron for the Fresco school was like trying to find a tall Japanese person, but Ilia insisted the Hollywood celebrity path was beginning to work.

Was he dreaming? Dino De Laurentiis, an Italian creative genius and art lover had just said no. They didn't know if he was mad or just really stupid. They hadn't even been able to give the art away. The only person who had accepted a painting was Tommy Lee and he had done absolutely nothing in return, they didn't even know if he still had it or what had become of that small piece of Ilia's soul. The final straw came when Tommy had let them down on Celebrity Art Interiors, causing all sorts of mayhem with the assembled professional film crew, who believed all the pieces of the project were solid. They were being paid when it went to Style. All that chaos aside, they had had no film to take to Barbara for the pitch meeting and Ilia was left staying up for forty eight hours drinking wine, smoking Russian cigarettes and painting their story board for the show. Had he forgotten that?

Even President Bush had said he would accept a painting but could do nothing to offer any exposure for Ilia's work so basically told them to bugger off and the Osbournes finished them off when their attempts to deliver "The Cat and The Mouse" had also failed. The truth rendered Ilia speechless.

They were backed into a corner with very little money, The Jailers breathing down their necks, Villa Pera, the house in limbo and no agent, to forward the script to Harvey. The thought of becoming check out girls in Ralph's, was enough fear to make anyone open a bottle of red. There was nothing for it but they had to get "real" jobs, at least for a while. And that was that. It was less appealing than dating a midget with a stammer but unfortunately until they received a check from Aga, The Girls had very few options left.

The next few weeks were spent revising resumes, CV's in American, dry cleaning suits and going for interviews. It was brutal for both but they had committed to this course of action. It was necessary for survival and that was that.

After a while they realized it was hopeless. Shirley, overqualified for everything she applied, continued on alone and Holly, desperate not to return to the corporate rat race from which it had taken her so long to escape, got a job selling document storage, even duller than selling software, her previous professional experience. It saved her temporarily from impending doom. Although after six weeks of abstinence from marijuana, she still failed the necessary drug test and was promptly sacked. Oh well. Holly was a writer now. It was to be expected she couldn't go back to selling her soul.

Once again in the safe confines of The Beach Cottage all the job hunting behind them they licked their wounds. Over the last year, The Girls had become very friendly with Steve, owner of Ashley's Deli. Their addictions became his profit. They were definitely, his best customers. Looking inside the large wine cooler for a cheap cold white, to help kick off the day they spotted something new, a man with one arm holding a bottle of Fat Bastard. The one armed wine rep promoted the hell out off his Fat Bastard. He had more in common with The Girls than he realized. The name itself stirred something in them. How ironic would it be to send a case to every single celebrity in the Rolodex including Harvey, who had let them down? The reluctance from anyone to even listen to them had reduced them to name calling.

Number five was added to the list of the Art Interiors rules and guidelines, easy to follow and never to be broken. Better to drink Fat Bastard than work for one. They bought a couple of bottles, Marlboro menthols and a packet of cigarette papers. Smoking weed was still an essential part of their creative process even though they were now heavily rationed after the loss of the job, due to drugs, which neither Jailer was at all happy about.

The wine went down well with a simple and inexpensive lunch of cheese, crackers and fruit. It was clear by now they weren't going to hear from Aga and they couldn't call Harvey. After a couple of hits on the joint and a glass of Fat Bastard, The Girls had a Plan B. Promoting Fat Bastard wine was an idea but they had no money or resources. They pitched the small vineyard in Washington their rolodex anyway and received a couple of complimentary cases to send out as gifts on the strength of something more formal being agreed. That was easy and all based on one phone conversation.

They couldn't believe it when the wine actually arrived. It was a blessing for drinkers with no money. Promoting wine with such a distinctive name was a better plan than trying to become television stars. While job hunting Holly had applied for a position with The Royal Academy of Wine Tasters and although the job was paying a pittance and totally unrealistic The Girls loved the marketing and branding possibilities attached to the name The Royal Academy.

After a peculiar dinner meeting in a swanky Beverly Hills steak house on Canon, when The Girls had met the Texan owner for the first time and John Cusack for that matter, a meeting was set for The Girls to present their ideas to him. He loved them instantly and although would have hired them on the spot, recognized the salary he was willing to pay fell way short of The Girls business experience and sales savvy, not to mention their ever growing rolodex of Hollywood Royalty and business heavy hitters like Harvey. They talked openly about their vague dealings with Hollywood's elite. With John Cusack at the next table and within earshot they neglected to mention, while they had all these personal telephone numbers and faxes, so far the only person ever to get back to them was the office of Steve Martin who incidentally, politely told them Mr. Martin would review any material once finance was attached. The Dirty Rotten Scoundrels log line for Villa Pera hadn't worked but at least somebody had rung back. It was a start even if it had taken two years.

It was the fat Texan's plain Jane secretary who made The Girls realize, celebrity stalking was not their true calling. She was overcome by John Cusack. The Girls politely asked if she would like to be introduced. She declined.

They had left the restaurant that night with no cash, to pay the exorbitant valet charge however they talked their way out of it and left excited. Finally someone was listening. This was a legitimate opportunity to make something happen. It meant a lot of hard work to prepare and even more if they pulled it off but at that point hard work was the very last thing on the list they were afraid of. Oh how things had changed.

They hatched a pitch for the chief, detailing a consulting gig through their own business. To work for themselves exactly what they wanted. With the pitch to "The Royal Academy of Wine Tasters" honed on a carefully written business plan proposing a $20,000 a month public relations, sales and marketing fee, they had their meeting scheduled with the man behind the company, the extremely wealthy overweight, Texan, polo player, Al McChief.

They already had big plans to sell wine to Hollywood, Fat Bastard loved them and they could tie in the longtime association between wine and Polo as the marketing hook. Big Al would love it. After reading an article in W magazine about how Londoner and socialite, Simon Nichols of Protocol Agency was revamping wayward royal public persona and doing so very successfully, they needed a name for their company and so Veracity Management, Public Relations and Talent was born. It seemed for now selling art was not the way to go. Their timing could not have been more perfect, or so they thought. It was not their wildest dream but maybe "The Royal Academy of Wine" was a way into Hollywood and art through the back door.

"Our best plan ever. We get free wine, The Royal Academy of Wine Tasters makes millions, we buy Villa Pera and the art gets elevated."

"Perfect. Roll another joint.'

They needed something new to concentrate on. Finding the perfect client to subscribe to the Royal Academy of Wine was critical. It had to be somebody with impeccable taste and loads of money. They needed a high profile celebrity with style to take to Al McChief and close the deal. It was clear from the beginning no such creature existed in LA LA Land. Perhaps they could find someone if they spread their wings a little wider. All the real players obviously lived in New York with Harvey.

"Who would really enjoy the English season? We need someone with a brain, from the world of business."

"Donald Trump. Perfect. We offer him the first complimentary membership and ask him to be our patron."

"Trump Tower here we come."

How hard would it be to get Donald to participate in their sociable business for the rich and the famous? All the top people modeled themselves on the English. He would be the ideal name to drop in the mix, creating enough excitement to make Mr. Al McChief cream his knickers and sign on the dotted line.

The plan for the newly established 'Royal Academy of Wine' was faxed to Meredith, Donald's private PA at the Trump Empire in New York, requesting an audience with her fabulous busy boss, Mr. Trump himself. If they could just get in front of him, all their problems would definitely be over. It was reminiscent of their hopes for Harvey but Donald was different animal all together.

"We don't have five hundred years to sell this guy our idea. We have to appeal to his level of personal pleasure. We need to tell him what he wants to hear. He won't be able to resist. Style and sex, the guy's addicted."

Within what seemed like seconds they were in the twilight zone once again, the phone was ringing. Meredith was responding to the fax. Bloody hell that was quick. Donald had his finger on the button. This was more like it.

Meredith conveyed Donald was flattered by the whole prospect of being the first member of the Royal Academy of Wine. He loved the idea and embraced their spirit but sadly could not help, not yet anyway. Donald was too busy doing other fabulous things but wanted to be kept informed of their progress. He was forgiven. It wasn't necessary to say yes to remain in The Girls good grace at that point. A polite no thank you would suffice. Anyway he was not dismissing the idea completely, just giving The Girls the heads up on his busy schedule. Maybe if they came back to him in January, things wouldn't be so hectic. Make a mental note. Call Donald in January.

For the first time in ages The Girls felt really sure about their new business venture. If they could impress Donald Trump they could sell it to anyone, including the fat Texan. Donald was another genius and had acted accordingly, doing unto others as he would wish done unto himself. The message perpetuated right down his chain of command. The Girls, his new apprentices would model themselves on him instead. Donald's leaf "Always plan for a success" was added to their book.

On the morning of their meeting with Mr. McChief dressed to kill, both coincidently in cream summer dresses and matching coats, very Royal Ascot, they headed to Santa Monica for their make or break meeting. Two copies of their six page proposal professionally bound in hand. The queue cards for their well rehearsed pitch at the ready. The only thing missing were the hats.

The apartment was smaller than they'd expected for a billionaire but it had spectacular views from Pales Verdes to Malibu and the atmosphere was airy and relaxed. Shirley took the meeting and within an hour it was over. Al was excited and The Girls left with parting kisses and a promise of a ride on the private jet.

When word came three days later that the plan, Al had so eagerly embraced, did not in fact fit their original business model, The Girls were stunned. Of course it was a change of direction but hadn't that all been discussed at the dinner. It had been at Al's insistence that he look at a more adventurous strategy for his company. Had he been drunk? It was the only sensible explanation.

When The Girls came back together they had only one option left. Plan C. The begging bowl was out. Shirley had to go to London and raise money for Villa Pera. The target was all the old wealthy City clients. The Girls would quash their egos and tell the truth. Surely somebody would help them. It was a fabulous project after all. With a one way ticket to London, for Shirley, now booked The Girls decided to use the six week window of time before her emergency impending departure, to sell their marketing concept to Wine Growers and Vineyards including Fat Bastard.

Convinced their business model was viable they would not to let the matter drop. They were back in their own arena, business. Now they were unstoppable. Two weeks of cold calling taught them one thing about Al's business and thus their own. The wine industry was in trouble. There were no marketing dollars available, however good their sales skills were and regardless of how many times they heard enthusiasm for their product no one had any money to spend on promoting their wine. Fifty canvas calls a day was not going to change that.

The main principle of The Royal Academy of Wine was to offer its prestigious members, like Donald Trump, the opportunity to socialize and be seen at two annual Polo events. One in the spring, one in the autumn to be attended by the world's wealthy, powerful, beautiful people and of course the press. The Royal Academy was now a school for scholars, with a heavy membership fee and a subsidiary of the newly formed Veracity Management. As I said everyone they spoke to, adored the concept so a local venue had to be sought. AB FAB running the Season? The Girls needed luxury sponsors so Range Rover and Hermes were approached. After favorable responses from the marketing teams within both organizations, reconnaissance of a local Polo facility was required. An article in Playboy stating clearly the rap icon Jay Z was seeking help to raise his profile produced the idea of all ideas. What better way to bridge cultural barriers than to get HRH Prince of Wales and the young rap star competing at the age old gentleman's sport of Polo. Jay Z did pride himself on being an amazing sportsman. He could easily learn to play polo, would presumably love to be associated with the future king of England and Charles, on the other hand, would receive huge credibility not only from William and Harry but internationally. It was perfect.

After a very pleasant conversation with Sir Michael Peat, Charles's private secretary The Girls carefully and respectfully penned a letter to his royal highness. It was certainly easier to get to Charles than it was anyone else.

The highlight of those two weeks of sheer hard work was a trip to the Santa Barbara Polo Club. One call to the man in charge quickly produced an invitation to a large charity event being hosted by the polo club's founder and longtime benefactor Ben Holden's daughter, Jeanie. What a gift. Having missed the season in England for yet another year the thought of donning hats and going for a lovely free lunch to watch Polo was all The Girls needed to lift their spirits. This wasn't dead in the water yet. Perhaps there would be some local big wig there who The Girls could talk into membership in The Royal Academy of Wine and financially backing their idea. Once again the wardrobes were raided for the perfect frocks and the hat boxes dusted off to reveal the selection of huge millinery creations from yesteryear, of which two had to be selected. Just because they had failed as art consultants, PR agents and television personalities they had not. With business cards bearing only the crest of the "Royal Academy of Wine" and their names, deemed a necessary purchase for credibility, The Girls set off on that sunny Saturday morning for Santa Barbara, confidence brimming, in the hope, once again, of saving their Picasso.

Before the fateful lunch at the polo The Girls had gone back to their friend, Donna Scavella at E! Television with the idea of Charles and Jay Z playing polo together. It had been Jeff Shore, himself at the very first green light executive lunch, saying anything with celebrities in it and E! was interested. The current content on E! confirms the truth in that statement from the then, newly appointed chief.

The Girls arranged to meet Donna for a casual lunch they couldn't afford to pay for, to catch up. As always she was enthused to hear from them. She had great news and wanted to show off. Making friends with the assistants, assistant had paid off. Listening to 'The Hollywood Penetration Manual' (where everyone gets fucked), as it had now been aptly renamed, had worked. Donna had been promoted to the development department and now had some pull. The Girls were delighted. Comforted once again success was all about building relationships. Their friend now in a position to help and it was off to the polo club that upcoming Saturday to close the deal. Well they did have, Jay Z and Charles as content for E! Sir Michael Peat had been so lovely and they knew Jay Z's personal phone number.

The meeting with Donna was in a small sandwich joint across the road from the TV network's Wilshire Blvd offices. It was nothing like the first time they had lunched together. The sad reality, Donna paid for her own sandwich that day and The Girls didn't eat, too embarrassed to say they had no money for lunch. Their humiliation was lessened by the fact they looked fabulous or so they thought. After talking excitedly of how explosive Charles and Jay Z would be together Donna helped them develop a pitch for the show. She then went into a pitch of her own.

Let's just say the less said about that the better. The Girls were mortified when Donna offered roles on 'Style Court', E's answer to Jerry Springer, criticizing losers dress sense and humiliating them on national television. After everything they had been through Donna had absolutely no idea the type of people she was dealing with. Her parting request was for Jay Z's telephone number. She, the television executive, was having trouble reaching his people. The Girls could relate and handed it to over without a peep.

Having completely fallen flat on their faces as celebrity stalkers, being offered the tragic E appearance was, they thought, the final straw then the polo club luncheon proved fruitless. Was it truly the end? Although they met many people all mesmerized by the Girl's quest to bring his royal highness to their club no one was actually able to help. It was nice to get dressed up but even after discussing the details of the proposed polo event with a very official club manager at length, the quote they requested never arrived. Weren't they the client in that situation? Los Angeles did indeed feel like the twilight zone. Everything they touched turned to shit.

The Jailers had taken great pleasure in executing the credit cards with a sharp pair of scissors, ouch, and their business account was frozen solid. Unless a miracle occurred the future looked grim for the two English art dealers from Yorkshire. Life in Hollywood for two English best friends, married to American jailers, was not working out. Without cash they were ineffective. They were despondent and for once silent.

"Let's pop into the Peninsula and see Peter Dickinson."

They had met the manager of the hotel, the day they had bumped into Ridley and had kept his card just in case. The Peninsula Hotel meant a fifty buck tab the minute one sat down. Those days were long gone. They couldn't afford a glass of wine, never mind a bottle. They needed a reason to be there. Peter became the reason.

The Girls didn't know what they would talk to him about but surely he would buy them one drink. While they waited on the patio, for the extremely busy hotel manager, The Girls had a legitimate window of opportunity to scope out the joint.

Many aspects of this tale are startling. What happened next for me is one of the highlights. Sitting in The Peninsula Hotel with not a penny between them, waiting for Peter Dickinson to join the table, there, not ten feet away was Mr. Michael Caine, The Dirty Rotten Scoundrel himself. Who said timing was everything? He was dressed very casually, a contrast to his exquisite luncheon companion, his wife Shakira. The Caines looked relaxed. The Girls were terrified. They had to do something but what.

If the truth be known neither wanted this job, approaching a massive Hollywood icon cold about a project took balls bigger than Winston Churchill. Totally stone cold sober was the killer. Their eyes discreetly glued to his table, The Girls witnessed Mr. Caine, politely but extremely quickly exterminate a fan who dared to approach. Ouch, poor woman, that was embarrassing. They wanted to talk to him but not end up as chicken fodder like her. As the responsibility was batted back and forth like a ping pong ball, You do it, no you do it, the decision was made. Shakira headed indoors for the bathroom and Shirley promptly followed her. Holly's stomach was churning so violently in that split second she thought she would throw up. She knew she had to act.

With a deep breath, head up, shoulders back, shitting herself she said the first thing that came into her head and offered him a drink. Although he politely declined, thank goodness on reflection she teased him about having to rush off. What happened to being English and sociable? Had he been in America too long as well? He immediately warmed up. He was heading to Dallas and with a little humor about Texans she was in. The Girls were as poor as church mice but the ancient couture told a different story. For once Holly looked hot.

The next two minutes were spectacular but totally unmemorable. It was a bit like being a victim in a horrific train crash then realizing you are still alive. Holly had the name of his agent in Hollywood, Toni Howard at ICM (International Creative Management) and Michael Caine himself saying he would look at Villa Pera, their movie script. If you believe in heaven, this was it. Who cared if they were broke? They left the Peninsula that day without spending a penny of their money or anyone else's for that matter. Today they didn't need a celebration high. They were high on life. Several weeks later the script was returned from ICM, unopened and unread with a very nice letter from Toni Howard. They never went to the Peninsula Hotel again.

Things were as dire as they could be at The Beach Cottage. The doorbell ringing startled them both. This was a first. They had a visitor? Who could it be? The boy was a friend of Filthy's, who incidentally had dropped off the face of the planet, after the gig at the House of Blues. The struggling Hip Hop artist with the face of an angel and the attitude of the Ayatollah, apparently needed an evangelist. They knew Roc A Fella Records inside out by now after the polo fiasco but as yet, had been unable to get the man himself to return one of the thirty or so messages they had already left him.

"Hey, what's up, it's Jay Z. If you need to reach Lenny in the A and R department…blah blah blah…"

So getting an artist to Jay Z was a stretch. Was this the route they should be taking? They didn't know anything about Hip Hop. The Girls couldn't help them selves. They grilled him like a tomato. They had nothing else to do. He was moody and quiet, both qualities totally forgivable, when the man in question has a huge bag of Chronic, the very best marijuana money can buy. He was willing to share the high and having a human being to chat to, in their impending financial doom, was quite a luxury. The gorgeous twenty seven year old Rastafarian with the big baggie of treats was a lover of women not pussy. They entertained his ideas of stardom, listened enthusiastically to his demo as the trio slowly got high. Before leaving he made a really strange but incredible observation, The Girls reminded him of Absolutely Fabulous, the drunken English sitcom duo, on Comedy Central. It was quite flattering to be compared to such veteran drinkers. The show was popular with great ratings, maybe it was something The Girls could capitalize on. And that was that really, the Reality AB FAB show was born. By the end of that day, when everything had seemed hopeless, they had a new pitch. Having already had a small and nasty taste of the Hollywood television industry, they were coming back for more.

After that first morning back from Cannes, now an age away, the message had been received loud and clear from Barbara. If they wanted to get anything else to Miramax it had to be done through the proper channels. They had managed to refrain from contacting Harvey again, the wrath of Barbara was just too scary, but Miramax was still in their minds. Starting all over again with the whole filming nightmare would take much wine and heavy duty, straight jackets.

"Challenge is probably still at his computer producing a cosmic invisible explosion. I don't have the stomach or the energy."

"Why don't we make our own pilot? We have a digital camera and all we need to do for reality AB FAB is film ourselves getting drunk and having a laugh"

"Hang on Woody. What the fuck do we know about making films?"

So it was decided they would make another pilot, find a Hollywood agent and go back to Harvey with a winner, before the day of reckoning, the flight to London, loomed. It wasn't about selling art anymore. It was about getting Weinstein's attention once and for all and fighting back. Winston Churchill came to mind again however the quote was paraphrased.

"If you can't beat the bastards join the bastards and then take advantage of them."

The Woody Allen phase of life began the next day. They would become Hollywood filmmakers and embark on a journey they would never forget. Both coming from the North of England with natural dramatic tendencies, making a film would be a piece of piss. Highly intelligent with three quarters of a performing arts degree between them, they knew they could pull it off. How hard could it be to win an Oscar? Ben Affleck and Matt Damon had done it as teenagers.

The chick they had used at Westside Talent to get their last project out to market was no longer in business. Although it was time to find a real agent, the stalking would be saved for a later date. It needed strategic planning. Getting to William Morris or Creative Artists, even with the Toni Howard, "fuck off and die letter", would not be easy. They had completed their internship in how to penetrate and manipulate the system and no longer green, they knew facing the beasts in Agent Land would take much wine and as much Dutch courage as they could muster. They would attack with the right commodity. Reality AB FAB would be everything. If they really wanted to make it in Hollywood, they had to become independently wealthy. If totally humiliating oneself on national television was the road, then they would take it. Surely, then, someone would listen to them about the art. With humiliation in mind they made a mental note to get back to Howard Stern.

Full of the joys of spring, they set out to write down the Reality AB FAB pitch. The pot, the rapper had left them was just enough to get their creative juices flowing. The day proved to be extremely productive. Clutching the high tech camera, the pitch was sculpted and the whole day caught on digital film. It was the very first glimpse of Reality AB FAB, the DVD.

The next day was spent planning for their new show and of course filming the process, it was reality television after all. They remembered Lulu, the producer from Extra they had met during their chance encounter with Gene Simmons and in the quest for some solid professional advice, made the call. She was delighted to hear from them. They explained their situation and shared ideas.

Lulu liked their honesty, was flattered by their request for help and agreed to meet with them in Studio City the following day at a small French Bistro, her choice. The only problem now, who would pay for lunch? They had to take this woman out. She knew all the tricks of the trade.

A table outside was booked for noon the following day. The nice Frenchman, on the other end of the telephone asked if they had any gastronomic preferences. They were delighted to arrange baby lamb chops with fresh mint sauce. It was a nice thought but the grim reality, the lamb, no problem, mint sauce, never heard of it. Even the French drop their standards after a certain period of time living in LA LA Land.

They were brassic but not desperate. A dress with tags still attached, in the original bag with the receipt, was the answer. For The Girls, returning clothes was going below their tolerance level, but it had to be done. The dress was far too small, obscenely expensive and they were broke. The digital footage from the trip to Saks Fifth Avenue is a legacy to that dire point in The Girls history. Being thrown out by the store detective did not change the fact, they had lunch money. The Girls would always find money for French food and wine somehow.

No mint sauce but they had lunch to enjoy and a television filmmaker to impress in that order. They picked out identical outfits, bright yellow tops and the faithful tight hipsters, gold Gucci sandals and the ever- present pouchettes. They looked absolutely fabulous as they set out to meet the real thing.

They arrived at the restaurant late. Lulu was later. She was a short, middle aged and struggled to ease herself into the cramped space between the, tightly packed, empty tables. Let's not forget no one ever goes to lunch in LA.

She was a perfect candidate for a make over. Sometimes being fabulous was not always glamorous. Non of the three women at the table were teenagers any more but Lulu seemed particularly mumsie. Could she be their saving grace?

The place had a real French atmosphere and a rather sexy genuinely French manager, Etienne. Red wine was served by the bottle as opposed to by the glass and large woven baskets filled with warm bread, gave a legitimate European feel. Lulu was only a field producer it turned out, the last in the food chain according to the Hollywood Penetration Manual. She didn't really seem like their kind of player but she had the experience and they needed her know how. The Girls humble and openly desperate, gave her their tale of woe. It was a mistake.

Lulu was brutal for a fat cow with no real power. Too old for Hollywood? Speak for yourself. This was something they had never even considered, something more horrific than they could ever have expected. How could they be too old? They were fabulous. The Girls were stuck for words. Lulu was immediately relegated to Wicked Witch of the West, only far too fat for her broomstick. It was bad enough having to sit and take her bull shit but having to pay for the privilege? That was taking the piss. They played take away. Being insulted was just not acceptable, especially by Lulu from Extra. No more wine or lamb chops for Miss Piggy.

Lulu excused herself spouting time constraints on some domestic emergency, leaving egos in tatters. On reflection she did actually give them one good piece of advice telling them to film everything they did, no matter how small or how crazy. That process had already commenced. Was she predicting their future?

The Girls needed conformation from somewhere that they were, indeed, well within their sell by dates. Even these two had pride for Gods sake. With a large restaurant bill to take care of and nothing to show for it except some more free advice they caught the attention of some sport on a table inside.

"Let's give those four an afternoon to remember. She thinks were too old? Watch this space."

They reached inside the pouchettes for the joints stashed earlier, they were outside after all, downed their wine and extinguished their cigarettes. A couple of hits and it was show time. Always flatter even if it's a blatant lie and make every man feel confident they are in with a chance. Later down the road these tactics had a tendency to come in handy.

The Girls loved the energy around the table and began making friends. They stuck to the same wine making merging the two tabs without detection, a possibility, if the opportunity arose. The quartet was made up of a Beverly Hills plastic surgeon, a filmmaker, a clothing designer, Jasper Conran peut etre? Big and beautiful was a new market for him and uh you guessed it an adult film star. With his striking white smile and over filled pouch, he pulled out chairs with sex symbol flair.

It was soon very clear Lulu was just a jealous cow. These Girls weren't passed it, they were about to dive into it, as the porn star said to the plastic surgeon. The conversation flowed like a raft on the rapids, dangerous and choppy. Principled slappers to the end, they tried really hard to sell the surgeon on buying their art but he was more interested in selling his idea. The buy one get one free face lift package. Wasting time in front of a cruel mirror waiting for lines to appear was something The Girls had no interest in. They might be ripe in years but they could still get blokes to buy champagne despite Lulus protestations to the contrary. Everyone in LA lives to be younger, tighter, trimmer yet the mirror in the bathroom after the fine Dutch was far from unkind. The Girls accessed the situation. The ensemble had suggested belting out a few show tunes. The Girls conceded things were going no where. They needed to get back to The Beach Cottage.

The bill was paid by the black dream team and they still had their money. On reflection it had been a most successful day. The Girls desperately hoped for a grope in the pants of Mr. Porno as they hugged him goodbye but it was not meant to be. He was far too pissed to rise to the occasion. His name was immediately erased from the Pussy Galore notebook. What use was a porn star without an erection? The Girls spread their goodbyes, like thick creamy butter on hot toasted bread and left in a cab with a tip from the filmmaker to keep their pilot short. Hollywood green-light executives had the attention span of a moth. The four suggested meeting up somewhere later but The Girls had made a promise to visit Challenge. Numbers exchanged and they all promised to call soon. By the time the taxi dropped them at the studio, The Girls were ready for another drink.

Challenge was over the moon to see them. Polly was out somewhere and that made them happy. She could be moody and they fancied having some fun. They drank wine and told Challenge about their new plans for Reality AB FAB. He was so excited he nearly pissed his pants. He agreed with the rappers assessment confirming The Girls even looked like Patsy and Edina. He took out his camera, filmed them with his own digital flair then played the footage back on his computer. Was he trying to sell them something?

"Challenge darling, forget it. You are the most useless filmmaker in Hollywood.'

"You have not managed to produce one single piece of photographic evidence from the last twelve months. We are still waiting for pictures to send to Hugh Hefner, by the time you sort that out, the poor bugger will be dead."

Challenge pushed buttons, played tapes and showed them all his footage. He had the Russian Madonna dancing with Filthy, Smirnoff eating a mouse and some random feet tapping to a New York State of Mind. It was the worst film they had ever seen. They had to smoke pot to make head or tail of it. He was such a superb photographer. Was he on the wrong track? It was clear Challenge needed to go back to his old career. He was their genius after all.

"We are supposed to be interviewing Filthy not the Russian Madonna and animal cannibalism never sells."

Challenge was mortified but fought back with a cosmic explanation for his stupid film. As he printed off the very first photograph Challenge had ever taken of his crazy Girls it was clear he had not heard a single word they had said. The music pounded from the Venice Beach studio and The Girls guzzled one more for the road. Those goodbyes were the last they ever said to Challenge. The next time they tried to reach him his phone was disconnected and on further investigation the empty studio had a for lease sign in the window.

The reality AB FAB of two drunken middle aged women was the perfect solution to all their problems. Now it was just a case of getting everything on film and producing a pilot themselves. The following morning they would deal with monumental hangovers but the recovery period works quite well, when the prospect of no booze looms.

As luck would have it the following day Ilia called with fantastic news. He had sold a painting and wanted to treat The Girls to a slap up lunch. Selling the pouchettes was put on hold for another day. Ilia was their knight in shining armor, a Russian lunatic artist, cash rich for a change. He would treat and they would capture it on film. It was another day and another miracle, as they accepted his kind invitation.

For two years they had spent all their savings on promoting his fresco dream. Ilia buying them lunch for a change made them both feel good. Of course they would make the most of such a rare occasion and choose somewhere flash and expensive. Ilia never complained. He just loved having deep thinking friends to get pissed with, The Girls especially. They always had a sneaking suspicion after hanging out, he went home and masturbated. Remember they are delusional. In truth he was petrified of them both and that day happily picked up the bill.

The lunch was life saving for them and extremely expensive for Ilia. Not only was he stuck with the huge tab, The Girls had some extras on top, a case of red wine, a carton of fags and a baggy of high quality weed. It was enough fuel to keep them sane for at least a week while they shot and edited the pilot. Judgment Day and Shirley's trip to London was drawing closer. This would be one last push.

Having an early night was never first choice but on the back of two consecutive lunches, Lulu, Challenge and then Ilia, it was inevitable. The downside, having to perform robotic sex acts with The Jailers, needed as much anesthetic as possible and their tired state made the horror, a little more bearable. The next day, filled with guilt and alcohol remorse they started the rationalizing and rationing phase.

It was a sad state of affairs for two such monumental snobs, even with Ilia's generous supplies. Every day from there on they could have only one packet of fags and one joint between them. They had already started re rolling the dog ends from the cigarettes to make them stretch a little further when not out in public. What was life coming to?

"This is like being in World war two, poor people waiting for the daily supply of essentials."

Making a film the way they looked was an art form in its self. Thank God for the remnants of Chanel foundation the following morning. With the digital camera positioned on the corner of the leopard print sofa, ready and waiting for action, they appeared from the bathroom. They both looked fabulous in different ways, so much like the real AB FAB it was scary. Shirley went for sexy in black and white. Holly was ridiculous in psychedelic sixties. Both girls were useless in front of the camera. The day was captured inside the camera and sits as a testament to this books veracity. They were following Plato's advice to the letter, "Create drunk, edit sober."

Surprisingly, the footage was hilarious and a perfect start for the AB FAB pilot. They embraced their new celebrity roles. Looking like Pasty and Edina, for them was so easy, it was uncanny. As the days passed, their clothes became more dramatic and their behavior reached an all time level of ridiculousness.

"How are we going to actually make this film?"

Once again it was amazing. Jailer one had another use. Movie editing software was his business. Apparently it worked like magic and any idiot could master it. The footage from the digital camera would be transformed over night. If all else failed in the States, Shirley would not only take Villa Pera home to England but a film as well.

The Girls decided to edit the piece and burn a DVD themselves. Being incredibly bright had its advantages. Reading the instruction manual was a piece of piss and it was almost eleven thirty. Hooray!

"I bet this is how Speilberg started out."

The Girls watched every single frame of footage and after many hours and many laughs, they had a twenty minute piece. The film was full of classic dysfunctional behavior just like the real AB FAB. Considering neither had ever picked up a camera before, they were naturals. The reality AB FAB pilot was finished and they were film makers. For the first time in a very long time, they had a sense of achievement. They still had the two hundred bucks from lunch with Lulu and anticipated success was just around the corner. The last few days of filming had been productive considering they had been drunk or stoned throughout the whole process, so a nice bottle of red sounded very appealing, it was Friday after all.

"Two middle aged art consultants with a home video, seek green light executive to help make their unbearable lives disappear."

They had some calls to make. Now they needed to find a Hollywood agent, a good one. The three bottle canvas call marathon was about to commence yet again. They dialed the number of William Morris, agents to the stars, aiming high but as always, determined to win.

In the blink an eye, the automated operator was chatting politely. These two were out of practice. The Penetration Manual, now dog eared, clearly stated in the agent section, don't call unless you have a name. They needed a name on a Friday afternoon.

After smoking some pot and racking some brain, they remembered something viable. Ilia had a collector who worked for William Morris. It was someone on the music side but it was a name. Ilia saved the day yet again and gave them the name of his agent collector. It made sense. If they made it, Ilia made it and the value of the name's collection would sky rocket.

After several calls and many left voicemails they finely had the person who would make it all happen for them, Colin Reno. He was the best reality agent Hollywood had to offer, dialed the number and got straight through. This was a first. What was wrong?

Colin was intrigued by the prospect of a reality smash and impressed by the recommendation. He invited them out the following Monday, lunch on William Morris in Beverly Hills. Now they were getting somewhere. The fear of being homeless was abated for a moment, they had a film, a potential Hollywood agent and money left over in the emergency fund. The real Absolutely Fabulous chicks had Bolli Stolli as their signature drink. The Girls were stuck with the remnants of Fat bastard to celebrate.

Monday came and dressed to kill in hipster jeans and bright velvet jackets, Gucci sandals and of course the pouchetes, they set out to impress their new Hollywood agent. He instructed them to meet him in the reception area of his posh Beverly Hills office. They would eat at a local hot spot and he would decide if they had what it took to be famous. He had no idea at that stage, their show was all about getting to Harvey Weinstein and Colin was just the necessary pawn. They needed him to lick the stamp and send all the properties to Barbara. That was it. She would then send everything to Harvey and he would finally acknowledge them, recognize the genius and buy some art. For The Girls, becoming famous didn't even figure. It was simply a means to an end.

As they nervously waited in the huge plush reception area they kept one eye open for a famous face. It was Hollywood and after the way their luck had gone up to now, it was time for this to be the real deal. They wished they had not smoked so much pot.

Surprisingly Colin was not small, fat and Jewish as they'd expected but young, funky and very good looking. A cute boy buying them lunch? Today was their lucky day. He liked them, they could tell, as he marched them out into the street. The chosen eatery was within walking distance.

The restaurant looked pricey and very chic, very Hollywood. Colin was pushing the boat out. It was the kind of place one might see P. Diddy having a bite. At the Girl's request the Maitre D' showed them to a table outside. They needed to smoke. Fortunately their host had no problem with their bad habit. He smoked too but another freak of nature, never in public. As Colin abstained he chivalrously lit their cigarettes and ordered some wine. My God this was too much for one day. Colin, the smoker in denial, not only drank wine but also could order the stuff? This was obviously meant to be.

The Girls with Woody Allen flair blew him to bits, raving about their work and all the marketing hooks attached. The DVD looked pretty impressive clipped to their typed pitch and ten percent for licking a stamp was a great deal.

For Colin it was a power lunch. He had to shoot back to the office within the hour, people to see, places to go and deals to make. Busy busy busy. He paid the bill and bid The Girls a fond farewell clutching all their material. It had been their most successful lunch to date. They finally had a real Hollywood agent. It was fantastic. If only Jeff Shore could see them now, Donna, development manager, formerly the assistants, assistant would lose her mind.

Of course by now, you understand the Girl's pattern. They just had to celebrate. With their emergency fund available if absolutely necessary they ordered a chilled bottle of Verve Cliquot, their second most favorite French pop, and some Marlborough lights. A restaurant filled with beautiful people assuming The Girls were famous and the Pussy Galore notebook poised and ready to be filled for Villa Pera, they now had a whole new audience to impress. Lots of name dropping with several of the surrounding tables and the notebook had three new entries.

After more champagne their bill was exceeding the $200 dollar limit and they didn't feel like going back to jail anytime soon. The Girls needed a victim to pick up their tab. Two Girls, drinking alone, was a perfect dessert for a dirty old man and as luck would have it, one was coming their way. It didn't take long to catch the eye of the tiger. Bernard Blackthorn with his platinum Omega and over sized wallet ordered pink champagne as he talked relentlessly about his Aston Martin. Too drunk to drive, The Girls needed a lift back to The Beach Cottage so talk of his flash wheels was exceedingly welcome. They didn't mind him showing off. He was a hundred years old.

The flirting worked and the bill was paid by Bernard. As they climbed aboard the green Goddess, the most fabulous car in the land, Bernard panted like a cheetah ready to devour her kill. He needed to breath. They didn't want the old fellow having a heart attack.

Their ride home in the $200,000 car was exciting and thrilling. All the agents in the land could not top that feeling. It was the most incredible way to feel sexy, everyone staring, whispering who are they? With money and more success, maybe the place wouldn't be that bad after all.

The following day was Hangover Alert! Surviving penniless was impossible. All those years of hustling men had come in handy, but they had a car to pick up in Beverly Hills, no taxi money and a huge car parking bill to face. The two hundred was history. Up to now they had managed with very little hard cash, thank you very much, although they did need a manicure in the worst possible way, things weren't that bad. William Morris was their agent. Always hopeful, forever positive, they picked up the car.

All the art work that once adorned the walls of The Beach Cottage was disappearing piece by piece as the artists slowly but surely lost faith in The Girls ability to promote their work and came to collect it. The Girls were expecting Amanda that afternoon. They had still had one of her paintings and she wanted it back. When they returned from William Morris, the invisible postman had left a strange air mail package on the step outside. The package had come from Crohord House, Fraggle Rock. It was addressed to Art Interiors and although there was no complete return address it had British stamps, $3.87 to be precise.

Inside the strange parcel was something even stranger. A small box of Titania's Fortune Cards and an instruction manual. Where the hell was Fraggle Rock? Neither of them had even heard of it. There was no note.

"Who's sent them?"

"I've got no idea."

"Are you sure they're not from your mother."

They pulled out the Atlas but couldn't find Fraggle Rock anywhere in the British Isles. It was very weird. Distracted by the package, they had forgotten about Amanda and both jumped when the doorbell rang. She was bubbly as usual. The three women embraced and then Amanda loaded her painting into the old Volvo station wagon outside. She was another struggling genius, a great talent with no money. She supported her self by running yoga classes at the local YMCA and giving therapeutic massage to private clients. The Girls had spent two years solid trying to promote her work but had never managed to get, even a whiff of interest. A healer and a teacher as well as an artist The Girls asked Amanda what she made of the cards. They were tarot she told them and asked where they had come from. Fraggle Rock was the reply.

The cards and that very first reading had to be included just because it was something, to this day, The Girls could not explain. Holly shuffled the cards and Shirley cut them. Amanda laid 9 cards in a grid form, like naughts and crosses.

BOOK	LILY	BIRD
MOON	WOMAN	SNAKE
TOWER	GARDEN	MAN

Anyone who reads the cards will tell you what this meant. It took The Girls a while to really get it. Amanda drew this conclusion that day.

The Book was The Girls card, but the centre of the reading and most important card was The Woman. The Book next to The Lily indicated professional writing and publishing. The Book, The Moon and The Tower was an incredibly powerful trio. The Garden, Amanda read as Villa Pera and The Girls future business there in, a lucrative enterprise, where people came together. The hotel perhaps, they thought. The Tower, The Garden and The Man she read as a good man from their past coming back into their lives, possibly at Villa Pera again. Was that Ilia? But he hadn't gone anywhere. Villa Pera was the place where everyone would come together in The Girls world, if things ever went according to plan. Was that what it meant? The only words of warning came from the final trio The Bird, The Snake and The Man. Amanda wasn't concerned about Snake next to Woman as the powerful Moon protected those cards but there was a man who was not what he seemed. The Snake was a clear indicator of that and the gossiping Bird was something to look out for in the future. As we now know, the Tarot predicted the future, clearly and accurately that day.

When Amanda had finished, The Girls, absolutely floored by the reading, needed a drink more than ever. Amanda had no money. The tab at Ashley's Deli, now at an exorbitant level, even they could not justify, meant no booze. As they waved Amanda off they thought about her words. The only way Harvey would ever help them, was if he heard the whole story from the horse's mouth, obviously. They already had made a film, written a play, pitched several TV shows and put together the huge art restoration project for Villa Pera, the house. He was a publisher. They needed to write him a book. Their story was fantastic and a novel? Now that would actually be highly profitable for Harvey and Miramax. So thanks to the unbelievable Tarot reading writing a best seller was the next thing on the agenda. They had one more week before deadline. Their separation was now imminent, Shirley was going back to London and the book had to be finished before she left. Could they write a bestseller in a weekend? Remember anything was possible with these two.

Reality AB FAB was now their identity. Arm in arm dressed identically in jeans and Ts, the Gucci sandals and the ever present, pouchettes, The Girls slowly strolled along the Strand in Hermosa Beach, taking in the fresh air and the beautiful view. They needed a deal and fast. The walk allowed them to momentarily soak up the California sun and contemplate life as famous authors. It was bliss and it didn't cost a penny.

When they returned to The Beach Cottage they dialed Colin's number and caught him at the end of his day. They had to know the film was on its way to Barbara. The film needed to be much shorter. Nobody in Television Land would sit through twenty minutes of such ridiculous behavior was the message. The Girls took his advice, went straight back to the computer, cut the pilot down to the best three minutes, then dropped it off at his office the next day. Things were really grim. They had no pot, no fags and still no hope of a close in sight.

After giving The Jailers a roasting, The Girls checked into The Beach Cottage. They would be out of circulation, until the book was written. They decided to tackle the journey completely free of any stimulants. If they managed to finish the job, Eli Thomas from Fred Segal would cut and color their hair. A reward for attempting to document their journey and a coiff they both badly needed. After three days and three nights, with no sleep, no pot and not a drop of alcohol, The Girls had a two hundred and forty page typed manuscript, Tawdry Tales from LA LA Land, a comical, fictional expose, about Hollywood and its useless celebrity. It was a masterpiece and dedicated to Harvey Weinstein.

The beautiful manuscript was immediately sent to Colin Reno even though The Girls had little confidence in him at this point. They had not heard back regarding the new film and the dozen or so messages they had left, were still unreturned. They needed him, but just how much was now in question. They couldn't make up their minds.

It was decided. Colin Reno was on ice for the time being. They would never get to Harvey without him on board, Barbara had made that blatantly clear but Colin was an entity unto himself and would not, under any circumstances, be manipulated by them.

Appointments with Eli Thomas, their friend from the House of Blues, would breathe fresh life into their tied locks. He had been confident he could provide the "TV look" for The Girls. Maybe it was possible. It had been a long time since either had set foot in a hairdressing salon and although they did not have a brass farthing between them it was agreed the new hairdos were a necessity. They stole a credit card from Jailer number one and made the call. Eli was heavily booked and getting an appointment was more difficult than they imagined. He was only twenty five, a baby from Vancouver. How many clients could he have for Christ sake? They concurred it was a good thing he was busy and booked the soonest available slot. Only in Los Angeles does the celebrity hairdresser work on a Sunday.

They arrived in Santa Monica, searched out the salon and pulled into the car park. It didn't look terribly impressive. It was supposed to be Jamie Lee Curtis's hairdresser. Was that a tramp in the corner? Always hopeful, forever positive, perhaps the cruddy exterior of the building, long over due for a coat of paint, was a cover for the haven of celebrities that awaited them, inside. As they passed by the homeless man, they opened their pouchettes and offered him a few crumpled dollar bills. He needed it more than them. The man was overjoyed and The Girls felt good.

The doors were cheap and the reception area small. The only furniture was a large red sofa opposite a beautiful painting, in a heavy, matte gold frame. It was the nicest thing in the space. Within a few minutes of their arrival, Eli's wiry form emerged. He was taller than they remembered. His face was not classically beautiful or distinctive but he was cool and real and it made him attractive. He seemed to savor the moment to get off his feet and leaned back on the sofa, comfortably stretching his arms above his head.

The three of them chatted with ease about the last time they met. Each gave a condensed version of the events in the months in between that were news worthy. He spoke openly. Eli was just like that.

The Girls discovered Fred Segal Beauty was renowned for its talented young team not its elaborate décor. Well that explained the crappy building. The owner ran a hair and make up agency for all the hot parties and shows and was well known for regularly getting the best gigs. He was on their wave length. The Hollywood set, like the staff at Fred Segal, got to go to all great social events, hence the celebrity connection. It was a perk of the job for the ambitious and hungry Eli. He had recognized early, his fastest way to success was to secure a handful of loyal and powerful clients. He already had the star of the Hollywood movie phenomenon, My Big Fat Greek Wedding under his belt.

The Girls told Eli all about their encounter with Tommy Lee. He was a huge fan of the rocker. Desperate to get in front of him, Eli convinced them he could do something fantastic with his rather orange highlights. The Girls, still trying to get to see Tommy away from the lovely Vinny Vignola, said they would see what could be done to get Eli an introduction. It would be good for Tommy, a free hair do from the best in the business. Maybe then he would give Ilia's painting some bloody exposure. How much more could they do for Mr. Tommy Lee, Esq. before the dude got some sense of give and take.

Personal grooming had taken somewhat of a back seat and as Eli examined both heads of hair with medical precision, the prognosis was harsh at best. They had both survived for over a year with a hair drier, several packets of L'Oreal and three sets of overly worked heated rollers. One set lived at The Beach Cottage.

It was not that The Girls didn't enjoy a good day out at the salon in the right hands, on the contrary. Yet following their lack of success selling art and constant pressure from The Jailers, getting one's hair done had proved to be a luxury they just could not afford. Although happy on this occasion to let Eli take over, The Girls were not convinced it was absolutely necessary to cut ones hair eight to ten times a year. It was more likely a sales tactic to encourage the client back more regularly and keep the struggling barber afloat. Although many areas of The Girls complex make up needed constant up keep and attention, it was safe to say, the hair in both cases had been low maintenance.

Eli was overly confident the night they had met in The Foundation Room. As Sunday had approached, The Girls had looked forward to his positive personality more than his prowess with a pair of scissors. Now as they sat in front of a large mirror, Eli milled about, gathering together his team of minions and briefing them on his plans. Eli talked about making them look younger, younger, younger. That bit was good. OK. Right. Right. Right. He decided what needed to be done and confidently announced they were about to commence with the transformation.

Could they get something to drink? Natalia aspiring hair stylist, Eli's girlfriend and general servant to wealthy clients was kind enough to bring The Girls two cups of coffee and biscuits. At three o'clock on a Sunday afternoon they were more in the mood for a glass of wine and a cigarette but the coffee was a start.

Eli tried to convince The Girls to don black cloaks. He was coloring their hair and was nervous of possible spills. Sorry, The Girls could not be seen dead in the cloaks so he would just have to be careful. Practicality aside, sitting in a hot salon wearing nothing but one's underwear and a black plastic cloak was not going to happen.

Placing color with the same care and precision Ilia used to produce a magnificent fresco he rolled his eyes realizing this battle he was not going to win. High standards must be maintained. In truth he was secretly worried about hair color on their clothes.

"I told him no bleach. My hair will fall out. Where is Eli, I need to talk to him. Ouch, it's burning!"

Eli appeared as if by magic to allay any concerns his client may have. He looked at the paste in the bowl and swirled it around. With a grand gesture and a confident smile all was well. He approved. He was courteous but firm. The Girls were on his turf and he was having none of their nonsense. He knew what he was doing. Give him a break. He was hung over. Immediately The Girls wanted the juicy details.

The night before Eli and Natalia had been in the thick of it at the MTV awards. They were the chosen talented stylists to coif the presenting celebrities' hair, quite a coup for the young pair. Eli had had to do something with, mother and daughter Sharon and Kelly Ozbourne and Natalia had styled several black rappers The Girls had never heard of. Eli did have a certain charm. He was very together in a modern sense, mature for his years, having a child at nineteen will do that for you and he was straight, a rarity in his line of work. Both had had far too much vodka, after the gig for MTV was over, to remember how they got home. The Girls probed further. Eli tried to silence them and Natalia blushed.

"You guys are cute together, ahhhhhhhh."

"No one knows your seeing each other? You're deluding yourselves. It's obvious."

"What do you mean sush?"

They were gaining momentum and volume and although he found them funny, the owners of the salon were stiff. Dealing with complaints from the other uptight customers was the last thing he needed. He separated them.

Three hours and twenty five minutes later The Girls stood to admire Eli's work. He was the master. They both looked and felt fabulously transformed. Eli had been true to his word. He had worked his magic with very little creative input from them. He and his team had taken unbelievable care of them and the results were stunning. As The Girls left that basic and bare salon they were on cloud nine. The whole experience with Eli and Natalia had been wonderful. The Girls vowed to get Eli the introduction to Tommy Lee. They owed him, big time. They privately hoped Tommy would at least say yes to a free haircut. He'd probably like that better than the painting if the truth be known.

As The Girls drove home that evening, admiring each other's new dos, they had a new hairdresser and believed for the first time in a while that anything was indeed possible.

They decided to call Colin about the manuscript. Although he was a reality television agent, being associated with a best seller would not do his career any harm. He hadn't had time to review it himself but had already sent a copy to Barbara, per their instructions. Now they had to wait. He warned not to expect fast answers. The business was renowned to be slow.

It was time at last, to smoke a little pot. They decided to do it in Vegas.

With their new hair dos they could be hookers for the weekend. Shirley was leaving on Monday. Being Principled Slappers had definitely not worked and sad goodbyes made them both crazy. The accommodation was easy. They had free passes at the Venetian Hotel from days gone by of extravagant lifestyle and lots of gambling. They were not really dissimilar to the Pera family, who had lost all their money in the Italian Casino. The flights were easy, The Jailers air miles once again. With the kids covered, having spent two days on the Internet learning to play craps they headed to Vegas.

Sitting on the cheap Southwest Flight, contemplating life as middle aged show girls, with free passes to the Venetian and a hundred dollars pocket money, cash between them, they knew life had hit rock bottom. These Girls had so much to offer. They just couldn't fit that final piece together. In reality this was even worse than the Lubbock debacle. Turning to prostitution in Vegas had always been a fantasy but never a reality. What would they say back in Yorkshire? There had to be other ways to make money in Hollywood.

Once again when all hope is dashed a ray of sunshine came from nowhere. No one would ever have imagined, by the end of that terrible flight they would have given Craps Lessons to a member of President's Bushes administration, Peter Dugas. They had his card. It was official. Was it just pure coincidence The Girls were off to the Venetian, Las Vegas, the closest they'd get to Italy for a while and the dream of fresco was alive and kicking.

In the months that followed Shirley pounded the grey pavement in London and Holly kept things alive at the office opening the post and answering the odd email. Hers was the easiest job in the world. Admittedly Peter Dugas did give his best effort in their plight to elevate the struggling artist but money in Washington was hard to come by. You only have to watch HBO K Street to realize where the cash is being spent. Peter eventually retreated knowing he had done his best and recognizing his best was all The Girls had ever asked of him, a good man to have in government. Not perfect, couldn't get anything achieved but at least told the truth. Once again the light went out.

Holly was missing Shirley. The time difference and the children made talking on the phone virtually impossible, not to mention the cost, so The Girls communicated by email. Shirley had been having a tough time getting things off the ground, even on their home turf and the future for Villa Pera looked hopeless. Needless to say they both tried to remain positive, each buoying the other with enthusiasm when absolutely necessary.

The Beach Cottage was dark and lonely without the bright light of Shirley, so visits were kept to a minimum. The phone never rang so the question of answering it was never posed. When it did on one of those dreary visits, instinct took over and Holly picked it up. It was Shirley.

"We have Penguin London at the table. Shall we save Harvey a seat?

She had met another agent, in the literary division at William Morris, London, Eugenie Furniss. She was hot and through a recommendation from a mutual friend agreed to help. Her largest client Penguin Books, she had a fabulous relationship with. If she liked the content of Tawdry Tales she could get it to Penguin just like that. At the table? Well not quite but as close as they had been for a long time. That call provoked the final fax to Harvey and then what happened as a result. Shirley got on the earliest flight home and Holly sent over a bold note to New York.

Dear Harvey,
Re: Tawdry Tales from LA LA Land (Read it you might be in it.)
Penguin London is at the table. Shall we save you a seat?
Peace
The Girls.

Shirley was back and it wasn't very long before The Girls found themselves back too; in the twilight zone with Miramax calling, Emily Harvey's assistant. Was she new, they had never spoken to an Emily before? She informed them Harvey was on holiday but she understood the importance of their fax. Then she did something unheard of in Assistant Land. She told The Girls she would fax it to Harvey Weinstein, on his boat. Shocked and stunned The Girls hung up. Barbara was not going to be happy, they needed to smoke a joint.

The phone was ringing but now feeling too high to care and too fearless to panic, they answered it ready to take on the world. Yep, you guessed it was Barbara. The prospect of what she had to say was enough to sober a judge. Surprisingly however she did not rake them over the coals for once. She was calling to say it was time to talk. Harvey was flying into LA in two days and she wanted a meeting with them. Was Harvey finally ready to talk deal? Even with Barbara as his puppet, The Girls didn't care. They were overjoyed to have done something right at last. They had achieved their goal. Harvey was at the table.

The next few days were spent resting and dealing with their agent. They wanted to make sure he was ready to close the book deal from his end.

"Are you ready to do a deal for us?'

"Ask her if we should save Harvey a seat."

Colin was in rather a bad temper for someone about to make millions. He told The Girls off for telling Harvey about Penguin's interest. He really told them off for going to Harvey behind his back. Colin warned The Girls yet again about being too pushy. They told him to stop being a chicken shit and get on the phone to Barbara.

The following morning all their materials, the book, the DVD, came back with a formal letter from William Morris. A nice fed ex man delivered the package. Colin was resigning, severing all ties and wishing them the very best of luck in the future? The Girls were devastated. They had a meeting with Barbara the next day and now no agent. It was fucking unbelievable.

Although for them being poor made life unbearable, the thing they longed for most was recognition for Ilia and to be taken seriously by someone they truly admired and respected. They had to remain positive and think quickly. Did they actually need Colin anymore? Surely the agent's job was over? They would close the deal and he would still get paid. It was only a matter of twenty four hours. Most people would view that as unlucky.

The day of the big bad Harvey meeting started off with an explosion, a strong bloody Mary with extra vodka for the kick. Smoking a little weed would be saved for the celebration high, on the drive back. As they climbed into the truck, dressed like Wall Street hookers, a bit of business with a lot of cleavage, they looked perfect. Black pin stripe business suits with short skirts. The crisp white linen shirts covered expensive gold lingerie and the ever present pouchettes finished off the ensemble, power dressing at its finest. The Girls for the first time in ages truly believed in themselves and their dream. Now Ilia would finally get some bloody exposure and they could get back to selling art.

The nice valet parking man, in the small underground car park at Miramax, remembered them from their last visit, tipping well always pays in the end. He parked their car and wished them luck. The deal they had in mind was one million dollars writer's gift, then royalties on all books sold. This was finally the big time.

As they stepped off the lift on to the fifth floor of boardroom after boardroom, the bare walls were still devoid of art. Harvey needed a telling off for that. His company was all about the art, or so they thought. The young blond receptionist, still wearing no make up and looking fabulous, was delighted to see them back. She told them to take a seat. As they sat down, tummies toppled. They were desperate for a large G and T. Barbara popped her head round the door and indicated they follow behind. She didn't look quite as happy as they had anticipated. Did she have her period?

After that meeting The Girls never really spoke to Miramax again. It had got pretty heated in there as Barbara coldly told them they would never get Harvey's ear. The Girls had fought back for the art with all they had but she was not budging. So Harvey just worked for Disney now, another cog in a very big and powerful wheel. Paid to be chief cook and bottle washer? Well so be it. They had died on their feet not lived on their knees.

"Penguin like our story maybe you should take the time to read it, you might be in it. Take care."

The pre rolled joint for the ride home was a godsend. Expecting a million and getting a roasting was a hard reality to stomach. It was back to the drawing board. Back at The Beach Cottage having a drink seemed pretty pointless, they had nothing to celebrate. They didn't have a mentor anymore. They didn't have a deal.

Several things had happened in the months Shirley was in London. As well as meeting Eugenie Furniss she was introduced by a friend to a venture capitalist, Mathias Hink. After uncertainty in the market investors were keen to give their money to this hot shot and his art fund was now approaching sixty million pounds. In a stylish private gentleman's club in Berkley Square he had showed Shirley the most impressive array of art projects. Villa Pera sounded quite piddly in comparison.

By the end of that meeting with the handsome forty something financier, it was unclear the role Mathias would play in their project but he was certainly interested to find out as much as he could about Ilia. Unfortunately while Shirley was talking to Mathias Holly was talking to Ilia. He could be intolerable at times and with half a bottle of cheap Pinot Grigio already downed a dose of his ego was something she just couldn't swallow. After everything they had done for him. The call ended abruptly with the two angry people screaming at one another.

At the time The Girls decided it wasn't too much of a tragedy. Mathias had clearly said things would take time, time they didn't have anyway. There was still Eugenie, maybe something would happen with Penguin and Tawdry Tales From LA LA Land.

Another influential friend in London was the chairman of Telstar records, Sean O'Brian. Shirley's chum gave her an internship in the label business and with 50 Cents hugely publicized visit to the UK and Jay Z performing at the Reading Festival the music industry and the world of rap was beckoning. They did have Jay Z telephone number let's not forget. Shirley had met with Bruce Flohr from B.M.G. in Los Angeles prior to leaving for the UK. Bruce was a big name and she had used it to impress Sean enough to secure her meetings with Virgin records and the Head of CBS records in London.

She had pitched him an English rock band Five Green Bottles. The joke of that meeting, Dave Matthews was sitting next to her. Shirley had no idea who he was. Perhaps music wasn't their calling after all.

With some contacts in place they could promote the London connection and pitch music to labels in Los Angeles. Now they were record producers. They had already collected a few demos along the way. Some of the stuff was jolly good, maybe they had something viable. They cold called Def Jam Records and set up a meeting.

DeF Jam's offices, above the Hustler store on Sunset, were funky, but the meeting with Nancy Walker was fruitless. They decided to pop into the Mondrian Hotel, famed home of the infamous Sky Bar for a conciliatory glass of wine. One glass was all they could afford in there. Their waiter, Adam Copeland, it turned out was not actually a waiter but a produced song writer trying to get his work distributed. Wow is life uncanny or what? He arranged to meet them at the Beverly Hills recording studio, Forster Brothers and introduce them to his producer and his attorney. Nancy at Def Jam had offered them non paying internship positions. She was obviously on the wrong track.

The studios were amazing. The walls had seen 'We are the world' and Michael Jackson's 'Thriller' produced. This was the music business and The Girls were catapulted right into the middle of it. Dressed in business attire, feeling extremely stiff they met the relaxed team, London a gorgeous producer with pony tailed dreadlocks right down his back and Steve the Jewish lawyer. Everyone, who is anyone, has one in Hollywood. The music was fantastic, brilliant. The boys just couldn't sell it. Everyone in the room was optimistic for the future. They knew The Girls could.

There were hints of jealousy and rivalry that very first day when their meeting was interrupted by one of the studio bosses, Evan Forster. The Girls euphoric once again failed to recognize the tension. People jumped to attention when he came into the room and The Girls were introduced. Eager to push his way in on the action within minutes he was talking about a British pop icon from the eighties. Of course The Girls had heard of Matt Goss, he was an international superstar. His videos had sold more copies than Thriller for goodness sake. Matt Goss was the Forster's next meal ticket.

A British independent A and R team was a gift that he greedily snatched away from Adam, the waiter. The CD, head shot and bio were tucked into the Louis Vuitton briefcase along with London's work. Matt was going home. That was an easy close. Before leaving that day The Girls met two other people who feature heavily in this story. Jimmy Brinks, a Philadelphia street gangster, the Forster brother's answer to Eminen and Bambino Brown who was to become their next genius.

Armed with the plan to re- launch Matt Goss back into the UK it was back home for Shirley. The Forsters were the men behind Pharrell and The Neptunes after all and the album was superb. The air miles had run out. It would be her last trip.

On the last visit home, penniless and with broken spirit she had had the good fortune to sit next a hugely powerful man in Hollywood, Isreal Baron. With nothing to talk about except her battered ego and the failed Royal Academy of Wine she was content to find out about his life, sip wine and bid him farewell with his business card securely tucked away for another day. They had called him before the final meeting with Miramax but he was extremely busy and unable to meet up with them.

"Oh well, next time."

Shirley now hopeful for this trip, had Matt Goss's career in her hands and Jimmy Brinks badly needing a break. All the CD's London had given her were fantastic. This would be exciting. Bruce Flohr had told her to contact, David, BMG London when she arrived. Bruce had recommended they talk. Perhaps she would get a second chance with another Isreal on the flight, anything was possible.

Sitting next to a breast feeding mother on the transatlantic flight while the nanny flicked through a magazine three rows back, was not Shirley's idea of fun but surprisingly she didn't care. She closed her eyes to prepare her pitch and slept the whole way.

As it turned out while Shirley was pitching BMG London, Holly was in the 900 Club, Manhattan Beach, entertaining Larry from BMG who worked for Monty Olsen, a big knob in Los Angeles. Holly of course had no idea who any of these people were but the name BMG rang a bell and she stashed his card, planning to tell Shirley about him, the next time they spoke.

Shirley had meetings with Ben Mortimer at Virgin Records head office and with Jay Z in town numerous faxes were sent from The Beach Cottage offering personal concierge services while he was in London. No one from Roc A Fella ever called them back, even when the offer from Top Shop came for a Jay Z/Top Shop clothing concession alliance. It left them with the age old question. What does one have to do to get any acknowledgment in this place? They had long given up on the hope of anyone ever saying yes.

The response to the American music in Britain was lukewarm at best. The industry was in such trouble due to internet downloading, they all wanted a sure thing. What was a sure thing? London's music was talking about a life and a culture alien to the Brits. Matt Goss was a has been, apparently. Hello Magazine were potentially interested in the photo rights to a Matt Goss, Daisy Fuentes, home coming. His beautiful fiancé and Latino model, now that was a media and public relations dream, the general consensus on the music however was no thanks.

With Fifty Cents in the news, the only sniff of a deal was for Jimmy Brinks. Rap was on the rise and the British teenager could not get enough of their American gangster idols. The Virgin guy told Shirley about Big John, an independent powerhouse in the music business, based in Los Angeles. Get him behind this kid and Virgin could make something happen was the message. Phoning frenzies could not provide Shirley with any information as to where she might find Fifty or Jay Z so there was nothing left to do than head back to Los Angeles and the Forsters with news of Hello Magazine and Big John.

Holly met the flight at LAX and calls were immediately placed. The recommendation from Ben was solid and Julie, Big John's assistant was polite, friendly and professional. She told them to get the packet to her and she would ensure Big John take a look at it. Lunch following and The Girls had their first visit to Pan E Vino, Beverly Blvd. It was not a very pleasant experience. Although Rod Dyer the South African owner was charming and immediately bought them a drink, when the brothers arrived things were obviously about to go down hill. They accused The Girls of not knowing what they were doing, lying and various other things that were totally untrue. They had called Big John directly, apparently and questioned the validity of the recommendation from Virgin.

This was dirty tactics. From the early headhunting days they knew calling the client directly was a no no even though they had been unable to take a leaf from their own book where Harvey was concerned. Things got ugly as Holly vehemently defended everything they had done to promote the angry brother's people. Without being paid a penny was the dagger that ended the lunch. Shit and they still had London to disappoint.

The Girls ventured back into the studio in the hope of finding London, while not being spotted by the Forsters and bumped into Bambino Brown. He was working and focused, in the middle of recording but being the charming soul he was he organized cigarettes and introduced them to two members of his team, Mr. Beloved and the Arch Bishop. The only smoking allowed in the bowls of the dark studio was marijuana. If nicotine was your vice, you were outside, it was LA.

Within moments of meeting, Mr. Beloved was showing off his semi erect penis as he puffed on a fag. It was the size of two coke cans end to end. Wow. He tried desperately to get his hands inside Shirley's knickers using every tactic possible. Feeling vulnerable and frustrated from their bashing in the restaurant The Girls enjoyed the open flirtation and sexuality of the black men. Were they just prostitutes after all? They had just had their hearts ripped out, Holly was still shaking and they had not yet imparted the bad news to London. Bambino saved the day that afternoon when his sparkly green eyes poked round the door saying they were taking a break and going to smoke a Dutch.

"A buzz, how lovely. Let's go inside."

The rest of the afternoon was spent in a purple haze on a purple couch, talking about music, art and the things that mattered in life. It was The Girls, five black rappers and their leader Bambino Brown, a cross between Lenny Kravetz and James Bond, or so The Girls thought. He was an entrepreneur in his own right, a DVD and a CD already in distribution with some of the Mom and Pop records stores around Los Angeles and a deal was pending with Violet Brown at Wherehouse. Mr. Beloved and several of the entourage vied for The Girls attention but Bambino stole the limelight without even trying. He was a star, a genius and would become their next protégée. They had committed to send Jimmy Brinks to Big John and would honor that even though the Forsters had been so horrible. That wasn't Jimmy's fault. Bambino would be their, own subtle, inclusion to Big John. That door was open, thanks to Julie and was an opportunity not to be missed. By the end of that amazing day, jet lagged and tired they had a management deal with Bambino Brown. Mr. Beloved was not too happy but he could smell the rose and the green and wasn't going anywhere.

In the weeks that followed they visited the studio many times, always managing to avoid the Forsters and London for that matter. They liked London and loved his music dubbing him the next Quincy Jones but his stuff was not saleable within their circles. They couldn't help him, not yet anyway. Most of the work on Bambino was done back at The Beach Cottage. They got a guy from an old friend able to get Bambinos DVD into a national retail distributor, Navarre, thus enabling The Girls to approach buyers in retail stores like Target and Walmart. They were certain the sell through would be massive.

Bambino's vision of a New Westcoast for rap, was so cutting edge at the time and later became a self fulfilling prophesy for him. His CD was brilliant and they played it constantly. His message was true, hopeful and raw, both sexually and spiritually. It took Bambino to re instill in The Girls that life itself was indeed a blessing.

Veracity Management's attack on BMG, Los Angeles was fuelled by Bambino's song 'Ménage Me', a tribute to sexual freedom. Let's not forget neither of The Girls had had good sex for a very long time so the controversial lyrics became their anthem.

Larry's card, from Holly's chance encounter, was pulled out and a monumental three bottle canvas call was made to the man behind Nelly, Derrick Thompson. His whistle was wet. He knew of Bambino already. Juan, Derricks assistant was bubbly and helpful. Always make friends with the assistant worked yet again and they had their meeting with Derrick. Lunch with Larry, much further down the food chain needed to happen first. Information about BMG gleaned from that meeting would be very useful if they needed a few nuggets for Derrick.

Larry, a scout for Monty Olsen and desperate to break into the music business was actually an accountant and hated his life but they did have some great stuff for him. They were in play and this could make his career. Responsible for the next Nelly or Fifty his future would be secure.

Larry had less drive than a Reliant Robin and didn't quite see things the way The Girls did. However at that lunch in a back street café off Santa Monica Blvd he did say he would listen to the music, then pass it on to Monty. They did make it clear if he didn't, they would phone Monty directly. The fear of that for Larry was surely enough to ensure he kept to his word. Then as if by magic Ozzy Ozbourne appeared from nowhere. My god, what was happening, they were sitting with a music scout from B.M.G. and there was their old mate Ozzy.

"Ozzy, it us, Art Interiors, The Girls from Yorkshire, remember."

"If that's a coke, I'm the Queen of England."

Ozzy disorientated holding a big gulp was quickly ushered inside the café by his attendants. Larry mortified his hour was up turned back into an accountant and bid The Girls farewell. They were staying put. That was obvious.

Several trips to the bathroom, lots of eye contact with Ozzy and he wanted to play. The entourage had him on a very tight lease, however. It reeked of the Tommy Lee and Vinny Vignola situation and The Girls were put off. They were just finishing two watered down diet cokes when Jon, from Newcastle, Ozzy's friend and long time manager joined them at their table. He wanted to know what all this art thing was about.

The Girls told the story of Ilia and the painting once again. How their endless conversations, messages and faxes to his office had been ignored and how they had failed to offer Ozzy a piece of Ilia's work, in return for some powerful media. The selected painting 'The Cat and the Mouse.' a satanic representation of the struggle the cold war produced for everyone in Russia, not just Ilia, they believed perfect for Ozzy. If the truth be known Jon felt like a complete arsehole and Ozzy invited The Girls to bring the painting to the studio across the road. He was recording with Ringo Star and they could all hang out.

The Girls didn't take Ozzy up on his kind invitation. They did not know where they stood with Ilia and getting the painting could prove very tricky at that point. Bambino was their new genius and they needed to focus and concentrate on him. Ozzy was a has been who couldn't return a phone call. So they left the restaurant nonchalantly considering they had finally met their third chosen rock star. As they drove home they thought about who might pop up next. Keith Richards was no longer far fetched.

A quick email to Ozzie and Jon thanking them for being so magnanimous and it was on to the meeting with Derrick Thompson. Once again, their attire was businesslike. He was the client and a very powerful one at that. When they arrived at the casual, hip offices dressed in black clutching the Louis Vuitton briefcase brimming with CD's, they felt like policewomen in high heels. They patiently waited to be attended to silently thinking, would they ever get it right.

Derrick was running a little late. Juan was cool, hugged them and offered them water. Minutes later the man behind Nelly arrived in a floury and ushered them into his spacious offices before excusing himself. He obviously needed to pee. The Girls alone and surrounded by more electronic equipment than they imagined N.A.S.A. would have, collected themselves. They re arranged the furniture putting them at eye level with Derrick when he returned from the bathroom. He was amused by the re vamp of the interior of his office but got straight down to business never the less.

The room shook as he played the chosen Bambino track at ear piecing volume. He was in the zone and The Girls knew better than to disturb him. When it was over he was curt yet positive. He told them there was a possibility if Bambino could get his act together. This was a road less traveled but had been certainly traveled before, Bambino's lack of professionalism leaving a bad taste in Derrick's mouth. On the basis of The Girls involvement he was prepared to give Bam another chance. He would listen to the whole album that weekend and get back to them with a plan. Success at last.

The Girls first mistake with the Bam Clan was to give Shaheem Beloved too much information they later found out but they were excited for Bambino and the future of Veracity Management. When word came that Derrick wanted a creative meeting with Bambino to discuss licensing one of his songs, Mr. Beloved immediately called Derrick Thompson and put the cat amongst the pigeons. This was the street after all.

The Girls tried to get something in writing with Bambino. They weren't doing anything else with these people until they had a formal contract. They even met with Bam's Jewish lawyer but were unable to get anything agreed on paper. Totally frustrated they called Beloved and told him to close Derrick Thompson. They were out of the loop. These people would never get anything accomplished. Calling the client directly? They had no idea how to operate in the real world even with a penis that size, God help them.

It had been on one of those fateful visits to Forster Brother's studio they had met Richard Glorious, an ex con independent music producer with a great attitude and a greater dream. He had found a young, homeless, magnificent freestyle rapper Ila and taken him under his wing. Ilia was an unusual name in itself but now to be listening to Ila, as he rapped for them like a pro in the car park of the studio clutching a huge bottle of Miller light beer, The Girls couldn't help but embrace the coincidence. They arranged to meet Glorious and his team the next day at Pan E Vino. Bambino was history and they needed new genius.

That lunch was incredible which ever way you sliced it. Glorious was making music, had his own studio and a stable of talent all with massive back stories just like Ila, the huge African with the voice of an angel. F.E.D.I.E. (For every dollar I earn) was a story unto himself, a kid out of the projects in Watts, riot and gang land, with an unbelievable gift. Several bottles of the House Pinot later, the crash course in street lingo and hand gestures commenced for The Girls, an education they will never forget. As they tried to mimic the cool rappers assembled, their guests guzzled the wine like water. Glorious of course had no money so The Girls were left using money put aside for marijuana to pay the bill. Oh well getting high would have to wait. They were going to Glorious' studio. He was bound to have pot.

The Girls caused quite a stir in the restaurant that afternoon. The message on the street from the Forster Brothers was that these women were not to be trusted and here they were sitting with three very large black men, bandying names about that everyone on the nearby tables recognized.

After their new friends had left The Girls were corralled by Rod and immediately invited over to his table. Hosting a group of gentleman friends for lunch The Girls provided an obvious distraction and they fancied some sport. Suffice to say, Nigel Shanley was sitting at that table that day. The mysterious man from Las Vegas they had never met but who had been in their lives since the very beginning. His company website www.nigelknows.com the ultimate concierge service to the extremely wealthy based upon his famed rolodex. Nigel's name alone had already opened countless doors for The Girls, namely the House of Blues, without even realizing it. They would go to Falls on Sunset that night, the new happening restaurant, as Nigel's guests and things were bound to happen. They believed in fate above all things, it was the bread of their world.

Glorious' studio, based upon their experience at Forster Brothers with Bambino, was a disappointment at best. Although their host was generous, pouring them large glasses of Kendal Jackson chardonnay as they arrived it did not detract from the fact they were in a dingy back room, quasi "music studio" with two large Doberman pinchers barking furiously close by and about to attack at any minute. The Girls gulped their wine and after confirming the dogs could not get into the house, started to listen to some music. Well Glorious had got them there and never judge a book by its cover. Maybe he actually had something. The previous night with Nigel at Falls had proved interesting in more ways than one and stories of Holly's first experience with a black lover were used to arrest Glorious' amorous advances toward both Girls. This guy could work the room.

They conveyed that although the sex had been magnificent the lack of flowers and Chanel number five afterwards was totally unacceptable. Glorious had no choice but to agree and kept his overt flirting to a minimum after that. As they talked about the dream of elevating the struggling genius and The Girls efforts to get to the elusive Hollywood celebrity, Glorious divulged, he had a celebrity, a big one who would help. Ecstatic, The Sky Bar was the chosen venue for their first official celebrity meeting. Glorious confirmed this guy would do anything for him. They were brothers, Glorious was The Girls' friend and the celebrity was willing and huge.

Falls, on Sunset had born some unexpected additional fruit on the celebrity front as well as in the bedroom department. The posh restaurant, named after its spectacular cascading indoor fountain was a magnet for the cool Hollywood set. The Girls had even met Jeff Bayliss, producer on Miramax, HBO's Greenlight Project collaboration, in there.

Pussy Galore entries were everywhere but one girl in particular had notebook star quality. A polished sharp spear, greased, dangerous and highly effective dressed in a red fishnet sequined cat suit, the perfect celebrity escort. Bill Maher obviously agreed with the Girls assessment as he had already bagged this elephant.

Someone else who came from that night was Chuck Tover, but not literally. Holly enjoyed chatting to him about the dream of Villa Pera but when it came down to carnal pleasure, the Rastafarian musician, a producer in his own right was a much sexier option. Chuck, though a little put out by the rejection, agreed to review the project. That was all that mattered. Shirley stayed up all night talking to Nigel while Holly went at it next door. With her ego stripped away she rediscovered the child in her and soon realized she was OK, just the rest of the world was mad.

The day of the celebrity meeting coincided with meeting Chuck Tover, (Chucked Over), the man holding the check book for Falls and several other large commercial restaurant properties on Sunset and around California for that matter, to talk about financing Villa Pera. These brothers were already in the restaurant and bar business, selling them an exclusive art hotel was not a stretch. They even had Nigel in place to run it. Nigel, being South African, had loved the vision of Villa Pera and thought Chuck would be able to help. If not, the producer had an in with Dr. Dre, apparently this was right up his alley. Holly had slept with him and the Dre introduction was promised in return. Meeting Chuck, the Jewish lawyer/accountant to the two brothers, seemed a stretch at best in an Irish pub. Not one of them was remotely Irish but the idea to name the bar Dublins was well thought out.

The Irish had no beef with anyone, cultural barriers vanquished, prejudice cast aside, everyone would come and they would make lots of money. They had. The Girls needed some of it to restore Villa Pera. With one brother sorted out in the bedroom department surely this deal would close. Chuck took all the paper work and said he would crunch the numbers. He was not excited. They could tell he had never been to Italy.

They had some time to kill before going onto the Sky Bar to meet the Hollywood celebrity. They called the conquest. The man related to the money. Could they visit the studio and have lunch, they were famished. The food was greasy and the conversation dull. The boys were busy and The Girls sensed they were in the way. The visit to the studio filled a window of time but little else. The Sky Bar beckoned so they said goodbye. Smart white people loitering outside, was a quite change for the bigoted property owners in the car park. The Girls gave street credibility, music people from London and their producer friends were happy.

They arrived at the Sky Bar wondering if Glorious would show. Thanks to Ani, the manager, they were on the list. Due to the crucial nature of this meeting they had been careful not to drink prior although one would go down a treat right about now to steady the nerves. They made their way through the throng of beautiful people to the stilted tented cabana where there was alcohol and hopefully a seat. It was early. They quickly got a table and a bottle of house wine, at the Sky Bar fifty bucks was inexpensive. They sipped it. Would the superstar pay? They couldn't rely on it.

It seemed like they had been waiting for ages and the conversation was unusually strained. They were shaky. They had left word with the concierge as to where they were sitting so there could be no confusion. The bar started to fill up with a snooty casually dressed crowd. It was six thirty.

The grand entrance of Ice T and his whole entourage was quite spectacular and something The Girls will have difficulty ever forgetting. Ice was a larger man than expected wearing an interesting black hat and oversized leather coat. The Girls expected Ice and Glorious not all their friends and family so additional seats were quickly included around the table to accommodate everyone.

At least half a dozen people shook Ice's hand before he actually made it through the throng of fans and sat down with The Girls. They knew he was on a TV show, Law and Order but they didn't watch it. He had been a rapper at one time but they had heard that side of his career had flopped. He was obviously someone pretty famous, they just couldn't place him.

Everyone ordered a drink, entourage included. The Girls scared about the bill drank water. After the recent break up of his marriage his date was unexpected. She threw The Girls off a little. Dressed as a Japanese Geisha with more make up than a circus clown, she thought she'd died and gone to heaven just sitting next to Ice. The Girls were threatened? Quite the contrary, it just meant extra work getting her on their side, something that proved more of a struggle than anticipated. Ice wasn't very respectful to the poor woman putting The Girls backs up immediately. The two sat side by side however he still managed to keep his back to her, talking mostly to Shirley about the promotion of Glorious' artists. He totally ignored his date even when she addressed him directly. Albert Einstein she was not, but that was just plain rude. Holly was afraid of him and felt sorry for her. Someone had to keep the rest of the gang happy so she entertained the entourage including Glorious ignoring the tension.

The Girls managed to upset Ice T so badly that evening they were reduced to yelling at one another and Ice left the table in a very bad temper, twice. The first time, they managed to calm him down and get him back. The second there was absolutely no chance of recovery. On reflection The Girls were very green and their knowledge of the roots and history of Hip Hop was non existent. Bambino had not provided them with a terribly good internship where that was concerned. Talking to Ice T about promoting something he was so passionate, educated and instrumental in, like a pair of losers who had no idea what they were talking about, not surprisingly, back fired.

The Girls saved face with Glorious, putting the problems down to Ice's abrasive manner and not their lack of information. When saving one's ego is the goal, always blame the other guy. They felt justified. His social skills had certainly been rudimentary and he had treated his girlfriend like a piece of shit regardless of anything else that had occurred. The Girls told Glorious, they had no interest in Ice helping them. They couldn't work with someone that rude and that was that.

If the truth be known it was Ice himself who thought this pair was crazy. If they thought they could ever be taken seriously by the world of Hip Hop they were dreaming. He was not going to attach himself to anything they were doing. He had too much to lose, he was already up there.

That week brought forth more fruit in the music world with Artist's Direct, Michael Whitted. Lunch with another decision maker, on him, from one cold call was a coup. Even though they had been unable to get anything signed from Bambino they decided to pitch his DVD and album anyway, it was finished product. Everyone in the business had told them there were no label deals available anywhere. However Artists Direct had an ambitious and unconventional chief executive in Ted Field who was spending money all over the shop according to Variety magazine. They planned to give him F.E.D.I.E and Ila, in the hope of raising some development money.

Veracity Management contracts were forwarded over night to Mad World records, Glorious' company. They were not going to have the same fiasco happen with Michael that had happened with Derrick Thompson. This was the street and blood thirsty rappers would rip your throat out at the first sniff of a deal. The Girls didn't play like that and weren't prepared to go down to that level. Unless they had something in writing they were not doing anymore work and that was final. The contracts were simple, a month commitment for Mad World, giving Veracity Management five percent of the artist only in the event they pulled of a deal in thirty days.

Glorious called several times after receiving the contracts, always promising his people were looking over them. As the weeks passed, still no contacts had arrived. Glorious' calls got fewer and fewer until one day he just didn't call anymore. He was someone else who wanted The Girls to help but didn't believe in them enough to give anything away. Did he think they were stupid? While he was in the can, they were in the City. They could pull off the dream and Glorious would be sorry.

Life as music producers was over for the time being. They had been let down so badly by their geniuses or more accurately the people that controlled them. Three years of struggle and these veteran business women could not close a door never mind a deal. They couldn't even get jobs. They were brilliant. How could that be? Now many months since that first depressing trip to London when their quest for a benefactor proved fruitless and all was seemingly hopeless Holly's lonely nights, after her phone was cut off for a while, were spent re living the fantasy of Villa Pera, their screenplay.

The previous year after writing Villa Pera as a way to impress Harvey, The Girls set their sights on HBO and Miramax's Greenlight Project, a screenwriting competition and reality documentary, the brainchild of Ben Affleck and Matt Damon. They wanted to enter Villa Pera but after being told by Barbara, if they entered it to Greenlight, it could never be considered by Miramax, they whipped up a different play, The Identical Stranger and entered that instead. Needless to say they didn't win although they were convinced they would and stayed up until midnight for the first cut to see if they had advanced to the second round. Anyone who has ever written anything professionally knows it takes months and often years to produce a quality piece of work. The artist constantly chipping away, revisiting, molding, sculpting until the genius emerges. It is extremely hard work and not for the faint hearted. When The Girls got over their shock of not being selected by Ben and Matt, the writing internship began. They reviewed their scores and read their critiques.

The comments made sense and the education about structure and dialogue, protagonists and antagonists would prove invaluable when editing Villa Pera down the road. The writers who reviewed The Identical Stranger were way more skilled and trained than The Girls. That much was obvious.

During the bleak period, the story of Villa Pera provided Holly with escapism. Her friend gone and no money to have any fun, she needed something to fill her evenings once the kids were in bed. She worked on the screenplay for weeks, refining the plot, weaving in sub plots and line by line, word by word, reviewing and changing, making every sentence, every word on the page for that matter, count. She loved being in Italy even if it was only in her head, it was certainly nicer than Los Angeles.

As the story evolved she could only cringe when she thought about the pile of drivel they had sent to Gold Circle Films and HBO. It was not surprising Robert Enriques from Red Baron Films has sacked them. It didn't matter how much he loved the idea, the script just wasn't ready. It was ironic to them, however many times they had tried to get Villa Pera to Barbara and Harvey they had hit a road block. Now after all the editing it was a blessing Miramax had never seen the 120 page piece of rubbish that didn't make sense. They would have been laughed out of the room. One thing The Girls did know by now, you only get one shot and the reason why, for the agent, credibility is everything.

With all ties to Miramax severed, their friendship with Ilia seriously in doubt, no money to eat let alone buy a house in Italy, the music business in trouble and genius everywhere nobody had the remotest interest in, they were defeated. The days that followed were the blackest they had yet to experience. The Girls spend no time together and when they spoke, it was about basic day to day rubbish, domestic nonsense. What they would do next they didn't know but the dream was over.

They didn't even flinch when an email arrived out of the blue from Mathias in London, inquiring about the wellbeing of the Russian Fresco Man. It had been almost a year since Shirley had met him originally and to hear from him now, after all this time was too little too late. They emailed back saying Ilia was the same but the project was dead in the water and thanked him for his interest. They will never forget the email that came back from Mathias that day.

"DO NOT GIVE UP, YOUR PROJECT IS FANTASTIC AND I AM GOING TO HELP YOU MAKE IT HAPPEN"

The answer was blowing in the wind according to Bob Dylan. A call had to be made to Ilia. He was the key and their relationship needed to be mended. He was the project. Holly made the call cautiously. She knew Shirley potentially could have a lot to say about how they reconnected. Holly was drunk and high and considering nothing else than Villa Pera when she dialed the number. It was possible she would say something terrible and potentially forsake the deal but it had to be done. She said hello, she didn't know what she would face.

Ilia extremely pleased to hear from her asked about the children and enquired how The Girls had been personally. He knew they had gone through a terrible time particularly over the last year and was sympathetic. He'd been living in poverty for years. Initially, he talked nothing of the dream and their mutual aspiration to raise fresco to the forefront of consciousness. He was sensitive that may open old wounds and was genuinely appreciative that the chasm in their friendship had been bridged.

To Mathias, Holly had paraphrased the master's words and spoke of a new beginning for art. The concept sold was a new renaissance, the re emergence of the master teaching the student, a traditional look at how and why art was so important in our lives today and understanding that to define new tradition we had to look to our past to glean the tools necessary to make the dream a reality. As she relayed the message to Ilia and explained what had happened as a result, she waited for words of inspiration from the teacher. He was inspired by how far they had come in such a short space of time. He had been on this sinking ship for 10 years let's not forget, never once giving up, always fighting. The Girls were only recently experiencing the intense pain of caring for something so much, by comparison. This struggle was harder than being a parent, ones children a very real testament to all the hard work put in. They had nothing to show for their efforts however it was mind blowing when you considered what they had actually achieved. The Girls had mentally evolved to a place Ilia had been for many years and he was overjoyed they had reached their enlightened state.

The chat steered to Ilia's new non profit status. The school was now a registered charity and could accept donations without a problem from Uncle Sam or George Bush for that matter. Lena his wife and Philip his son were doing well and he was overjoyed The Girls had finally got it. He had been way ahead mentally from the start. For Ilia, regardless of his meeting of The Girls that fateful day, one pregnant with her second child, the other reeling from a two million dollar loss on the stock market, his message remained constant throughout. He believed, not only in his art but more importantly in his talent as a teacher. The role he was to play out in his own life was that of true creative genius and it was clear to every single person he touched.

The conversation concluded with his necessity to be a parent. Philip needed picking up. Ilia didn't need a revelation he was the revelation, The Girls simply had to play catch up. The Girls had no idea really why they had chosen Ilia in the first place. Let's just say it was fate.

The logistics of all the telephone conversations, faxes and emails that followed are probably the most boring part of this story. Harvey Weinstein has not been involved in the project to date, that's not to say he won't be in the future. The truth is The Girls didn't need Harvey to make their dream come true. They didn't realize it at the time but he was always there anyway, right from the very beginning.

So now you have read Shirley and Holly's true tawdry tale of trial, tribulation and triumph. Surely that proves that anything is truly possible. You just have to find the Harvey Weinstein in yourself. Cheers to mental genius.

"Thank God that's all over."

"So we'll be the patrons of The American Fresco School."

"What do we know about the Medicis?"

"Can you roll a joint?"

EPILOGUE

DEBUSSY TAUGHT US TO DREAM IN COLOR. DA VINCI TAUGHT US ABOUT JESUS. JESUS taught us about life. Life is teaching us the work of a creative genius is a personal attack on the establishment and without that voice being heard we are doomed. We don't believe in Debussy, Da Vinci or Jesus; we believe in ourselves.

And so in recognition of all the untapped genius out there in everyday people we would like to acknowledge all the geniuses we encountered on this incredible journey without whom, this book would not have been possible.

Mr. Ilia Anossov-Russian Fresco Master
Mr. Challenge Roddy-Photographer
Mr. Howard Stern-Entrepreneur and Media Voice
Mr. Jimmy Brinks-The next Eminen
Mr. Bambino Brown-Entrepreneur
Mr. Tommy Lee-Musician
Ila-Musician
F.E.D.I.E-Musician
Mr. Mathias Hink-Banker
The Filthy Immigrants-Band
H.R.H Prince of Wales
Mr. Peter Dugas-Politician
Mr. Israel Baron-Film Distributor
Mr. Nigel Shanley- Entrepreneur
Mr. Steve Martin- Actor
Ms. Suzanne Somers-Business Woman
Mr. Donald Trump-Entrepreneur
And of course Mr. Harvey Weinstein

ISBN 141202822-1

9 781412 028226